COST-
ESTIMATING
AND PRICING
With Machine-Hour Rates

Also by Spencer A. Tucker:

SUCCESSFUL MANAGERIAL CONTROL BY RATIO-ANALYSIS
McGraw-Hill Book Company, New York, 1961

COST-FINDING AND CONTROL
Haywood Publishing Company, Chicago, 1961

WAGE INCENTIVE SYSTEMS
Haywood Publishing Company, Chicago, 1956

Every man who knows how to read has it in his power to magnify himself, to multiply the ways in which he exists, to make his life full, significant and interesting.

ALDOUS HUXLEY

COST-
ESTIMATING
AND PRICING

With Machine-Hour Rates

SPENCER A. TUCKER, P. E.

Industrial Engineer
Partner, Martin and Tucker, Management Consultants
Little Neck, N.Y.

PRENTICE-HALL, INC., *Englewood Cliffs, N.J.*

To my sons

Michael and Harry

PREFACE

How cost-estimating and pricing is made profitable and equitable by the use of the Machine-Hour Rate technique is the subject of this book. Machine-Hour Rate (MHR) estimating is concerned with allocating fairly to each product and facility a share of various segments of overhead or burden expenses in advance.

The MHR given in this book divides product "conversion" costs into its variable (direct, volume, out-of-pocket) costs and its fixed (period, time, standby) costs. This will allow the user to apply MHR in either the *direct-costing* or *absorption-costing* (full) pricing concepts, or in both at the same time.

The author believes that, in our present competitive economy, it is unrealistic to assume that selling prices are based directly on "full" costs. Pricing decisions must consider out-of-pocket (direct) costs as well as full costs in selling products so that the margin of fixed expenses and profits likely to be contributed by an order can be evaluated. The direct-cost level establishes the selling price floor and allows ready determination of the products that will yield the greatest cash profit before a consideration is given to fixed costs.

The reader is also shown how to use MHR as a managerial tool for directing sales effort towards products and facilities of maximum profitability, for selecting an optimum product mix, for make or buy decisions, and for evaluating acquisitions or disposals of equipment.

The presentation given in this book is simple and straightforward; it does not require previous accounting knowledge although this type of training will undoubtedly be helpful. MHR and its applications are not complicated by extensive theory or sophisticated techniques, making it useful and practical in application for anyone having an understanding of his company's operations.

Machine-Hour Rates:

The MHR system as given in this book solves the knottiest costing problem in industry, namely the allocating of all variable and fixed expenses to the product. This book shows how to do this in a simple and practical form (step-by-step) regardless of the caprices of the product mix, changing product lines, different equipment usages, and vagaries of the market. Instead of hampering costing problems with illogical, convenient, or traditional theories, which have no logic or traceable source and which cannot be supported in fact, the MHR system develops a consistent and provable method that allows realistic cost and pricing decisions.

MHR maintains a continuous reading of the profitability of each production center or facility as well as every product, territory, product class, market, and customer in which the company has an interest.

The term Machine-Hour Rates is not new. There are many systems operating today that carry this name (or similar names). Unfortunately some of these cost systems still carry over conceptual errors from the illogical, traditional methods, which continue to victimize their users and at the same time create a false sense of security as to their equity. The MHR presented here is new so far as a formally published book is concerned, besides, of course, the various articles and papers that the author has presented before various groups and published in several trade journals.

The author has pioneered the refinement of MHR during the last 23 years. He has simplified existent accounting confusion by separating the MHR from the general accounting books and applying manufacturing criteria easily understood and usable by businessmen. He has developed MHR into a costing and managerial tool rather than an accounting device and has included in MHR every cost element in the company other than materials cost. Most importantly he has added the concepts and procedures necessary for keeping the system up-to-date without extensive periodic overhauling. Unlike the older machine-hour plans, this system has been refined by the author to include all work centers or stations, whether machinery, hand assembly, inspection, etc. Naturally in this context the term *Machine-Hour Rate* is theoretically not applicable. However, the term is retained to attract and encourage those who use the older plan to up-date and modernize it.

The MHR presented in detail in this book is the refined result of experience in developing, installing, testing and cross-checking thousands of machine-hour rate installations in almost every type of industry. Because of the detail in which this material is developed, it should be clearer to readers how this MHR system can be installed successfully in every type of manufacturing enterprise.

Manufacturers who act as government contractors have found this refined MHR system to be invaluable in developing a "full" cost of their products and contracts. Many use this system, among other reasons, for solving the problem of proving to government auditors the equity and consistency of their overhead allocations. The use of this MHR system, when government contracts are anticipated, is preventive medicine.

Many trade associations have adopted this MHR plan in an effort to develop among their members realistic costs and sound individual pricing practices. These associations have also sponsored industry-wide MHR manuals based on the concepts outlined in this book.

Accountant-readers may wish to tie the MHR system into their accounting records; this has been done easily many times by clients. However, the MHR is regarded and presented in this book as a "memo" cost system that does not require that it be tied into and balanced to the last cent with the company's set of books. The information presented is designed so that a company can install a proper cost-estimating system quickly and equitably without going to the time, trouble and expense of endless, obscure, and formal academic gyrations, which, incidentally, greatly hamper managements' understanding and, therefore, implementation of cost information. This MHR does not require constant, expert accounting know-how. It requires intelligence, common sense, and a knowledge of the company's processes.

Allocating Overhead:

The day has long passed when the market would tolerate a mere estimate of the sum of labor and materials required for a product, and then the arbitrary addition on a flat sum for overhead expenses. Competition and technological advances have seen to that. Today the manufacturer is faced with the dual and coexisting effort of pricing competitively and at the same time recovering his large investments in manufacturing facilities.

The estimating of direct labor and materials usually poses no special problem because these cost elements are readily identifiable with the product. But with the wide variety in the cost of facilities, products differing physically and in cost, volume, function, sales mixture; and in the demands each places on the different facilities, the allocation of overhead expenses to the product becomes difficult. In an attempt for quick estimating, managements were driven to search for convenient ways of allocating overhead to the product. They turned to short cuts, "magic numbers," formulas, ratios and percentages, each promising to solve the allocation dilemma. The use of these traditional devices did not *find* costs, it *forced* them. And, as the product mix varied, management was victimized by their current magic number and alternately rode the peaks of profit and loss (through under- and over-pricing) as their overhead formula approached or departed from their actual costs. And reams of paperwork continued to be generated to justify the particular allocation method selected.

The traditional percentage methods assume fixed conditions which cut profits on undercosted articles. It also depresses sales volume on products carrying overstated costs. This means the company lost the good orders and got the poor ones. A proper cost-estimating system, as exemplified by MHR, must be flexible enough to cope with the myriad changes and fluctuations typical of modern manufacturing. With competition emphasizing the smallest and subtlest cost area, there is an ever-increasing need for "tight ship" costing. Averages are out because of the need for discriminating cost data. The keenness of competition and the complexity of processing demand that cost finding be accurate. The system must also permit inevitable changes to be made simply and quickly without endless detail. More importantly, the facts emanating from the system must pinpoint the action targets for management without requiring them to make technical accounting interpretations first.

Contents of the Book:

This book is divided into four sections. The first section outlines what costs are and how they are used. It then goes on to discuss, by examples from various industries, the dangers of using traditional cost-estimating methods. It explains the effect of facility usage and product mix on profits and concludes with the proper approach to the allocation of overhead expenses to products and orders.

Section II deals with the actual development of the machine-hour rate system in step-by-step fashion. For utmost clarity and ease of applying the procedures, the specific case data of two companies are presented (ABC Company and XYZ Corporation) and carried through all the steps of the MHR development without a break in continuity. In Chapter 12, "Additional Considerations," many different expenses are given together with the allocation factors used by different manufacturers. Besides there being a chapter on organizing and collecting the basic data, a section on problems and discussion follows each of the major installation steps to answer practical questions that have arisen in actual MHR installations.

In Section III the developed MHR is applied to finding product costs of articles in various industries. Then the MHR costs are applied to the flexible pricing of products and the problems of relating pricing to costs and volume discussed. The section concludes with a chapter on the use of MHR cost data as a managerial tool for the coordination of sales efforts with the production function.

Section IV gives instructions for periodically testing the equity of the MHR, for making corrections to reflect changes in operating conditions, and for keeping the system alive and current in the face of movements and changes that occur naturally in all manufacturing companies. If these steps are followed, the MHR structure never becomes obsolete and obviates the necessity for gigantic periodic overhauling.

MHR as a Managerial Tool:

In this advanced form for the first time, the MHR has become a managerial tool. Besides, during the course of a period, continuously testing the equity of developed rates to insure that they are consistently recovering the expenses of the operation, so that changes can be made before negative pricing problems become precedent, this MHR system gives a running account of facility profitability, which is its cornerstone. By this technique, management can key its sales efforts to work centers and products of maximum profitability, a rarely attained goal of cost-estimating.

MHR Is Practical:

This is a practical book, as indeed all cost-finding books should be, and requires a firm grasp of the internal operating processes of a company. The manager, cost supervisor, controller, or whoever is charged with the administration of the cost system must understand production processes from the shopman's point of view, sales activity from the marketing aspects, expenditures from the merchandising and financial viewpoints, and so forth. The mechanics of order estimating can be routinized and assigned to an intelligent clerk performing within the framework of an established policy that is regularly tested by the methods discussed here.

The process of finding costs for managerial decisions or pricing purposes should not be clouded by theoretical hair-splitting concerning academic theory. The author contends so much time and energy is spent rationalizing these theories before applying them so that the larger issues become somehow lost in the shuffle. During the same amount of time these theories need for airing and settling, specific production changes and new marketing policies, new equipment, and products, which inadvertently go unconsidered can get initiated under MHR. The purpose of every business is to make a profit, not to adhere to strict academic theory. The sooner cost thinking is similar to the thinking of the production manager, sales manager, industrial engineer and owner, the sooner number inflexibility will give way to realistic data and sound profit-planning decisions.

MHR Administration:

Ideally, the *finding* of product costs should be supervised by the cost accountant or controller. In smaller companies this may not be feasible because of staff and budget limitations. The procedures spelled out in this book are easily applied, without previous formal cost training, by any intelligent person who has a knowledge of the operations of his company. In several instances, in smaller companies, the development of MHR has been carried out by the owner, office manager, the accountant, or the industrial engineer, or, even in some cases, by a bright shipping clerk who was not fully occupied.

Applying product costs is another matter. Using the MHR costs for coordinating sales and production is a task for upper management. And in the most difficult area of application, the use of costs for pricing purposes, the cost *developer* has a limited view that must be augmented by other members of the management team. They must consider the interrelationships of return on investment, market demand and price effect on volume, customer reaction and product acceptability, competitive activity, volume effect on costs, and evaluating countermeasures to price change by competitors.

While in the larger companies, the pricing practice is often carried out by a team comprised of different staff specialists, in the smaller company this function is usually residual in one person, the owner. In either case, both types of companies need a separation between product cost-finding procedures and the pricing practices discussed in this book.

Conclusion:

The science of product costing must not only keep pace with technological progress and competitive needs, but it must also achieve status equal to the other branches of the management sciences. It is the author's fervent hope that, by the time the theses and methods given in this book have been firmly grasped, the readers will have become convinced that the cost-estimating function is one that should be given equal weight with the other vital activities in a company, and not relegated to the background as a necessary evil lacking significance in the over-all profit-planning picture.

ACKNOWLEDGMENTS

I am indebted to many people who read this manuscript and offered helpful suggestions. These include trade association executives, controllers and managements of many client-manufacturers. Thanks are due Mr. Sergio Gazitua for his assistance in editing and clarifying this material and to Mrs. Elizabeth Prendergast, my secretary, who labored over the typing of this manuscript. I am grateful also to my wife who endured, with patience and understanding, the creative pains with me. Last, but certainly not least, thanks and love are due my mother who did the formidable job (in spite of her age) of proofreading this manuscript with me.

SPENCER A. TUCKER

Little Neck, N. Y.

TIME IS MONEY

We have all heard the old bromide that "time is money." Yet this idea, no matter how trite the phrase, can never be forgotten by a management interested in the growth and prosperity of a business enterprise. This is especially true for those organizations having a variable product mix, a variable volume mix, or both. For those organizations in particular, and all organizations in general, proper and precise cost information is a *must* if selling prices are to properly reflect cost as well as increase sales and profits.

To develop realistic and profitable selling prices which will meet the pressure of competition, management needs a pragmatic costing system. The costing system now recognized by the more far-sighted experts in the field as most fully meeting these criteria is the Machine-Hour Rate System. This system, when properly installed, not only does an extremely fine job of costing and cost estimating, but, as the author of this book so clearly indicates, is also capable of performing other valuable functions for any business organization. The Machine-Hour Rate System of cost analysis can also present meaningful information on the profit margins from a product mix as well as supply data for determining the maximum use of facilities. This indicates a flexibility not ordinarily achieved by other cost systems.

The proper approach to overhead cost allocation is a topic covered in painstaking detailed by the author, as is the development and the installation of the Machine-Hour Rate System. He also compares traditional costing systems such as Prime Cost, Direct Labor Dollar, and Unit of Product Method with the Machine-Hour Rate System. Not only are the advantages of each system shown, but, more importantly, he points out the disadvantages of these systems when they are compared to the Machine-Hour Rate System. Examples as well as exposition enable the reader to follow the step-by-step approach.

Obviously the value of the Machine-Hour Rate System is derived from the use made of the data which the system develops. Here a precise determination of the product cost is naturally an essential step in the application of the machine-hour rate data. Once this benchmark has been firmly established, we find that the machine-hour rate can very well be used in the pricing of the product as well as being employed as a control over its production and sale. This, then, completes the spectrum of analysis and establishes the system as a management tool not only for the estimating department but for all departments of the organization, from manufacturing to general administration.

It goes without saying that any costing system will become obsolete unless a determined effort is made to keep it up to date. This principle applies to the Machine-Hour Rate System as well as to any other costing system. By recognizing this problem, the author has wisely included detailed information on methods for testing and correcting the MHR System.

As with all general systems, it should be recognized that this system must be cut and tailored to fit the needs of any specific organization. These adaptations are, however, those of application and in no way disturb the fundamental principles and procedures essential to the effective operation of the plan. By a studied and careful analysis of basic information, any organization can fit its raw data into the Machine-Hour Rate System.

The chapter, "Profit Effect," contains an analysis of product mix and facility usage which should be *required reading* for everyone concerned with the profits of a business organization. Although most people say they realize the importance of product mix and facility usage on the profit margin, it can be assumed that they either do not understand the principles involved or are only giving "lip service" to the subject since, in practice, they pursue the opportunistic approach by taking anything and everything which is offered to them in the way of an order, regardless of the effect on their profit margin. As the author dramatically illustrates, the proper attitude toward the planning and execution of a program of maximizing the use of facilities through a proper product mix can have such a profound effect on profits that it could, in effect, nullify other factors generally considered important.

The chapter, "Proper Approach to Overhead Cost Allocation," can well be studied by all top management men since these principles are generally either misunderstood or improperly executed. The usual procedure of analyzing totals and spreading them across the expense sheet will invariably result in a distortion of the cost picture. The more precise method of analysis provided by the Machine-Hour Rate System offers many advantages to the cost-minded executive.

Obviously any exposition on the Machine-Hour Rate System must be concerned with its development and installation. Here the author is at his best and gives a step-by-step analysis, beginning with a discussion and description of the basic data needed from production, administration and sales, proceeding to the integration of this raw data into the Machine-Hour Rate System. His discussion of the classification of converting facilities, as well as the accumulation of computation tables and procedures for developing the operating budget, will give any serious-minded manager sufficient background to enable him to check his computations when he develops his own machine-hour rates.

The author makes a significant contribution to the literature of cost analysis by outlining how a properly installed, properly maintained and properly used machine-hour rate system can be utilized by any manufacturing organization in costing and cost-estimating. However, costing and cost-estimating are only two entrepreneurial functions. He also points out how the system can be used to determine adequate profit margins and develop realistic selling prices which will meet competition and provide the best product mix for the most profitable utilization of equipment.

What more can a reader expect from a book?

GUSTAV L. NORDSTROM,
Executive Director
Folding Paper Box Association of America

CONTENTS

SECTION 1. INDUSTRY COSTING PROBLEMS

Chapter 1. **The What, Why and How of Costs,** 3

What Are Costs?, 4; Estimating Systems Must Answer Questions, 5; Classification of Costs, 6; Fixed and Variable Costs, 6; Manufacturing and Non-Manufacturing Costs, 6; Reporting of Costs, 7; Costs for Pricing, 8; Costs for Facility Costs, 8; Costs for "Make or Buy," 9; Costs for Optimizing Product Mix, 9; Costs for Long-Range Planning, 9; Costs for the Shorter Term, 10.

Chapter 2. **Traditional Costing and Machine-Hour Rates,** 11

The Big Problem, 11; Traditional Costing Methods: Prime Cost Method, 12; Materials Cost Method, 13; Direct-Labor Dollar Method, 13; Direct-Labor Hour Method, 15; Unit of Product Method, 15; Machine-Hour Rate Method, 15; Arithmetic Comparison of HR with Direct-Labor Method, 17; Summary of Machine-Hour Rate System and Advantages, 18.

Chapter 3. **Profit Effect of Product Mix and Facility Usage,** 19

Industry Costing Problems, 19; Expense Recovery, 20; Cost-Profit Averaging, 20; The Goal of Cost-Estimating, 22; Test Cost Recovery, 23; How Product Mix Affects Profits, 26.

Chapter 4. **Proper Approach to Overhead Cost Allocation,** 31

Allocation Equity, 31; Allocation of Overhead to Facilities, 33; Distribution Bases, 34.

SECTION 2. **HOW TO DEVELOP AND INSTALL THE MACHINE-HOUR RATE SYSTEM**

Chapter 5. **How to Organize the Basic Data,** 39

Cost Activities in Manufacturing Enterprise, 39; Classification of Costs, 40; Materials Costs, 40; Labor Costs: Direct Labor, 42; Indirect Labor, 42; Productive Workers Daily Tickets, 42; Reports: By customers' order and operation, 45; By department or group of machines per day, 45; By factory order and worker per day, 46; Overdesigned ticket, 49; Factory Expense, 50; General, Administrative and Selling Expenses, 52; Misclassification of Expenses, 55; Reporting for Job Costing vs. Facility Costing, 56.

Chapter 6. **Introduction to Machine-Hour Rates,** 58

Development of the Rate, 58; Company ABC and the XYZ Corporation, 59; What is a Machine-Hour Rate?, 59

Chapter 7. How to Develop the MHR. Step 1: The Converting Facilities Classification Sheet, 61

> Production Center, 63; Service Cost Centers, 64; Number of Units, 65; Horsepower, 65; Net Working Space, 65; Present Value, 66; Production Center Annual Hours, 68; Problems and Discussion: On Production Centers, 72; On Space, 73; On Present Value, 73.

Chapter 8. How to Develop the MHR. *Step 2: The Crew Composition Table,* 76

> Number of Units, 76; Standard Crew Per Unit, 77; Workers' Hourly Base Rate, 77; Hourly Pay Rate Per Center, 77; Maximum Annual Center Hours, 77; Fringe Benefits: Rest Periods, 80; Holidays, 80; Vacation, 80; Available Annual Center Hours, 80; Scheduled Production Hours, 80; Hourly Balance, 81; Transfers, 81; Idle Time, 81; Non-Productive Cost, 82; Problems and Discussion: On Crew Rates, 82; On Transfers, 82; On Arbitrary Crew Additions, 82; On Indirect Assignments, 83; On Working Group Leaders, 83; On Hourly Shortages, 83; On Man-Hours vs. Machine-Hours, 83; On Indirect vs. Direct, 84; On Handwork, 84; On Redistributing Operations, 85; On Indirect-Direct Ratios, 85.

Chapter 9. How to Develop the MHR. *Step 3: The Operating Budget,* 86

> Costs for Financial Reporting vs. Pricing, 86; Budget Form, 87; Judgment Essential, 87; Object and Preparation of Budget for MHR, 88; Budget Classification, 88; Direct-Indirect Charges, 91; Economic Depreciation, 92; Chameleon-like Profits, 93; Price-Level Changes, 94; Fairness to Customers, 94; The Method, 95; Flexible Budgets, 96; Flexible Budget Formulation, 96; Electricity, 97; Depreciation, 98; Problems and Discussion: On Allocation Variances, 104; On Capacity, 105; On Recovery-Sales Variances, 107; On Depreciation Methods: Straight-Line Method, 107; Diminishing Balance Method, 107; Sum-of-the-Digits Method, 108.

Chapter 10. How to Develop the MHR. *Step 4: The Expense Assignment Worksheet,* 110

> Costs vs. Allocation Factors, 110; Allocating Expenses to Production Centers, 111; Development of the EAW, 113; Allocation Factors Selected, 113; Not All Similar Plants Use Same Allocation Factors, 116; Different Plants May Use Same Set of Allocation Factors, 118.

Chapter 11. How to Develop the MHR. *Step 5: The MHR Summary Sheet,* 120

> Composite Rates, 120; Other Plant Examples of Summary Sheets, 121; Activity-Capacity Levels, 122; Summary of Rate Determination, 124.

Chapter 12. How to Develop the MHR. *Additional Considerations,* 126

> Assigning Service Expenses, 126; Other Expenses: Distribution Costs, 127; Shipping and Delivery Expenses, 127; Advertising Expenses, 128; Storage Costs, 128; Production-Line Centers, 129; Some Special Industry Cases: Meat Packing, 129; Milk Products, 131; Forging Industries, 131; Paint Industry, 132; Allocation Inconsistencies, 132; Typical Expenses and Some Bases Used for Their Allocation, 134.

SECTION 3. HOW TO APPLY MHR DATA

Chapter 13. How to Find Product Costs, 141

Production Standards, 141; Standards, 142; Development of Production Standards, 143; Dimensions for Tabulating Production Standards, 144; Formats for Developing Production Standards, 145; The Estimate or Cost Sheet, 150; Fixed and Variable Costs, 155; Sample Estimate Sheets, 155; Deficiency of Forms, 160.

Chapter 14. Using MHR for Pricing Products, 162

Price Acceptability, 162; Costs Start the Pricing Process, 162; Nature of Costs, 163; Pricing Influences, 163; Costs and Pricing, 164; Adjusting Historical Costs to Current Price Levels, 166; Pricing of Marginal Business, 166; Marginal Pricing Considerations, 168; Fixed and Variable Costs, and Volume of Production, 169; Fixed-Variable Flexible Budget, 170; Fixed-Variable Expense Assignment Worksheet, 172; Fixed-Variable Flexible MHR Summary Sheet, 172; Fixed-Variable Product Cost, 172; A Philosophy of Pricing, 176; Elasticity of Demand, 178; Pricing Strategy, 181; Pricing and Costing Methods, 182.

Chapter 15. Using MHR to Coordinate Sales and Production, 184

Separate Functions, 184; Costs and Profits, 185; Product-Volume Mix, 185; Sales Integrated with Production, 186; Production-Center Costs, 187; Products Converted to Operational Hours, 187; Product-Cost Breakdown, 190; Sales Targets, 191; Product Expense-Recovering Ability, 194; Needed vs. Attained Recovery, 197; How to Integrate Sales with Production, 199; The Impact of Product Mix, 199; Selling-Price Latitude, 200; New Product Mix Selected, 200; Recovery Ability: Condition B, 202; Hourly Recovery Volatility, 202; Production's Needs vs. Actual Attainment, 203; A Ratio Integrating Production and Sales, 204; Productivity Increases Capacity, 206; Sales-Contact Effort, 208.

SECTION 4. HOW TO KEEP THE MHR SYSTEM CURRENT

Chapter 16. Pre-Testing the MHR, 215

Cost Recovery, 215; Selection of the Capacity Base, 216; Practical Capacity, 217; Average Capacity, 218; Summary of Capacity Base Selection, 218; Capacity Balancing, 219; Effect of Product Mix on Capacity Base, 220; Operating Budget Pre-Tests, 220; Crew Composition Pre-Tests, 222.

Chapter 17. Testing the MHR, 223

Testing the Equity of the MHR, 223; Production Center Monthly Activity Report, 224; Cost Recovery Statement, 224; Using the Cost Recovery Statement, 225; Production Center Recovery Test Form, 229; Using the Production Center Recovery Test Form, 230; Testing of Product and Order Costs, 233; Variance Reports, 234; Testing Fixed and Variable Cost Recovery for Pricing Control, 241.

Chapter 18. How to Correct or Change the MHR, 243

Why Change or Correct?, 243; Practical Considerations, 244; Activity, 244; Machinery, 245; Labor, 246; Expenditures, 246; Allocation Factors, 246; Occupancy, 246; Summary, 247.

EXHIBITS

Exhibit 3–1.   The Profit Gap, 23

Exhibit 3–2.   Are Your Estimates Recovering Your Expenses?, 24

Exhibit 3–3.   Compositized Direct Labor, 25

Exhibit 3–4.   How Profit Mix Affects Profits, 28

Exhibit 3–5.   Variations in Total Overhead Cost with Product Mix, 30

Exhibit 5–1.   The Box of Cost Elements, 41

Exhibit 5–2.   Production Report By Order and Operation, 46

Exhibit 5–3.   Production Report By Machine-Group, 46

Exhibit 5–4.   Production Report By Factory Order and Worker, 47

Exhibit 5–5.   Downtime Form Envelope, 48

Exhibit 5–6.   Production Report By Order and Operation, 48

Exhibit 5–7.   Overdesigned Worker's Time Ticket, 49

Exhibit 7–1.   The Converting Facilities Classification Sheet, 62

Exhibit 7–1a.   Converting Facilities Classification Sheet (XYZ Corporation), 63

Exhibit 7–2.   Determinants of Production Centers, 64

Exhibit 7–3.   Determination of Net Working Space, 66

Exhibit 7–3a.   Determination of "Net Working Space" (XYZ Corporation), 66

Exhibit 7–4.   Converting Product Mix to Annual Machine Hours, 70

Exhibit 7–5.   Testing the Balance of Annual Machine Hours, 71

Exhibit 7–6.   Monthly Movement of Overhead Portion of a Machine-Hour Rate, 72

Exhibit 7–7.   Effect of Inflation on Purchasing Power, 75

Exhibit 8–1.   The Crew Composition Table for a Corrugated Sheet Plant
                (Company ABC), 78

Exhibit 8–1a.   Crew Composition for XYZ Corporation, 79

Exhibit 9–1.   Condensed Operating Budget for Company ABC, 89

Exhibit 9–1a.   Condensed Operating Budget for XYZ Corporation, 90

Exhibit 9–2.   Price-Level Depreciation Chart, 95

Exhibit 9–3.   Condensed Flexible Budget (Activity Based on Direct Labor), 97

Exhibit 9–4.   Condensed Flexible Budget (Activity Based on Sales), 99

Exhibit 9–5.   Example of "Step" Type Semi-Variable Expense: Supervision, 101

Exhibit 9–6.   Example of Straight-Line Type of Semi-Variable Expense: Electricity, 102

Exhibit 9–7.   Development of Total Departmental Flexible Budget in Relation
                to Productive Activity, 103

Exhibit 9–8.   Example of Calculation of Sum-of-Digits Depreciation Method, 109

Exhibit 10–1.   Simple Example of How Budgeted Expenses are Allocated
                to Production Centers, 112

Exhibit 10–2.   Valid Allocation Factors for Five Different Companies, 114

Exhibit 10–3.   Corrugated Sheet Plant (Company ABC), 115

Exhibit 10–3a.   Metalworking Plant (XYZ Corporation), 115

Exhibit 10–4.   Corrugated Sheet Plant (change in Allocation Factors), 117

Exhibit 10–5.   Setup Box Plants with Identical Production Center, 119

Exhibit 11–1.   MHR Summary Sheet, 121

Exhibit 11–1a.   MHR Summary Sheet for XYZ Corporation, 121

Exhibit 11–2.   MHR Summary Sheet, 123

Exhibit 11–3.   Effect on MHR Interchange, 123

Exhibit 11–4.   Setup Box Companies A and B, 124

Exhibit 12–1.   Percentage Comparisons of Different Allocation Factors in Meat Packing, 130

Exhibit 13–1.   Table of Production Standards Used in Screw Machine Plant: "Miscellaneous Cutting," 147

Exhibit 13–2.   Table of Production Standards Used in Screw Machine Plant: "Clamping," 147

Exhibit 13–3.   Table of Production Standards Used in Screw Machine Plant: "Turret Lathe Loading," 148

Exhibit 13–4.   Table of Production Standards Used in Screw Machine Plants: "Setup," 149

Exhibit 13–5.   Table of Production Standards for Operating Boring Mill, 150

Exhibit 13–6.   Table of Production Standards Used in Corrugated Container Plants: Run Printer-Slotter, 151

Exhibit 13–7.   Table of Production Standards Used in Corrugated Container Plants: Band Saw Cut Pads, 152

Exhibit 13–8.   Table of Production Standards Used in Corrugated Container Plants: Bale Waste, 153

Exhibit 13–9.   Table of Production Standards Used in Corrugated Container Plants: Warehousing, 153

Exhibit 13–10.   Table of Production Standards for Soldering Electrical Terminal, 154

Exhibit 13–11.   Table of Production Standards for Machine Wrapping of Setup Boxes, 155

Exhibit 13–12.   Sample Screw Machine Shop's Estimating Sheet (front side), 156

Exhibit 13–12a. Sample Screw Machine Shop's Estimating Sheet (back side), 158

Exhibit 13–13.   Sample Estimate and Job-Cost Analysis Sheet, 159

Exhibit 13–14.   Sample Cost Sheet: Novelty Manufacturing, 160

Exhibit 14–1.   Flexible, Multi-Level Operating Budget, Showing Segregation of Fixed and Variable Expenses, 170

Exhibit 14–2.   Expense Assignment Worksheet—Fixed and Variable (for 50 Percent and 90 Percent Activity Levels), 173

Exhibit 14–3.   Fixed-Variable Multi-Level MHR Summary Sheet, 174

Exhibit 14–4.   Three-Operation Full Conversion Cost Estimate, 175

Exhibit 14–5.   Three-Operation Fixed-Variable Conversion Cost Estimate, 175

Exhibit 14–6.   Fixed-Variable Order Estimate and Job Cost Analysis, 177

Exhibit 14–7.   Table Showing Net Profit Trend Based on Committed Selling Prices and Estimated Expenses, 179

Exhibit 14–7a.   Comparison of Fixed Recovery with Operating Budget at End of Three Months, 181

Exhibit 15–1.   Production Center Costs, 187

Exhibit 15–2.   Conversion of Product Sales to Production-Center Activity (Condition A), 188

Exhibit 15–3.   Condensed Cost Sheet (Condition A), 191

Exhibit 15–4.   Target for Sales Profitability Potential of Production Centers, 192

Exhibit 15–5.   Recovery Characteristics of Products and Production Centers, 193

Exhibit 15–6.   Actual vs. Budgeted Recovery vs. Maximum Recovery Before Duplication of Facilities, 194

Exhibit 15–7.   Product Recovery Ability (Condition A), 195

Exhibit 15–8.   Recovery Ability of Products vs. Recovery Attained by Sales (Sales Working at Cross Purposes with Production), 195

Exhibit 15–9.   Recovery Ability of Products vs. Products' Sales (Sales Not Supporting Needs of Production Recovery), 196

Exhibit 15–10.   The Influence on Recovery of the Drive for Commissions, 197

Exhibit 15–11.   Expense Recovery Per Dollar of Sales (Condition A), 198

Exhibit 15–12.   Recovery vs. Sales Booked vs. Sales Effort, 199

Exhibit 15–13.   Conversion of Product Sales to Production Center Activity (Condition B), 201

Exhibit 15–14.   Product Recovery Ability (Condition B), 201

Exhibit 15–15.   Recovery Ability of Products vs. Recovery Attained by Sales (Sales Supporting Production Economy), 203

Exhibit 15–16.   Economic Effect of Product Mix (Yearly Basis), 204

Exhibit 15–17.   Economic Effect on Both Product Mixes, 205

Exhibit 15–18.   Hourly Effect of Both Product Mixes, 206

Exhibit 15–19.   Annual Breakeven-Recovery Needs vs. Actual Attainment, 207

Exhibit 15–19a. Condensed P & L: Conditions A and B, 207

Exhibit 15–20.   Conversion of Production Center Added Profitability to Products, 209

Exhibit 15–21.   Sales Contact Effort, 209

Exhibit 15–22.   Products' Profitability Index vs. Contact Effort, 210

Exhibit 17–1.   Production Center Monthly Activity Report, 225

Exhibit 17–2.   Cost Recovery Statement, 226

Exhibit 17–2a.   Cost Recovery Statement (end of First Quarter), 228

Exhibit 17–2b.   Cost Recovery Statement (end of Second Quarter), Showing Action Taken to Improve First-Quarter Results (Exhibit 17–2a), 229

Exhibit 17–3.   Production Center Recovery Test Form, 231

Exhibit 17–4.   Direct-Labor Cost Summary Form, 234

Exhibit 17–5.   Labor Operation Report Form, 235

Exhibit 17–6.   Product and Operation Direct-Labor Cost Sheet, 236

Exhibit 17–7.   Summary of Standard and Actual Conversion Costs, 237

Exhibit 17–8.   Distribution of Current Overhead Expenses by Product Classifications, 238

Exhibit 17–9.   Weekly Production Report, 239

Exhibit 17–10.   Fixed-Variable Cost Center Recovery Statement, 241

Exhibit 17–11.   Fixed-Variable Production Center Recovery Test Form, 242

COST-ESTIMATING AND PRICING

With Machine-Hour Rates

Section 1

INDUSTRY
COSTING
PROBLEMS

1. THE WHAT, WHY, AND HOW OF COSTS

2. TRADITIONAL COSTING AND MACHINE-HOUR RATES

3. PROFIT EFFECT OF PRODUCT MIX AND FACILITY USAGE

4. PROPER APPROACH TO OVERHEAD COST ALLOCATION

Chapter 1

THE WHAT, WHY, AND
HOW OF COSTS

Business enterprise is organized for the purpose of making a profit. The more consistently profits are made, the more reliable future planning will be. Further, as its level of profits is raised, a company has the opportunity to recuperate the money invested in its facilities. The risk of capital investment is taken in the hope of generating enough sales income gradually to pay off the investment, meet expenses and have enough money left over as a fair return for the investment risk taken.

Simply stated, profit is the difference between income from products sold and the costs of making and selling those products. You may call the income sales or revenue, and you may like to differentiate between expenses and costs. In this book, we make no such distinction in terms, only in content, and we shall supply criteria for both expenses and costs.

Sometimes sales income is a reflection of what price leaders and competitors do; in other cases it is based directly on a markup above the figures on the cost sheet. And perhaps prices may even be reached by instinctive estimate. In any case, knowledge of costs and of how to use them is one of the most powerful competitive tools in the present razor-sharp industrial economy. Some companies have modern *cost-reduction* programs but with *cost-estimating* systems so antiquated that they actually drain off some of the profit potential.

A cost-estimating system worth anything must reflect accurately and currently all changes in the company so that management may price effectively in its markets, channel its sales effort for maximum profits, enhance profitable facilities, discard unvirile facilities, and plan for expansion. Management must know its costs while the events in manufacturing are current, not "after the fact" when the events have become ancient history. A proper cost-estimating system must be able to predict in advance, within close limits, the ultimate costs of running an order.

For pricing, however, costs are only the starting point. Since competition and customer demand must be considered, selling prices rarely have a rigid relationship to cost. Pricing is more an over-all total-product planning task where management analyzes the possible courses of action, balances one against the other and then selects the one which promises to be the most advantageous. For the selling effort, management must key sales effort not only to the most favorable markets but also must peg these efforts to the most profitable company facilities so that the investment capital is made as virile as possible.

No matter from what areas profits ultimately are produced, the basic function of a cost-estimating system is to help management to operate at a profit. Profits can come from a proper markup on sales, from a change in the sales mixture to produce the most effective use of equipment, from a change in production methods based on provable cost data, or from other sources.

What Are Costs?

For a company to operate profitably, expenses must be properly identified, classified, reported and allocated to the various products so that the customer pays for these in the selling prices, leaving a fair return to the owners. Of course, where "competition sets the price" the profit return may not be so attractive, but the manufacturer who enters into this type of transaction should enter with full knowledge of his own cost "floor" even though he sells this cost at someone else's price level. The traditional cost systems leave much to be desired in these marginal situations, since there is a lack of advance measurement of the cost floor and often companies find themselves selling below their actual out-of-pocket costs.

While, in general, selling prices of certain products are not established on the basis of production costs, the total aggregate selling price of a firm's products over a period of time must exceed the total cost of making those products. Within a specified period there are many fluctuations in cost and selling price, because of the nature of the particular product, the time of year, the customers' demand. A proper set of cost data skillfully used will allow the manufacturer to exploit such factors to his own advantage and thus obtain a greater gap between the total period costs and sales income. Of course, costs on the estimating sheet must be a reflection of actual costs, or the manufacturer will lose the good orders and get poor ones.

But what are costs? How are they identified? What do we do with them?

A cost or an expense is generated in every molecule of a company's geography, on every square inch, from every act and activity—during each second of the company's life. Costs never stop being born while the company is breathing although some costs grow at different rates than others. Indeed, costs, which are created in myriad ways, never remain static. In one second, a plant incurs labor, depreciation, and occupancy costs, and each of these costs acts in varying degree on every aspect of the company's economy.

A cost is born when a lathe is purchased; another when a switch to operate it is thrown. Direct costs are incurred in production: when a setup is made, bar stock is loaded, a piece turned or a product inspected. Indirect costs also enter in: when the floor is swept, the tool crib attendant issues a tool, a grinder is repaired, or when the supervisor checks a dimension on a print.

Some costs are quiet and proceed unobserved: rental is paid, interest expense is paid, depreciation expense purrs along 24 hours per day, 365 day per year. Other costs are generated outside of the factory: a salesman knocks on a prospect's door, the manager counsels the foreman, an invoice is typed, a pack of estimating blanks is ordered.

All these costs, to some measurable degree, have to be paid for by the customer via the product's estimating sheet. First, however, all cost must be reduced to the same dimension; that is, all cost elements have to be considered "by product." Here is where we encounter the first difficulty, because incurred costs are not paid for "by product."

Rent is paid for space, by the month; payroll is paid for human labor, by the week; material is paid for per lot, by invoice; and depreciation is paid for ownership of machinery, by the year. Nowhere in manufacturing enterprise, where converting of raw materials is being performed and where, in effect, plant and machine time is being sold, can expenses be imputed to each individual manufactured product. Expenses are incurred in blanket form, and it is the task of the manufacturer to segregate them and apportion them to products so that they may be recovered without overpricing the customer but leaving enough room for a reasonable profit.

Estimating Systems Must Answer Questions

If the estimating system cannot be depended upon to recover costs consistently, regardless of product mix, volume mix and facilities usage, then profits cannot be planned and pricing becomes insecure. The estimating system must have the inherent ability to answer questions such as these:

How does a foreman's salary get converted so that it can be charged to the customer?

How can depreciation expense on a lathe be allocated to an order?

How is the running time of a press charged?

How can the cost of stand-by facilities be added to all orders?

How are storage costs added?

Cost is the composite result of many different elements, some of which are actual and others estimated, some fixed and some variable, some easily noticeable and others obscure. For this reason, there is no single exact cost, but, on the contrary, total cost will vary continuously and its amount will depend upon the system used to determine it. This dependency makes it of the utmost importance that a company employ the most correct costing system possible.

Classification of Costs

The first differentiation to be made is between direct and indirect costs. *Direct* costs are those which are the result of a direct contribution to the manufacture of a product. For example: a setup is made, a bar is loaded, a piece turned, a product inspected. *Indirect* costs are those generated by activities which, although necessary for the operation of a factory, are not a direct result of the manufacture of a product. Such expenses are the sweeping of a floor, the issuance of a tool by the tool crib attendant, the repairing of a machine, supervisory checking of dimensions on a print, and the like.

Fixed and Variable Costs

This book will also deal with the separation of *fixed* (period) and *variable* (direct, out-of-pocket) costs, how these costs apply to product costing, and to the development of flexible operating budgets. The task of pricing will also be discussed.

In general, fixed costs may be defined as those costs which do not vary with volume, but rather are incurred with time. They are also known as stand-by costs or period costs.

Fixed costs include diverse elements. For example, depreciation expense is one form of fixed cost. It is referred to as sunk cost because very little can be done to change its magnitude; the expense was incurred in the past with the purchase of the machine. Other fixed costs are cash outlay costs, such as executive salaries. These fixed costs rarely change except for wide variances in the operating economy of a company.

Variable costs, on the other hand, are those costs which are known to vary fairly directly with volume. As far as orders are concerned, there are out-of-pocket expenses, such as direct labor, direct materials and direct overhead costs. Often we desire to know just what variable or out-of-pocket costs are involved in producing an order. In the case of the Operating Budgets, used in the development of the MHR, it is desirable to separate the fixed from the variable costs so that an Operating Budget for varying levels of activity can be projected. This step provides the basis for flexible marginal pricing and will be discussed at length later.

Manufacturing and Non-Manufacturing Costs

Two other categories vital in the development of the MHR, are the classification of expenses into *manufacturing* and *non-manufacturing*.

Manufacturing expenses are those factory costs which represent payments for space, occupancy, power, machinery, fringe benefits, and indirect labor. This is the primary group of factory overhead expenses.

Non-manufacturing expenses are those which support the productive effort but are non-factory expenses, such as delivery and warehouse charges, and selling and administrative expenses.

The manufacturing and non-manufacturing expenses comprise the overhead segment of the individual machine-hour rates. When the hourly direct labor cost, found in the Crew Composition Table (Figures 8–1 and 8–1a), is added to these costs the total or composite MHR for the product, by center or operation, is obtained.

Cost Allocation

The function of a manufacturer is to make his services, facilities, and technical knowledge available to the customer. Consequently, the customer must pay for a portion of each one of these items so that the manufacturer gets back all of his incurred costs. The industrialist suffers the risks of operating his business in terms of investment capital, that is, machinery, buildings and working capital for maintaining an inventory, a labor force and other factors of production. Against these risks the manufacturer balances his profits, and the selling prices that should bring in the expected profits. When estimated costs are wrong, anticipated profits may be a mere hope.

The manufacturer must apportion his expenses to products, so that these expenses are recovered without overpricing the customer and leaving enough room for a reasonable profit. However, as will be shown in future chapters, the direct allocation of blanket costs to products victimizes the manufacturer, making him a slave to illogical theories and magic formulas. If an estimating system cannot be depended upon to recover costs consistently regardless of product mix, volume mix, facility usage, and other influencing factors, then profits cannot be planned and pricing becomes insecure. The man who knows his costs has the best chance for profit-making and survival.

The charge for the use of machinery should recover a part of the machinery's fixed cost through the product, based on the time the equipment is used. Consequently, an indirect allocation, via the facility usage, is considered to be an equitable means of costing, and it is one which will lead consistently to profit-making. The machine-hour system of costing, to be discussed later on, also makes such recovery possible, as this system is based on the allocation of expenses according to equipment utilization and ownership cost.

Reporting of Costs

After a cost is identified, it must be reported in a suitable form for convenient evaluation. As mentioned earlier, costs take several forms. They occur in different geographical and financial areas of the company. They also move and change at different velocities and so require means of reporting them especially adapted to the manufacturer's needs. Machinery depreciation is not reported in the same way as the purchase of a lubricant. The former is accounted for automatically in the general ledger as a regular accounting routine, while the latter is reduced to product usage by the estimator. But each must be handled separately so that it finds its way to the estimating sheet properly. As another example, consider how totally different the reporting of an interest loan expense is from the cost of a machine make-ready. Again, the former expense is extracted from the general accounting books, while the latter is calculated from a payroll analysis.

Costs for Pricing

One of the most important benefits of a knowledge of company costs is its application for pricing purposes. Although in practice prices are affected by many forces over which the manufacturer has little or no control, still good cost information is the basis for any correct estimating system used for pricing purposes. A company that has an intimate and accurate knowledge of its costs can base its price estimates on a sound foundation that will bring few miscalculations.

A proper costing system will, in the long run, improve the company's competitive position within the industry. This may help explain the fact that today trade associations are trying to promote good accounting practices among their members, rather than emphasizing monopolistic activities, such as price fixing, as a means to increase profits.

Costs for Facility Profits

A proper cost system also helps determine which machines or production centers in a plant are the most profitable. This is an important consideration, since it enables management to reflect this profitability in their sales emphasis. The product mix should maximize profits through the optimum use of the production facilities. It is possible that because of inaccurate cost information the sales emphasis may be placed on the less profitable products, thereby altering the economy of the company by misdirecting the sales effort. For example, if a company manufactures a product on expensive facilities, it is essential that enough units will be sold to justify the maintenance of these facilities. Otherwise, the company will find itself in the position of a poor investor, because the monies liberated by the sales will not provide sufficient return on its investment. Invariably this also results in tying up excessive capital in inventory. Therefore, instead of merchandising the time of his facilities, the manufacturer becomes merchandiser of his raw material inventory—a condition that may well overburden his financial structure.

Costs for "Make or Buy"

Costs are also used in decisions involving purchases and manufacture. With the help of a proper cost system, a manufacturer can evaluate the desirability of maintaining or establishing a department as opposed to having the operations performed for him on the outside.

Costs for Optimizing Product Mix

In a multiproduct company, proper costs also help determine which products will be manufactured, according to the profitability with which the facilities can be operated in support of the product mix. A proper costing system also shows the relationship of profitability of facilities or products to the marketing costs required to promote and sell the product. In addition, costs allow the manufacturer to evaluate the profitability of his sales territories.

Costs for Long-Range Planning

Costs are also essential for the planning of expansions, regardless of whether these expansions are physical or functional in nature. In this instance, proper costs will indicate where and when facilities should be added. If, for example, sales keep a major facility active 90 percent of its capacity, the decision to add an additional facility to absorb a new sales drive which will utilize this type of facility, must revolve around the cost of the inactive portion of the duplicated facility. For example, an offset printing press costing $80,000 is kept active 1,800 out of 2,000 potential hours, and there is no possibility of operating a second shift. A sales drive which requires an additional 1,200 hours of this facility center is anticipated. To support these additional hours, management is faced with the purchase of a second offset press at the same acquisition price. The decision that management now has to make, since both presses operating together will provide 4,000 potential annual hours, is whether the company will make more profit with one press at 1,800 hours of activity, or with the 2 presses with 3,000 hours of activity, considering the impact of the cost of the 1,000 hours of inactivity that will be the result of the two-press operation. Unless management has sufficient cost data on which to base this decision, it is possible that they will fail to take advantage of a market opportunity, or may be committed to an equipment expansion which will limit their future profit elasticity. This means that the company may be faced with a greater loss or less profit at a greater sales level.

In planning for the long term, a company must know in advance the impact of a non-producing expansion, such as addition to sales offices or to administrative staffing. For example, how much more must be made in sales to justify the addition of a new executive, so that the company remains at the same dollar profit level? And if a sales office is to be added, what will have to be the increase in sales to maintain the same financial position? If a company plans a price reduction in one of its product lines, what increase in sales will be required to overcome this reduction without disturbing the dollar profit level? And if the company increases productive or non-productive facilities, how much more vulnerable will it be to recessions as balanced against its opportunity for higher profits in boom times? Proper costs provide the basic information for making these determinations possible.

For example, in one company the addition of a $30,000-a-year executive may require an increase in sales of $225,000 to maintain the same margin of dollar profits, whereas in another company, in the same industry and with the same volume of business, an increase of $500,000 in sales may be required. The case may also be that one company can justify a 10% price reduction by an increase of 22% in sales, while another company in the same industry, also doing the same volume of business, may require a far different sales increase to justify the same price reduction.*

Costs for the Shorter Term

For the shorter term, proper costs, when separated into their fixed and variable elements, will give us the out-of-pocket and break-even point of specific orders and specific facilities. Having this information, a company is in a position to accept marginally priced work. In so doing, it is seeking to recover its out-of-pocket expenses, on the theory that its fixed sunk costs (depreciation and the like) are present irrespective of volume. However, discretion should be used in this case to avoid booking work which causes bottlenecks in the plant, or which occupies facilities at a time when more profitable work is available.

* See S. A. Tucker, "How to Use Break-Even Charts in Your Decision-Making," *Iron Age*, March 24, 1960.

Chapter 2

TRADITIONAL COSTING
AND MHR

A company that does not know the cost of making its own products is like an unguided missile. It may take off but nobody knows where it will land. So it is with cost-estimating systems. A company manufactures products, but if it cannot predict in advance the amount of profit it will earn, it must wait until the periodic profit-and-loss statements are published—which may be too late. As far as sales orders are concerned, this late knowledge of the financial results certainly comes too late for useful managerial action.

Yet, numerous companies operate on the basis of poor cost information—which, of course, may be a source of delight to their competitors (or a major headache due to the necessity of having to meet lower competitive prices). That doesn't mean that these companies have poor production methods. It does mean that regardless of their methods or the degree of streamlining in their plants and offices, the product costs are not an effective guide to their pricing nor to other decisions.

The Big Problem

The key to the cost-estimating puzzle lies in the allocation of the overhead costs to the product. This problem will be discussed in greater detail in later chapters. As we have said earlier, the apportioning of direct materials and direct labor costs to the product is fairly routine. That is, you *can see* the material that goes into a product and by tracing a product through its manufacturing process you *can see* what labor it took to produce it. From this point on, simple records will give the materials and labor costs.

We are up against a much bigger problem when it comes to adding an amount of cost to the labor and materials costs to account for the overhead expenses, because, as we have said earlier, overhead costs are not directly identifiable with specific products. You *cannot see* the piece of the manager's salary in the product, nor the machine's depreciation expense, nor the cost of the material handlers who came in contact with the product.

Therefore, over the years myriad formulas cropped up, each claiming an ability to allocate to products a proper share of overhead expenses. Cost-finding became hampered by unnecessary complications and illogical theories. Shortcuts, formulas, magic numbers, factors and percentages confused the cost-finding process and generated tons of paperwork. Often these methods arose out of a need for quick quotations, and many managements never recognized product costing as a science. Once the idea of the magic number became implanted, it was hard to pry loose. It became even more difficult to do when owners pointed to a profit figure on a profit-and-loss statement as proof of their judgment in applying overhead. Even today, a large part of the discussion at local trade association meetings revolves around overhead formulas. This practice is tantamount to swapping medical prescriptions. What is fine for one may be poison for another.

Unfortunately, the use of the magic number does not *find* costs, it *forces* them. Overhead gets spread with a bulldozer, filling in holes and levelling peaks. Management is victimized by the current shortcut formula and alternately rides the peaks of profit and loss as the overhead formula approaches or departs from actual costs.

Traditional Costing Methods

Outlined below are a few of the more commonly used systems for allocating overhead to the product. In common to all of them is the use of a ratio or percentage. This percentage is related to one or more cost factors, depending on the particular method.

PRIME COST METHOD: Under this method, the overhead is added to the production order on a percentage basis. The rate percent is determined by the ratio of the total overhead of the cost period, usually a profit-and-loss reporting period, to the total prime cost of the products manufactured during the cost period. Thus, if the total materials cost during the cost period is $500,000, the total labor cost $300,000 and the total overhead costs $400,000, the rate is 50%. (Overhead is one-half of prime cost = materials + direct labor costs.)

This method is simple, conveniently developed, and easy to use. An estimator is given a percent rate and after he sums up labor and materials on his estimating sheet, he adds on overhead simply by taking this percentage of the total.

The disadvantages, though, are serious. For one thing, there is no sensible relation between overhead expense and the amount of raw materials used. Raw material can be very high and the cost of facilities used to manufacture the product very low, so that the product becomes overloaded with overhead expense because of its inherently high material-cost content. Naturally, the reverse is also true. The product may consume little in materials cost but may require very expensive equipment in its manufacture, leaving it shy of sufficient overhead-expense loading.

Exactly the same thing is true concerning the relationship between overhead expense and direct labor costs. It is perfectly possible for low labor items to require massive overhead expense support, and vice versa. When the reader considers that in the usual multiproduct company products contain varying amounts of direct labor and materials cost, he will find it unlikely that this fixed percent rate will equitably distribute overhead expense to all.

MATERIALS COST METHOD: Under this method, the overhead expense is added to the order cost as a percentage of the materials cost. Thus if the total materials cost for a cost period is $500,000 and the total overhead cost amounts to $400,000, the rate is 80%.

This method is also simple to develop and apply but except where used in very special cases, it will widely distort the distribution of overhead expenses. This method, while still a convenient compromise compared to the machine-hour rate method, can be applied to bulk materials industries such as forgings, cement, sugar, paint, bread and the like. However, it can be applied only on a weight instead of a dollar basis.

For example, if a brass foundry produces 800,000 pounds of castings per month of uniform style and weight and the overhead expenses for the month are $80,000, the overhead per pound is 10 cents. Thus the overhead expense estimate for a casting weighing 5 pounds would be 50 cents. If, however, the foundry's products are *not* uniform and it produces a variety of castings which vary in weight, shape and style, requiring all manner of coremaking, then this method becomes inequitable. Under this circumstance, the simple but heavy casting will be overpriced, because of excessively allocated overhead, and the foundry will lose business. On the other hand, the complex but light casting will be underpriced because of the insufficient overhead allocated and it will attract brisk sales activity, but not sufficient profits.

Some bulk product plants have refined this method by subdividing their overhead expenses according to types or classes of castings. The paperwork and fine dividing lines required to support this modification of the basic system is not worth the effort, especially if one compares it to the similar effort required to develop and maintain a machine-hour rate system, which has the further overwhelming advantage of being equitable and fully logical.

DIRECT LABOR DOLLAR METHOD: With this method the overhead expenses are added to the order cost as a percentage of the direct labor cost. Thus, if the total direct labor costs in a period amount to $300,000 and the overhead expenses are $400,000, the rate is 133%.

Again, this is a simple method to develop and establish but it contains the dangers discussed under the Prime Cost Method. Adherents of this method claim that each article made incurs overhead expenses in direct proportion to the direct wages paid for its production. This is a false theory, since there are so many items of overhead expense which are neither a function of direct labor nor vary in proportion to it. Take the president's salary or machinery depreciation, for example. Regardless of how the direct labor varies, neither the president's salary nor the depreciation expenses will change. Yet, of all of the traditional overhead formulas, this one seems to be the most popular.

Rarely is the Direct Labor Dollar method equitable for distributing overhead to products. The type of plant in which some resemblance of equity is found is one in which the operations and rates of workers' pay are uniform and the type of equipment they all operate is similar. Further, to make this method valid, the class of work and type of product involved would have to be very much alike. Handwork or non-machine industries are the safest for this method.

In some cases, departmental or product overhead rates taken as a percentage of labor are used to reduce some of the inevitable inequities raised by such a procedure, as discussed under the Prime Cost Method. While this is a better approach than applying the overhead percentage factory-wide, the effort it takes to do this can be better spent in developing a far better cost-estimating system, namely Machine-Hour Rates.

In a furniture company that makes both upholstered pieces and highly polished tables, the total overhead rate amounted to 90%. Developing rates for each of the major departments resulted in the following rates: Mill department, 80%, cabinet making, 95%, finishing, 76%, upholstering, 72%, packing, 91%. In a metalworking plant which had used an over-all overhead rate of 190%, the departmental rates were: punchpresses 370%, drillpresses 216%, small lathes 210%, automatic lathes 476%, hand assembly 142%.

To summarize, the disadvantages of the Direct Labor Dollar Method are that it does not consider the cost value of the product made by services other than direct labor, viz.: machinery; in some departments, and for some products, expensive facilities constitute the largest cost element. The method assigns overhead based on the dollar which may not be a true measure of cost, since many overhead expenses, such as taxes, insurance, and depreciation, are functions of time. Also, this method penalizes operations performed by highly paid workers with more overhead than operations performed by lower-rate operators. This means inequitable allocation of overhead to the product where two or more operators do the same operation on different jobs or product groups, but are paid varying rates per hour. Worst of all, the Direct Labor Dollar Method deprives the owners of the enterprise from a consistent recovery of monies invested in productive facilities, since the criterion of large recovery in this method is the existence of a sizeable direct labor content in the product's sales dollar. This direct labor content may or may not have been produced on expensive facilities.

DIRECT LABOR HOUR METHOD: This method is similar to the previous one but includes one refinement. It is based on the assumption that overhead expense is a function of time and that therefore products should carry overhead in direct proportion to the time of the *direct labor* employed to produce it. What may baffle the conscientious but inexperienced investigator is the fact that this method deals with time and hence seems equitable, since overhead expenses also are incurred with time.

Such is not the case. For if the products, facilities, and labor skills vary widely, no average overhead cost per direct labor hour will be indicative of the actual overhead of any department or product. This method is, therefore, practically as illogical as the previously mentioned Labor Dollar method. Consider the wide variances in production-machinists' pay and acquisition costs of precision machine tools.

UNIT OF PRODUCT METHOD: This is the method whereby the overhead expenses are divided by the number of product units manufactured in a cost period. Thus, in a period wherein the number of assemblies total 10,000 and the overhead expenses $50,000, the overhead cost per assembly is $5.

Obviously, this is the most direct method for obtaining the overhead component of product cost, since the product itself determines the amount of the overhead expense. However, this method has severe limitations and can be used only where one product is made or where products are few, closely related and have some common denominator such as weight or volume. Examples of industries where the use of this method may be considered safe, but still not logical, are the shoe industry and the mattress industry, where the size is standard and the grades held fairly closely.

Conceptually, it is easy to understand that all percentages developed from previous data immediately imply that the coming period in which the rate will be used will be exactly the same as the period from which the rate was drawn. They assume that the same products will be made, in the same quantities; that the same facilities will be used for the same length of time; that labor, material and overhead expenses will be the same; and that the expenses of the conduct of the business will be the same. Obviously, the plant that uses systems drawing no logical relationship between overhead expenses and the base on which they are allocated is taking an exercise in faith and chance.

MACHINE-HOUR RATE METHOD: In contrast to the previous methods, the machine-hour rate system allocates overhead to the products in accordance with their direct consumption of overhead load, and makes each product carry its fair share of the overhead expenses. Instead of assigning overhead expenses based on some illogical base that is not a function of the way overhead is used, the machine-hour rate method apportions the various components of overhead to the production facilities, on an appropriate base equitable for each of the different expenses. Thus, electricity expense is allocated to each facility on the basis of horsepower-hours, rent on the basis of square feet occupied by the machine, and so on. This procedure continues until a portion of each expense has been assigned to each producing facility. When all the expenses of a facility are added and then divided by the expected hours of operation of that facility, the cost of operating that machine or work station for one hour—the MHR—is obtained.

Then, in estimating the operating time for each specific facility involved in the manufacture of the product, and multiplying this operating time by the machine-hour rate, we obtain the total cost of the operation—which automatically includes the correct overhead. Summarizing just the operational costs (conversion costs) gives the total labor and overhead costs of the product. Thus, in the MHR System only those labor and overhead costs which enter into the actual manufacture of the product are charged. There is no average overhead figure applied which acts to undercost products when expensive facilities are used prominently in their manufacture; nor is there overcosting which penalizes products which require the use of little expensive equipment.

In effect, under the MHR System each machine or production center becomes a total economic entity, as though a separate company. In fact, because each production center carries a piece of every expense incurred in the operation of the total enterprise (except materials) it can be evaluated individually for profitability and for return on the investment. Profitability of each machine can be emphasized in sales to bring in orders for products which make long use of its activity and capacity. Without such integration of sales and production, expensive facilities which have high annual ownership costs may remain relatively inactive, their use depending on the vagaries of accident rather than being adroitly planned. Unused costs become a charge against profits.

While Section 2 of this book will deal in great detail with the actual development of machine-hour rates, it may be useful to explain here briefly the calculation of a machine-hour rate. If it is estimated that a small grinder is to be operated 1,600 hours during the coming year, with an overhead expense totalling $32,000 (this sum composed of numerous items of overhead expense which have been allocated on various equitable bases, as discussed previously), the *overhead portion* of the machine-hour rate is $32,000 divided by 1,600 hours, amounting to $20 per hour. If an order for a certain product requires the services of this facility for 2.5 hours as part of its operational process, the total overhead cost of this facility is 2.5 hours × $20, or $50. If the direct-labor worker receives $3 per hour in wages, the total cost of the operation, excluding materials cost, is:

Order No. 8081
Part 2–676

Grinding Operation:

Direct Labor	2.5 hrs. × $ 3 =	$ 7.50
Overhead Cost	2.5 hrs. × $20 =	$50.00
Total Conversion Cost of Grinding		$57.50

As will be shown in Section 2, modern MHR practice combines overhead per hour with the hourly direct labor cost, since both are incurred by the same dimension, namely, time. This composite rate or hourly conversion rate is what we will refer to as the machine-hour rate. Thus, in the above example, the MHR is $23 and this rate carries a piece of every expense in the company except materials.

Arithmetic Comparison of MHR with Direct Labor Method

As an illustration of the inequities introduced by the Direct Labor Method of cost-estimating, let us consider the comparative estimating rates of two pieces of equipment. One is an expensive horizontal boring mill and the other an inexpensive small engine lathe:

Expense Category	*Total Cost*	*Boring Mill*	*Engine Lathe*
Building Expenses	$ 3,000	$ 2,500	$ 500
Machinery Costs	$22,000	$20,000	$2,000
Indirect Labor Expenses	$10,000	$ 8,000	$2,000
General Expenses	$ 8,000	$ 5,500	$2,500
Total Period Costs	$43,000	$36,000	$7,000
Normal Period Hours	2000	1000	1000
MHR (Overhead Portion)	—	$36	$7
Hourly Rate	$21.50	—	—

It should be clear to the reader that if the hourly rate of $21.50 is added for overhead expenses to all products for every hour of operational time, then products which do not use the boring mill very much in their manufacture will be unfairly penalized by the presence of the large expenses contributed in the average figure of $21.50. This figure will tend to overcost those products. Conversely, for products which do use the boring mill for considerable lengths of time, an insufficient cost will be developed, and while this may result in attractively priced products, the sales revenue will be insufficient to repay the company for its large investment in the boring mill.

This is a vastly oversimplified illustration of the relative equities of both methods.

In actual manufacturing there are numerous production and machine centers, hand-work stations, and a much longer schedule of overhead expense categories. These elements will be further discussed in Section 2.

Summary of Machine-Hour Rate System and Advantages

The overhead rate for a machine or work center per hour is obtained by dividing the estimated overhead expense by the number of normal hours the facility will operate. This hourly overhead rate is then added to the direct hourly wages of the workers required to operate the facility. The composite rate (MHR) then costs the overhead and labor to the job or process by multiplying by the number of facility hours involved in each specific operation.

Thus, the MHR represents a *predetermined estimate* of the actual overhead and labor cost per hour for operating each facility or production center. And because of the nature of the testing and correcting features of the MHR plan, to be discussed in Section 4, it is simple to keep a running check on the accuracy of the estimates. Fast corrective action can be taken where required.

The advantages of the MHR are numerous:

a. From the accounting viewpoint, it gives the most accurate method of apportioning overhead expenses to the job or order;

b. From the production viewpoint, it gives an ideal method for estimating the cost of a job on a process sheet with a high degree of accuracy;

c. From management's viewpoint, the overhead allocation method is scientific, logical, sound, consistent and provable. Management's reports are realistic and there are no doubts about the dangers of undercosting or overcosting. Thus operating losses or failures to obtain jobs may be prevented.

d. MHR overcomes the problem of charging correct overhead when one worker tends several machines or where more workers have to be added to production centers to accommodate certain types of work.

e. From the financial viewpoint, it gives the profitability of each machine, work station, and process as if each were a separate operating entity. Accurate check is had on the speed of investment return of each facility, and when to add facilities or discard existing ones is decided based on the velocity of the monies recovered by the activity of each facility.

f. From the sales viewpoint, MHR makes possible more accurate quotations of the selling prices of jobs and permits the efforts of the sales department to be keyed directly (in terms of products) to the facilities of maximum profitability.

Chapter 3

PROFIT EFFECT OF
PRODUCT MIX
AND FACILITY USAGE

Product costing usually fails in the area of overhead expense allocation; no other costing inequity stands out so dramatically. Managements work hard at improving internal methods, but if the gains from this activity are not accurately reflected on the estimating sheet, the effort becomes academic. Improvements, obviously, may even produce an increase in costs.

Management unfortunately tends to view cost-finding or cost-estimating only as *paperwork*, a somehow needed evil. And yet, with just a little more effort, and in some cases not as much as they presently use to develop cost estimates, managements can have an excellent system for profit-planning.

Industry Costing Problems

Most industries have investments of some sort in equipment. Some of these investments involve sizeable capital, the graphic arts companies, for example, use expensive printing presses. Other industries have little or no machinery and their investments in equipment are restricted to work benches, hand tools and testing equipment. This case is typical of radio assembly plants.

Industries which use expensive equipment generally use it in processing raw materials, in taking the raw materials, and, at each successive operation, converting them to other shapes or sizes until they have all been converted into the finished product. This operation is typical of foundries, brass mills, and heavy machining companies. Industries in which little capital equipment is used usually assemble the finished products of other industries; and their main item of expense, outside of materials costs, is usually direct labor.

Expense Recovery

When converter-manufacturers buy a piece of processing equipment they do so in the hope that it will make profits for them. However, before profits can be made, the cost of owning, operating, and maintaining this equipment must be paid for. This is what is meant by *expense recovery.* In costing and pricing its products, the company must first recover the money it advanced for the use and ownership of its equipment. If the equipment is used to its maximum capacity and this use is costed equitably and priced properly, profits will result. If the equipment is kept idle, then the difference between the money recovered in sales of its products and the break-even money required to operate the equipment will be a loss, a charge that is, a charge against future profits.

Unfortunately, what keeps a facility idle is not always general business conditions. Very often it is a poor cost-estimating system which overprices products made on the facility, thus discouraging sales of products involving the facility. Idleness is also often the result of the particular product mix sold—which the sales department might have autonomously decided was easy to sell without considering the production department's need for expense recovery on costly equipment.

It is characteristic of converter-manufacturers to operate a wide variety of equipment of different sizes and capacities to accommodate myriad varieties of work on which many different operations are required. The cost of the equipment may vary. In addition, these manufacturers generally make more than one product, even though the difference may be only in size, style, shape, color, weight, or volume; or they may produce a variety of lines. Often more products are added simply to utilize equipment that has not been fully used. Sometimes the motive in adding new products is the utilization of existing *non-production* facilities, such as sales offices, warehouses, distributors, and even retail outlets. A recent example of this motive was the manufacture and direct sale of wax decorative candles by a prominent candy manufacturer, who thus was able to utilize more fully his existing retail stores.

Planned profits are the result of selecting a product mix which supports the needs of expense recovery in production. A proper product mix will provide a balanced condition of machinery use, which can then be reflected in selling prices to yield optimum profits. Of course, a consideration of the state of the market during the period is also in order.

Cost-Profit Averaging

Sometimes manufacturers inadvertently lose revenue on a large amount of their production and gain revenue on a small part because of the cost-estimating system in use. For example, in the corrugated container industry, some plants still cost out orders on the basis of square feet of board in the total container order. This assumes that the labor and overhead will be the same per square foot regardless of the type of container or the operations performed on it. But this is not the case. It is only so for one type of board passing through the corrugator. But once it leaves that facility it may be sold as sheets, or converted into containers which vary widely in lengths and widths and which may incorporate printing or include inserts and the like, making the actual square foot cost for labor and overhead vary from one up to twenty times the basic cost. If the product mix of such a plant gradually shifted to more expensive containers, the company would find itself losing more and more profits. The usual practice is to raise the square footage charge, but this, in turn, overprices the less expensive containers, which might constitute a large portion of the firm's sales income.

In a foundry, as another example, there are also wide ranges of equipment costs. In a gray and malleable iron foundry the practice was to use a percentage of direct labor cost for allocating overhead. This meant that the cost of uncored moulds still carried the overhead of the core room, even though the core room was not in the slightest way involved in the casting process. Weight also was considered inequitable because of the wide variety and the intricacies of the finished castings.

The use of weight as an allocation factor for overhead on parts produced on automatic screw machines is fair only if all of the screw machines are of the same type and size. Where secondary operations are involved, then the final cost figure will be distorted by the use of the secondary operations in the manufacture of the finished piece.

For the same reason, a direct labor base is improper. For while a piece may have considerable direct labor content, it may be that this is the result of operational work on inexpensive, slow equipment. This high direct labor content instantly acts to boost the cost of the piece, as it inherits unnaturally high overhead expense. Sales resistance may then result. And what happens-to the expensive facilities? Their overhead expenses are put in a pool together with the lower overhead costs of the inexpensive facilities and averaged down. The costs, so developed, will not recover in the selling prices a high enough amount of cost to compensate for the use and ownership of the expensive facilities.

An analysis in a plant making races for bearings, after the installation of machine-hour rates, showed these operational variances in the relationships of the overhead percentages to direct labor: Cut-off, 430%; Stamp, 560%; Harden, 310%; End Grind, 710%; Cork, 190%. And yet, until MHR was installed, the manufacturer was using one flat percentage for the over-all operation. No wonder they were losing money, even though their sales remained fairly stable. The clue was their product line: part of it was very popular and always backlogged with orders, the other part of it was extremely sluggish. Invariably the slow-moving items involved the company's most expensive equipment, and the losses caused by the lack of fixed-expense recovery at these centers were sufficient to put them in the red.

In another case, a plastic plant in the business of molding plastic buttons, levers, knobs and the like decided to add to their operation facilities for making similar items out of metal, including painting and finishing operations. The motive was obvious. They wanted to supply these parts in either plastic or metal to improve their competitive position. Heretofore they had a battery of molding machines and were using the weight method of allocating overhead. With the introduction of the operations of paint-mixing, dipping, anodizing, polishing, spraying and finishing they switched over to the direct labor basis of overhead allocation, with very poor results (not that the continued use of the weight method would have been any more equitable). A considerably lower level of sales for these metal parts was obtained than projected, even though the market for the parts existed.

Here was the trouble. In the metal finishing operations, the labor was more important than the equipment as a cost factor. The reverse was true at the plastic molding centers. Totalling all overhead and applying it uniformly to all products lowered the profits on plastic parts because insufficient overhead was charged, and overcosted the metal parts, because of the presence in the figures of the larger overhead expenses of the molding machines.

The Goal of Cost-Estimating

A proper estimating system should state in advance the probable cost of an article in production. In effect, a group of estimates, representative of the major components of product mix of a company, comprises a condensed profit-and-loss statement.

The P & L statement tells what happened *after* it has happened; each cost estimate plays an *advance* role in determining just what the P & L will ultimately show. The cost of a product is divided into three major segments: cost of materials, cost of productive labor and cost of total overhead. As previously stated, most companies have little trouble with the first two of these items; these are straightforward. The difficulty, of course, starts with the third: allocating overhead to the product. As we have said, it is this segment of costing that widens the gap between actual and estimated costs. Usually the actual costs are higher than those estimated, rather than the reverse; hence, as the gap grows, profits shrink. (See EXHIBIT 3–1).

If an estimating procedure is sound and equitable, it should recover all expenses consistently to provide the expected profits as they are stated on the estimate sheet. Here is a simple test to determine whether your estimating procedure accomplishes this goal.

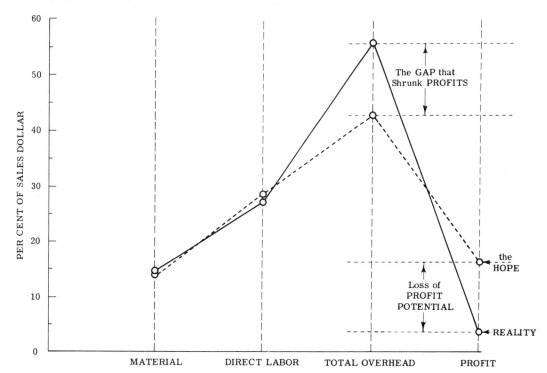

The uncharged-for overhead (by improper allocation) was taken out of profits and amounted to:
$. 135 × $2,750,000 = $371,250. (Net reduction in profits: $. 126 × $2,750,000 = $346,500)

Exhibit 3–1. The Profit Gap

Test Cost Recovery

EXHIBIT 3–2 shows how this test was made for a company that uses a variety of machining facilities and produces a wide range of products. Listed under each of the five parts is a condensation of the major expense elements that appeared on the actual estimating sheet. No matter how the estimate sheet was set up, it was possible to deposit the expense figures into the three categories of Direct Labor, Total Overhead and Materials Cost. The method of allocating overhead to each product was to assign uniformly 150% of the part's direct labor. This percentage was obtained from the 1959 P & L statement.

By this method of overhead allocation the company stated, in effect, that it was disregarding the facts that:

a. One piece of equipment cost more to operate than another;

b. The five products made varying use of facilities;

c. The circumstances which produced the 150% occurred in 1959 and were not necessarily the same for the current year.

The estimated total cost represented the addition of the three cost segments. Then the profit margin expected was added to get the actual selling price.

The product mix percentages indicate the dollar volume of each of the parts comprising the major product mix. This percentage, while not directly translatable into facility usages for the parts, does indicate comparative activity.

The weighted composite cost estimate is obtained by the addition of the three weighted cost categories. To get each weighted cost, multiply the product mix percentage by its expense for each part, and then add for all five parts. As an example, to get the compositized estimate for Direct Labor, the steps shown in EXHIBIT 3–3 were performed.

I: CONVERT YOUR 1960 MAJOR PRODUCT MIX INTO A COMPOSITE PRODUCT ESTIMATE							
	Part A	Part B	Part C	Part D	Part E	Weighted Composite Estimate	Per Cent of Compositized S.P.
Direct Labor	$5.20	$3.00	$ .86	$ .21	$ .06	$ .791	28.2%
Total Overhead @ 150% of Direct Labor (From 1959 P & L)	7.80	4.50	1.29	.315	.09	1.187	42.3%
Material	.41	1.66	1.26	.015	.01	.385	13.7%
ESTIMATED Total Cost	13.41	9.16	3.41	.540	.16	2.363	84.2%
" % Profit	15%	20%	10%	15%	10%		
" Profit	2.366	2.29	.379	.095	.018	.446	15.8%
SELLING PRICE	$15.776	$11.45	$3.789	$ .635	$ .178	$2.809	100.0%
PRODUCT MIX	5%	10%	15%	40%	30%		

II: CONDENSE YOUR 1960 PROFIT & LOSS STATEMENT			
SALES		$2,750,000 -	100%
Direct Labor	$742,500	-	27%
Total Overhead	1,534,500	-	55.8%
Material	385,000	-	14%
PROFIT		88,000 -	3.2%

III: COMPARE "HOPE" WITH "REALITY"				
	COSTS		Per Dollar of Sales	
	ESTIMATED	ACTUAL	GAIN	(LOSS)
Direct Labor	28.2%	27.0%	$.012	
Total Overhead	42.3%	55.8%		($ .135)
Material	13.7%	14.0%		(.003)
PROFIT	15.8%	3.2%	NET	($ .126)
Overhead as a % of Direct Labor (for academic interest only)	150%	207%		

Exhibit 3–2. Are Your Estimates Recovering Your Expenses?

The weighted composite estimate, if developed from the entire mix of products, should be the mirror of the profit and loss statement. In practice, an exact reconciliation cannot be expected because of fluctuations in material costs, the performances of labor, and those omitted elements of product mix.

If estimating is done "at standard," that is, at the level of productivity which equals a fair day's work for a fair day's pay, then higher productivity will show up as a figure in the compositized estimate higher than that shown in the P & L. This means that the gains from, say, incentive stimulus were not passed on to customers, but instead were retained to swell profits.

5% × $5.20	$ .26
10% × $3.00	.30
15% × $ .86	.129
40% × $ .21	.084
30% × $ .06	.018
Weighted composite direct labor....................	.791

Exhibit 3–3. Compositized Direct Labor

If the estimating assumes standard productivity attainment and the actual performances are below standard, then the company is kidding itself and a lower figure shows up in the compositized estimate. In this case the company must absorb the cost of subsidizing sub-standard workers.

While this test is effective for evaluating the real gains from a wage incentive system, its most important function is to show where the largest gap is between actual and estimated costs. When overhead is allocated to products on the basis of direct labor, the area of disparity is, typically and usually, the total overhead cost, as will be shown later in this test.

The weighted composite estimate is then assigned percentages of the compositized sales dollar so that later comparisons can be made. The P & L statement for the same period from which the individual estimates were drawn is then condensed to the same expense categories as the estimates and assigned percentages of the sales dollar.

In the third section the percentages for the composite estimate are inserted under the "Estimated" column and those for the P & L under the "Actual" column and the two compared. The adjacent columns show the differences or gaps between estimated and actual costs. The gain refers to an over-recovery. The loss is an under-recovery for which customers should have been charged. In the case of materials, this difference ($.003 × $2,750,000, or $8,250 annually) is usually the result of underestimating waste, or overestimating yield or having high reject experience.

The real offender is in the under-recovery of total overhead costs. For each dollar of sales, $.135 was lost from the undercharging of customers. See EXHIBIT 3–1. The case illustrated does not call for a mass markup of prices to recover lost overhead. The estimated overhead was 150% of direct labor, whereas the actual overhead for the year was 207%.

If that 207% had been known in advance and applied, the estimated and actual costs would reconcile on paper, but still not in practice. First of all, overpricing, leading to a decrease in sales, would result. The consequent loss of activity and the unrecovered expenses due to that activity loss might more than wipe out the gains of higher prices. For example, Part A in EXHIBIT 3–2 involves some small single spindle work and lots of hand assembly. The cost of facilities is comparatively low. Yet it is penalized by having to carry more than its share of overhead because of the "magic" percentage in effect. This practice artificially inflated its selling price, and as a result it had the lowest sales of all.

On the other hand, Part D involved the highest priced equipment in the shop and carried the same overhead percentage. The machine-hour rate showed that the proper overhead charge would have been the equivalent of 370% for this part. Pricing by means of the "magic" number obviously resulted in brisk low-profit sales.

How Product Mix Affects Profits

As the product mix changes, the company is victimized by the overhead-as-a-percentage-of-direct-labor method of assigning overhead costs. EXHIBIT 3–4 shows how product mix affects profits. This company had a $1,000,000 annual sales volume in three types of products, represented by Parts A, B, and C.

Section 1 shows the information taken from the actual estimating sheets. Sections 2, 3, and 4 show what happens to company profits under three different conditions of product mix, for the same $1,000,000 sales volume.

EXHIBIT 3–5 shows the parameters of the three products and the effect on overhead cost exerted by three different states of product mix.

The data in EXHIBIT 3–4 is self-explanatory with the exception of the actual total overhead cost figures. These were developed from a machine-hour rate structure which, of course, allocates overhead in accordance with the use of facilities.

Note the losses for Parts A and B under the Condition A product mix; these losses turn into profits under a different product mix represented in Condition B. And in Condition C, Parts B and C are the losers. These circumstances occur at the same total sales volume, with the labor and material cost of each part being held at the same level and the selling prices for each remaining the same. The only change is the individual level of sales of each, that is, the product mix. This product mix, reflected back into the specific operations, meant changes in equipment use and hence in the amount of overhead used by each piece.

	PART A	PART B	PART C	
I: ESTIMATES				
Direct Labor	$ .06	$ .60	$2.40	
Material	.05	1.05	.90	
Total Overhead @ 150%	.09	.90	3.60	
(taken from historical data)				
ESTIMATED TOTAL COST	.20	2.55	6.90	
ESTIMATED Profit @ 10%	.02	.28	.77	
ACTUAL SELLING PRICE	$ .22	$2.83	$7.67	

TOTAL SALES-- $1,000,000
"Hoped-for" PROFIT--- 100,000

II: REALITY: CONDITION A

	PART A	PART B	PART C	
Assumed product mix:	30%	10%	60%	
Quantity sold:	1,363,636	35,335	78,226	
Direct Labor	.06	.60	2.40	
Material	.05	1.05	.90	
Actual Total Overhead	.14	1.20	3.16	
ACTUAL TOTAL COST	.25	2.85	6.46	
From I: ACTUAL S. P.	.22	2.83	7.67	
ACTUAL PROFIT OR (LOSS)	(.03)	(.02)	1.21	
SALES	$300,000	$100,000	$600,000	$1,000,000
"Hoped-for" PROFIT	30,000	10,000	60,000	100,000
ACTUAL PROFIT OR (LOSS)	(40,909)	(707)	94,653	53,037
		NEGATIVE Estimating Gap		$46,963

III: REALITY: CONDITION B

	PART A	PART B	PART C	
Assumed product mix:	70%	20%	10%	
Quantity sold:	3,181,818	70,671	13,037	
Direct Labor	.06	.60	2.40	
Material	.05	1.05	.90	
Actual Total Overhead	.07	.60	10.70	
ACTUAL TOTAL COST	.18	2.25	14.00	
From I: ACTUAL S. P.	.22	2.83	7.67	
ACTUAL PROFIT OR (LOSS)	.04	.58	(6.33)	
SALES	$700,000	$200,000	$100,000	$1,000,000
"Hoped-for" PROFIT	70,000	20,000	10,000	100,000
ACTUAL PROFIT OR (LOSS)	127,273	40,989	(82,524)	85,738
		NEGATIVE Estimating Gap		$14,262

Exhibit 3–4. How Product Mix Affects Profits

	PART A	PART B	PART C

IV: REALITY: CONDITION C

	PART A	PART B	PART C	
Assumed product mix:	85%	10%	5%	
Quantity sold:	3,863,636	35,335	6,519	
Direct Labor	.06	.60	2.40	
Material	.05	1.05	.90	
Actual Total Overhead	.055	1.20	14.20	
ACTUAL TOTAL COST	.165	2.85	17.50	
From I: ACTUAL S. P.	.22	2.83	7.67	
ACTUAL PROFIT OR (LOSS)	.055	(.02)	(9.83)	
SALES	$850,000	$100,000	$50,000	$1,000,000
"Hoped-for" PROFIT	85,000	10,000	5,000	100,000
ACTUAL PROFIT OR (LOSS)	212,500	(707)	64 ,082)	147,711
		POSITIVE Estimating Gap		$47,711

SUMMARY

P   R   O   F   I   T   S

| THE GAP | | ACTUAL | | |
	ESTIMATED	CONDITION A	CONDITION B	CONDITION C
Estimating Loss----------	$100,000	$53,037		
		--$46,963		
Estimating Loss----------	$100,000		$85,738	
			--$14,262	
Estimating Gain----------	$100,000			$147,711
				----$47,711

Exhibit 3–4 (Cont.)

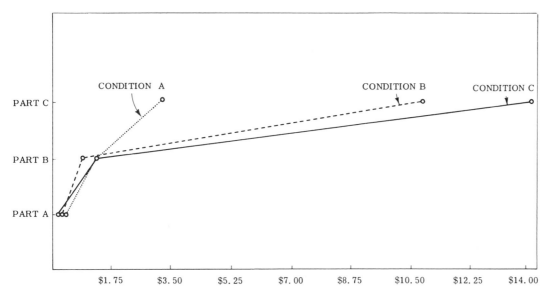

Exhibit 3–5. Variations in Total Overhead Cost with Product Mix

Selling prices in Section 1, EXHIBIT 3–4 (*estimates*) were developed from allocating overhead on the direct labor base. With this method, the more volatile the product mix, the more the company will suffer from insecure pricing and capricious profits. At one extreme, the company will lose from overpriced and therefore slow-moving items, and, at the other, it will be deluged with break-even or loss business. The three conditions illustrated here, certainly typical in machine-shop operations, cause a profit range of from 4.3% to 14.7% on the same $1 million volume.

The reactions of some manufacturers to correct costing deserves mention at this point. Some ask, "Can I raise my prices just because I have a new cost system?" This question shows that our message does not always come through loud and clear. Actually, some prices will be lowered, with the volume increasing enough to overcome the drop in the original price and going on to provide higher profits. Some prices will be increased perhaps so slightly as not to be felt. Maybe, for realistic reasons, a price that should be increased will not be to an existing customer, but will be to a new customer.

See Part C in Condition A. Raising the price from $7.67 to $7.77, just 10 cents, adds $7,822.60 to annual profits. Or raising the selling price on Part A to $.225, a matter of one-half cent, increases profits by $6,818.18. The goal is knowing what to raise or lower, when and by how much. The magnitude is not the criterion—not as long as we have competition.

Others ask, "What's the good of knowing my costs since competition sets the price?" This is like telling a man in the air-conditioning business that there is no point in measuring temperatures, because the measurement in itself will not change the weather. Picture the dilemma of a producer who does not know his cost floor. In important situations, where marginal profits are acceptable, how will he know when he is selling safely above his cost? If he is prepared to make concessions, how much will he unnecessarily give away? Or by how much will he lose an order?

Chapter 4

PROPER APPROACH TO OVERHEAD COST ALLOCATION

Because of the highly competitive character of present industrial activities, adequate cost control is becoming increasingly the major concern of every industry. As we already have said, where there is inadequate cost control, product pricing becomes insecure.

Different industries incur different expenses for different reasons. Some expenses are common to all industries, such as rent, depreciation, and so forth. However, there are a number of expenses peculiar to some industries that require individual handling, such as that of burning sawdust for heat in a lumber millwork plant. All such expenses, when they do not originate directly in the process of manufacture, constitute what is commonly known as "overhead" or "burden."

Allocation Equity

It is common knowledge that most companies, when determining product costs, stress the determination of manufacturing over non-manufacturing costs. This is a critical oversight, as certain products originate quite specific non-manufacturing charges of substantial size.

Let us consider marketing expenses. Differences in marketing costs will arise as a result of the sales methods used, the types of transportation systems employed, the product's requirements for handling, and so forth. If the total expenses of the marketing operations of a company are distributed among the products by means of an average, as is usually done, the individual costs obtained will not reflect the differences in the actual marketing costs of each product. The ratio of marketing costs to sales may be many times higher for some products than for others.

The assignment of overhead to product should be done in an equitable form. This is an area of costing which has elicited wide discrepancies of opinion among cost experts. In this book we hope to prove why the machine-hour rate system of costing offers the most adequate method of overhead and cost allocation.

Overhead distribution is primarily a problem of selecting the proper base for the allocation of the various elements of overhead. Industry uses, in addition to the MHR system, a number of methods for the application of overhead. Some of these were detailed in Chapter 2.

An over-all plantwide base is the simplest we have seen. To list the more common bases used, we find:

Rate per direct labor hour;

Rate of standard earned labor hours;

Percentage of direct labor dollars;

Percentage of direct materials cost;

Rate per unit of product;

Percentage of prime cost;

Percentage of total sales;

Percentage based on market prices.

The above rates are calculated by dividing the total overhead figure by the total of the base in use.

This arbitrary assignment of overhead on the basis of direct labor, or any basis other than the actual use of the facilities, is very wrong. Burden must be allocated to the product on the basis of the overhead expenses that are actually incurred in its manufacture. In a metalworking machine, for example, there are small, inexpensive drill presses, and then there are horizontal boring mills that cost many times more to own and maintain. The assignment of a flat percentage for distributing overhead expenses averages out the individual costs of these facilities and tends to overcost items produced on the inexpensive facilities and to undercost those products made at the more expensive production centers. It is obvious that these distortions can have a serious and possibly a disastrous effect on selling prices and profits.

Such a method of overhead allocation assumes that (1) each expenditure of the base used to calculate the rate will generate a directly proportionate expenditure in overhead, or that (2) all products will use the manufacturing facilities in the same form and for the same length of time. But, unfortunately, these conditions are not always existent in modern industry, where different products require different production techniques and machinery. It would be absurd to say that it costs the same to operate a 3,000-ton press, a turret lathe and a 1,000-pound steam hammer, that they would all run the same length of time, and that their costs would fluctuate only with changes in the operating crew, if direct labor were being used as the distribution factor.

Therefore, the most equitable way to reflect each facility's cost to the product is to charge to the product the specific operating cost of each production center used in its manufacture, according to the length of time the center was used in the article's production. This means that overhead costs first have to be charged against the facility and then, through the center, to the product. This is the goal of the MHR. Thus, when a piece is being costed by means of the MHR, (1) the operations involved are determined, and (2) the time to be taken by each is listed. Against this tabulation, the hourly cost of each facility is calculated and the operational or conversion cost is obtained by multiplying the time taken by the specific facility hourly cost. By adding these costs together, the correct total or "full" cost of the piece or product is determined.

There can be no doubt that the MHR provides a more accurate cost, since the allocation of overhead is based on the actual costs incurred by each type and size of equipment.

Allocation of Overhead to Facilities

In order to charge overhead or "burden" expenses to each facility, a basis must be found for distributing each expense according to the principles discussed above. Thus, *insurance* costs pertaining to buildings can be allocated according to floor space. Insurance costs on machinery and equipment can be charged pro rata to each cost center according to the dollar value of the machinery in the respective centers. Insurance costs on product inventories can be charged directly to a receiving and storing department (a service center) and can be reallocated upon the distribution of the service center to the various production centers. Distribution of *property taxes* can be made on the basis of floor space occupied by each cost center. *Depreciation on buildings* can be charged to the building center (a service center) and then be redistributed to other centers on the basis of floor space occupied. *Depreciation on machinery* and on permanent tools can be charged pro rata to each cost center as with insurance on machines.

The distribution of *water consumption* should not present any difficulty where a plant has individual meters for each cost center. However, where there are no meters available, then estimates will be in order. These estimates should be furnished by the engineering department or some individual who is qualified to make such calculations. If the water expense is nominal, it might be more practical to classify it as part of general factory expense distributed to other cost centers.

Electrical energy is utilized in many different ways in the average manufacturing plant. It is present directly in the motors of machines. It is utilized in processes such as arc welding, plating, and so forth. It is also used as a conductor of heat in liquid vats and heat-training furnaces. Last but not least, it is present for general lighting. An accepted method for distributing electric current costs is on the basis of horsepower hours. A total of horsepower hours is obtained by preparing a schedule of the horsepower hour capacity on each motor located in each cost center throughout the plant and, at the same time, multiplying the horsepower capacity by the number of hours this equipment is in operation each month.

The expense of the *receiving and storing centers* can be distributed to production centers on the basis of the tonnage handled for the class of materials involving each group of machines. The costs pertaining to the inspection center can then be redistributed to the production centers on the basis of ratio of direct labor incurred by each production center to the total direct labor.

Maintenance center costs can be distributed on a basis similar to that described for the distribution of a tool room center, as follows (the costs of operating the *shipping center* can then be distributed to production centers in the same manner as inspection costs): Job orders which entail tool costs stemming from services to cost centers could be charged directly to the center being serviced but, due to management's desire to have "under one roof" the cost of operating the tool room, all expense should first be cleared through the tool center. At the close of each accounting period, the tool room center should be credited with the cost value of all job orders completed during the period, with an offsetting entry to the various centers for which work was performed, as the specific job orders indicate. Any general expense remaining in the tool room center which has not been charged out in the form of job orders is prorated over the cost centers in proportion to the job order work.

The recovery of *general, administrative and institutional* expenses presents a greater problem, as usually the allocation of these costs is a matter of company policy rather than of a cost system. Many companies prefer to apply these costs to those products that offer a larger profit, leaving other products facing greater competition free of this charge.

It should be remembered that each company must take stock of its own situation in adopting or adapting particular allocation methods. There are no ready-made procedures and one company's experience and characteristics can be used only as a guide, never as a rule, for other companies.

Distribution Bases

With this in mind, we are giving below a list of distribution bases that have been used in one company for the allocation to facilities of the elements of overhead expense. If these expenditures are included in the calculation of the MHR, several allocation factors can be considered, namely:

Type of Expense	*Distribution Basis*
Depreciation of machinery & equipment	Present market value
Depreciation of furniture & fixtures	Present market value
Repairs to building	Area occupied
Power and light	Actual consumption
Heat	Area occupied
Water	Actual consumption (engineering estimates)
Group Insurance	Employee participation
Insurance on buildings	Floor space occupied
Insurance on machinery	Present market value of machinery in center
Insurance on contents of buildings	Inventory values
Salaries and expenses of sales department	Products served
Use and occupancy insurance	Gross profits
Advertising	Products advertised
Real estate taxes	Area occupied by center
Taxes on machinery and equipment	Valuation
Personal property & other taxes	Gross profits
Depreciation of buildings	Area occupied
Insurance on product inventories	Service of warehouse to each center

It must be emphasized that these allocation bases have been indicated only to show the cause-and-effect relationship between the expense and the physical factor that logically relates to it. In general, the appropriateness of a proposed basis of allocation of overhead expenditures can always be tested by studying this cause-and-effect relationship between basis and cost. If the cost varies directly with movements in the amount of the basis, then the latter will be appropriate. For instance, if group insurance increases proportionately with increases in the number of employees, the size of the plant's payroll will be a proper allocation basis for this expense.

Section 2

HOW TO DEVELOP AND INSTALL THE MACHINE-HOUR RATE SYSTEM

5. HOW TO ORGANIZE THE BASIC DATA

6. INTRODUCTION TO MACHINE-HOUR RATES
   How to Develop the MHR:

7. *Step 1:* THE CONVERTING FACILITIES CLASSIFICATION SHEET

8. *Step 2:* THE CREW COMPOSITION TABLE

9. *Step 3:* THE OPERATING BUDGET

10. *Step 4:* THE EXPENSE ASSIGNMENT WORKSHEET

11. *Step 5:* THE MHR SUMMARY SHEET

12. ADDITIONAL CONSIDERATIONS

Chapter 5

HOW TO ORGANIZE
THE BASIC DATA

The basic purpose of any cost-estimating system is to help the company to operate at a profit. Better stated, the object should be the earning of a consistent profit with due consideration given to longevity and financial health.

A useful cost-estimating system should be simple to operate, flexible in its application, and reliable. It should not be so cumbersome that it cannot be used effectively as a basis for pricing, and it must be understandable enough to allow it to serve, in addition, as a managerial tool with key personnel.

Before any cost-estimating system will work, basic information on the incurrence of all costs must be developed. Data being constantly fed into the cost-estimating system must be reliably and consistently reported. Before this can be done, all cost data must be indentified and classified. The collecting and organizing of the basic data must be done in a form suitable for use in the cost-estimating system. Listing information from memory or guessing at various expense elements only leads to confusion and insecurity in pricing and decision-making.

Cost Activities in Manufacturing Enterprise

The three major activities in manufacturing are:
1. Producing the article
2. Selling the product
3. Administering the business

When the costs or expenses incurred in operating these three efforts have been deducted from the revenue from the sale of the company's products, the remaining sum represents the profit. To assure a profit, the expenses must be controlled and held below the selling prices and held low enough to compensate the enterprise for the risk of having invested in the business. Besides control of individual expenses, there must be control over the utilization of investment previously paid out, as in capital equipment. More than a control over out-of-pocket costs, this involves the selection of the optimum product mix to utilize more effectively the investment in capital equipment.

Classification of Costs

The following is a list of the principal cost categories encountered in manufacturing industries:

1. Materials Cost
2. Labor Cost
3. Factory Expense
4. General, Administrative and Selling Expense

Of course, there are other elements of cost—engineering costs and distribution costs, for example; but it is not necessary to go into detail on these cost elements once the basic concept of handling the general cost classifications has been explained.

In the machine-hour rate method we use the term *conversion costs,* which include all the costs of manufacturing except materials cost. A graphic representation of the various cost and expense terms is given in EXHIBIT 5–1.

Materials Costs

Materials costs are those costs which enter into and become part of the sold product. These costs should be separated into those that enter directly into the finished product and those that represent manufacturing supplies and repair parts. The former are called direct materials costs, the latter indirect materials costs.

Direct materials costs consider the purchase price, plus freight and trucking charges incurred in conveying the materials from the place of purchase to the factory where they are to be used. Do not include internal transportation or materials handling in this cost, as this is considered indirect labor and is treated differently.

Examples of direct materials are the bristles, ferrules and handles in paint brush manufacture; kips in leather tannery; paperboard in folding carton plants; copper wire, lugs, and epoxy resin in electrical resistor manufacture. Examples of indirect materials are sweeping compound, grease and oil, belting and shafting.

Labor Costs

A going business requires human effort. A company uses labor of many types: administrative, clerical, productive, and so forth. Some of these people are farther from the scene of production than others and those we must identify and classify. We must use the identities and classifications consistently; otherwise comparisons, for identification, control and evaluation purposes, are difficult. Labor can be divided into the following functional categories:

I. Direct
  A. Productive
  B. Non-Productive
    1. Unavoidable delays, viz.: a mechanical breakdown
    2. Avoidable delays, viz.: waiting for material

II. Indirect
    A. Supporting production (materials handlers, etc.)
    B. Maintenance
    C. Factory, general (porters, etc.)
III. Supervisory and Control
    A. Department foremen
    B. Factory manager (line control over production and plant only)
    C. Supporting factory clerks

Exhibit 5–1. The Box of Cost Elements

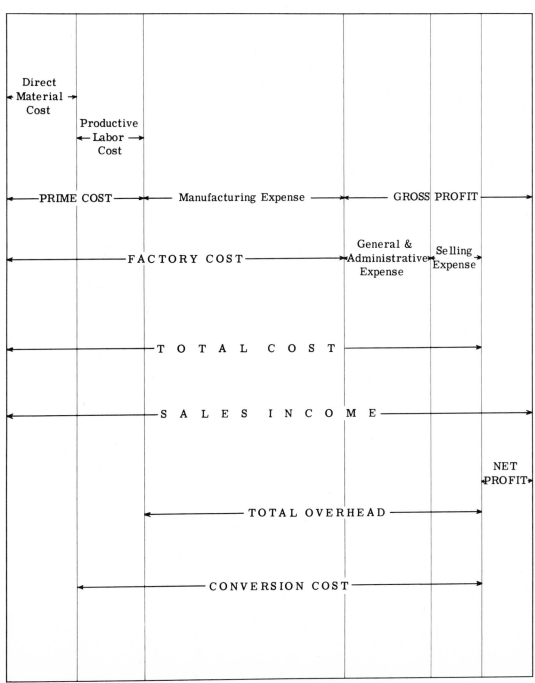

Exhibit is not to scale and proportions are not significant

Categories IA to IIB are reported on written production tickets. IIC to IIIC are usually reported by weekly clock card or, in the case of supervisors, may not be reported at all.

Direct Labor: Productive labor, sometimes referred to as direct labor, is considered the actual applied human effort which causes immediate physical changes to occur on the form of the material and/or product. It may also be considered as those acts essential to the making of the product. In this latter sense, the labor involved in the setting up of a machine is considered direct and that of sweeping the floors would be indirect.

Not all of a worker's time is productive. At times, he has delays which are either avoidable or unavoidable. At other times he may be assigned to product salvaging or to helping another worker. All this unproductive time should be reported clearly in the daily production tickets.

Each productive worker should be required to report his time and production in consistent and written form. Productive time, the items to which it was applied, the machines on which the work was performed, the nature of delays and other indirect work to which the direct-productive worker is assigned, all should be reported. Separation of delays provides targets for trouble-shooting in an elusive cost area where economies can be made markedly more efficient.

Indirect Labor: This category records all indirect labor in all factory classifications. The following are some typical accounts under this category: tool room labor, stock handling labor, chip separators, supervision, maintenance, inspection, shipping and receiving, incentive subsidy of production workers, incentive premium pay, lost time and production workers, and reprocess labor.

Productive Workers Daily Tickets: The card hung in the rack alongside the clock in the employees' entrance is used to comply with the requirements of the labor law. It is of little value in costing, for it does not identify the person with the operation performed, the customer for whom it was performed, the machine worked on, the quantity produced, or the time taken.

The output and the time consumed at each operation should be charged to the machine used, to the job or customer's order, and to the operator. Each of these charges serves to inform management of the utilization of the machine (a maximum consideration affecting the profits of the company), of the profitability of an order (useful in determining the product mix and price adjustments), and also of the productivity of the individual worker (the item affecting unit overhead cost the most).

There is positive need for a daily system of time production reporting from the shop. In addition to its use in building up estimating data, such a system always inspires an immediate gain in productivity. The first reaction is psychological; workmen know that their output will be watched. Supervisors, also, realizing that this is an indirect appraisal of their efforts, tend to plan their activities better and to keep them closer to the scene of production.

The second positive surge comes when people know that the daily tickets are actually being analyzed and evaluated. The study of the production tickets is the giant step forward in industrial plant management and control. But as soon as the shop people feel that no one looks at the daily time tickets, the reporting system collapses of its own weight.

Daily time tickets should show the following information:

1. Operator's name and/or clock number
2. Date
3. Department
4. Job, order, or customer's name
5. Operation performed or codified operation number or standard operation names
6. Quantity produced
7. Machine number
8. Unit
9. Time standard (inserted by office)
10. Earned hours (computed in office)
11. Elapsed hours (computed in office)
12. Time in and out for each job.

Here are the reasons for reporting the above data:

Operator's name: Some companies keep production records by machine and build up statistics which they use to evaluate their machinery economy. They feel that a report on the output of machines is a way of appraising the efforts of their labor. Unfortunately, this method just does not work. For if the machine output report is lower than what management thinks it should be, a machine cannot be counseled; only workers can be talked with. Machinery output is a function of labor; so why postpone the problem of getting right to the core of the matter? In addition, workers usually switch production centers, so that a production report by machine is only an average of the productivity of all the operators who worked on it. Manufacturing is basically the work of *people.* Keeping daily production records of operators tells how well they are working and shows what management must do to help them.

Date: The reason for this is obvious. A well-functioning reporting system must enable action no more than 24 hours after an event occurs.

Department: This subject is discussed in greater detail in another section of this book. Briefly, each major department has its own characteristics of downtime, materials handling requirements, setup time, and so forth. When operators are listed by department on a payroll analysis, it is easy to derive the simple ratio relating elements of downtime to running time for control purposes.

Job number: Even though the machine-hour rate system obviates the need for job costing (actually a duplicate cost system) it is convenient to list this number for the purpose of scheduling and order tracing. In some cases, important job costs can be extracted for determination of order profitability. It must be kept in mind that this part of the labor ticket extracts labor time only. The method of how overhead is allocated is left to the product as the final determinant of profit.

Operation performed: Labor expense must be pinned to the job number and the quantity, as, otherwise, the reporting is practically worthless. This category should not be mistaken for the name of the position held by the person. "Pressman" written in this space doesn't say enough. What he *does,* not what he *is,* should give the context. The honest reporting of one pressman, followed by an analysis of his idle time, proved that he could service two adjacent presses. As a result, the company saved the labor of three pressmen per year. The best way to look at this segment is to remember that in each second of the day everyone is performing an operation. In the boxboard container industry, this could mean getting material, waiting for materials to arrive, waiting for the make-ready to be completed, feeding or stripping. Only by accounting for every time period, and labelling it with an operation name or number, can a company maintain control over production.

Some operators exercise their sense of humor at the start of a reporting system by listing operations as having required one minute of time, 5½ minutes, and so forth, thus filling up many tickets in one day. At first patience is required. Then, taking the listings seriously, supervisors should tell the workmen that at the beginning it is impractical to list periods in less than quarters of an hour; that later, perhaps, a decimal-hour clock will be used and .1-hour (6-minute) intervals could be the minimum time period used.

Quantity produced: This data is obvious. With proper controls, as will be discussed later in this book, the self-seeking or insecure operator who claims excessive quantity credit can be discovered.

Machine number: Never leave out this number. This number is as vital as job number, operation performed and quantity produced, as it is the foundation of the machine-hour rate system. In most segments of converting industry, machinery costs form the largest portion of total factory overhead at each production center. Therefore, it is vital to know a machine's activity during any period in which cost recovery is being evaluated.

Unit: This refers to the unit of measure, which may not be the same at all operations in a company. In the process industries, units start at batches of so many gallons or pounds and wind up as quarts or packages. An operational sequence may start with sheets and wind up with pieces. Production may be listed by the piece, dozen, gross, or in hundreds, or thousands. The important thing is that the report indicate the size of or the quantity in the unit.

Time standard: The time standard is the allowed time for performing an operation at the unit rate. Thus, feeding a printing press may be .75 hours per thousand; for assembling transformers in place, the time standard may be 7.5 hours per thousand; for inspecting certain castings, the standard may be 3 minutes each. Production time standards are a vital piece of information for cost-estimating and should be established scientifically.

Earned hours: This is the product of the quantity turned out by the time standard and is vital for comparing the value of what a worker accomplished to the actual money he was paid. Thus, if a standard for a punch press operator working on a certain part is 1.25 hours per thousand pieces and he turned out 6,000 pieces in a pay period of 8 hours, the number of hours he earned was 6×1.25, or 7.5 hours. Since he is paid for 8 hours, the company has to subsidize or absorb the cost of the unearned half-hour. Since workers do not usually work near their standard rate in plants that do not use wage incentives, the cost of unearned time must be anticipated and budgeted as part of the cost of the company's operation. More on this later in the book.

Elapsed hours: This is the actual record of the passage of time by the clock. This information is used as a check against the earned hours to uncover the amount of effort or productivity that a worker expended on the various jobs that he worked on during the day.

Time in and out for each job: This can be written in by hand or punched in and out by means of small punch clocks located conveniently throughout the shop.

Some plants use running time meters electrically connected to machines as a check against time reported and punched. These are valuable for uncovering variances in the reporting of repairs and maintenance labor. Where wage incentives are in effect, time meters are extremely valuable as a check against the amount of day work claimed.

A production- and time-reporting system is a worthwhile investment in company energy. The gains are tangible, especially at the beginning. And these gains provide management with a first steppingstone toward a modernization of management methods and control.

In addition to the production workers' daily tickets, the following forms can be kept:

1. *Report by customer's order and operation:* As shown in EXHIBIT 5–2, all labor applied to produce the customer's order is listed on this one ticket. Obviously, since this method gives a job cost, it makes somewhat difficult the appraisal of individual operator efforts.

2. *By department or group of machines per day:* These forms, shown in EXHIBIT

ORDER NO.	CUSTOMER			QUANTITY		STYLE AND DESCRIPTION				
OPERATION		MACH. NO.	DATE	CLOCK NO.	QUANTITY		ALLOW. TIME	EARNED HRS.	ELAP. HRS.	CLOCK TIME
					GOOD	REJ.				
DIE MAKE										
COMPOSE										
PRINT	MAKEREADY									
	RUN									
	RUN									
CUT AND CREASE	MAKEREADY									
	RUN									
STRIP										
GLUE	SETUP									
	RUN									
PACK										

Exhibit 5–2. Production Report by Order and Operation

DATE		DEPT.	S & S WRAPPER			
MACH. NO.		MODEL	QUANTITY		CUSTOMER ORDER NO.	CLOCK HOURS
			BOXES	LIDS		
		A				
		D				
		HNS (2)				
		NJSF(2)				
		B				
		B				

Exhibit 5–3. Production Report by Machine Group

5–3 and 5–6, are used to get total departmental productivity. Thus, management can get the total number of impressions per day, for example, and if the output is unsatisfactory, can extract each operator's statistics before making an evaluation. In some plants, operator's name and/or clock number is left out and management is left with the impossible task of taking remedial action against lifeless and in-human objects, that is, machines. (EXHIBIT 5–6 is used in punched-card installations.)

In the methods discussed above (nos. 1 and 2), there is always the task of re-porting the non-productive time of productive people. It usually requires an addi-tional form, listing downtime of various types, to correct this difficulty.

3. *By factory order and worker per day:* This form, shown in EXHIBIT 5–4, com-

bines the advantages of the other systems in that the work is initiated by factory order and reported by worker under the factory order. This system requires considerable care in designing, since the cards follow the work, and means must be used to prevent the destruction or loss of the ticket. In this type of system, generally, a master copy remains in the office and the top of the ticket, used for scheduling, controls the return of the ticket from production.

As each operator in turn works on the order, the appropriate operation ticket is separated from the long top strip and placed in a small daily envelope. This step automatically collates the daily production time of each operator per day, and provides on the bottom strip, which is not perforated, the accumulated job time against the order. The operator's downtime is left unreported, but a downtime form can be printed on the small daily envelope. This is shown in Exhibit 5–5.

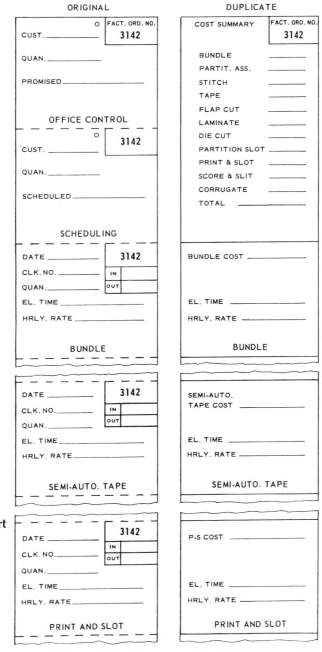

Exhibit 5–4. Production Report by Order and Worker

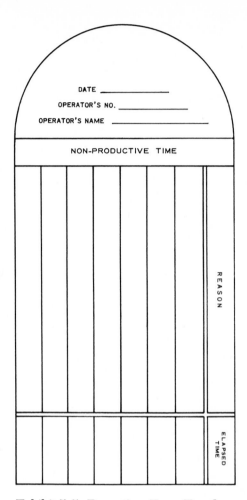

Exhibit 5–5. Downtime Form Envelope

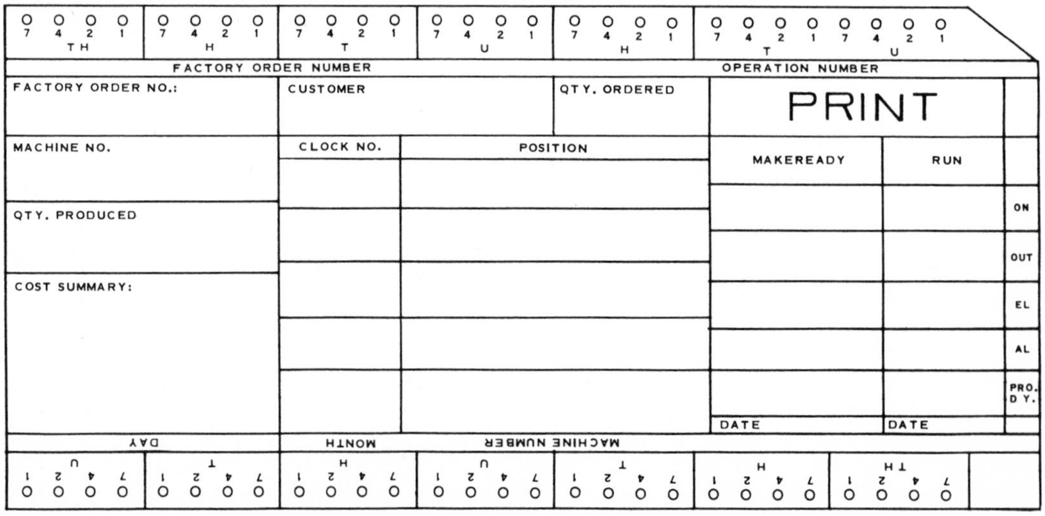

Exhibit 5–6. Production Report by Order and Operation

4. EXHIBIT 5–7 is an example of an overdesigned worker's time ticket for use in punched-card systems. Here, a separate ticket must be made out every time a different operation is performed by a worker. This leads to an accumulation of a vast number of tickets.

A good rule to follow in designing production reporting tickets is to sketch them out in rough form and then consider who will write on them, how many times and where; who will look at them and for what purposes; and, finally, why the ticket is necessary and if it can be done away with.

Installing a daily reporting system and getting it to work takes time and patience. Especially at the beginning, when by practice workers are not formally requested to give an accounting of their work output, there is bound to be fear and suspicion. These feelings must be dispelled by careful explanations. Cards must be reviewed and questions asked of foremen, who must go to the workmen concerned for the answers. Including the foremen in the process plays a large part in getting them to understand the goals of the system. Even when the reporting system works perfectly, it is good practice to go through the motions of asking for clarifications from workers, so that they will know the cards are being reviewed.

When time standards are in effect, it is also good practice to rate productivity for each operator daily so that necessary counselling can be done immediately, rather than after the event becomes ancient history. In some plants, daily or weekly operator or departmental productivity is posted in graph form and friendly competition is promoted, to the benefit of the company.

Where wage incentives are in effect, the productivity is adjusted to include

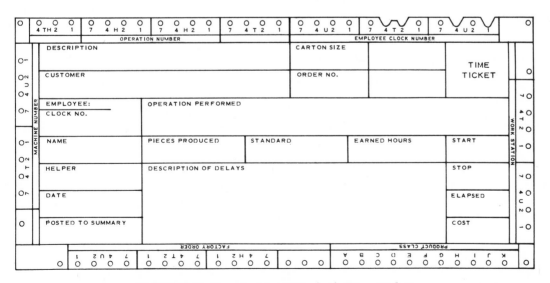

Exhibit 5–7. Overdesigned Worker's Time Ticket

rejects and other excess costs, so that productivity comparisons are made on a valid economic basis.

Factory Expense

Factory expense includes those expenses, other than materials and labor, incurred in the ownership and operation of a factory. It does not include the expenses of managing the business, or of selling, or of any of the other general or administrative activities. Ownership of the factory and its production equipment involves such expenses as taxes, insurance and depreciation, and these are the fixed or standby costs of the business operation, since these remain at the same level regardless of the volume production. The operation of the factory requires production management and supervision, repairs and maintenance, indirect supplies, toolmaking, sweeping, and so forth, and the variable costs of heat, light and power. All these expenses are known as factory overhead or burden (the former term is used throughout this book).

In general, factory expenses are grouped into four categories:
1. Indirect material
2. Indirect labor
3. General expense
4. Period expense

1. Indirect Materials

This category should record the total expenditure on materials which are not part of the product sold, such as electricity, brooms, belting, and the like. It should also include maintenance supplies—paint, grease, and so forth. Some of these expenses can be charged directly to a machine or a department; others are necessarily incurred by operation of the plant as a whole and must be spread over all processes and products.

Sometimes it is convenient to group indirect materials under several departments in order that the whole cost of any service department, as distinguished from a processing department, may readily be determined. Thus, steel rules are charged to die-making, and materials used in repairing the building to building maintenance. If possible, the record should show the *use* made of the indirect material rather than the reason behind its purchase. Typical general accounts under this category (which may be charged to specific departments or machines) are:
a. Heat, light and power
b. Water
c. Gas
d. Perishable tools
e. Maintenance materials

   f. Die-making supplies

   g. Boiler room supplies

2. Indirect Labor

This category should record all indirect labor as classified on the typical payroll analysis. Some of these indirect labor expenses can be charged directly to a department or a machine, as can maintenance labor, but rarely to a product. Service expenses, such as for inspectors and timekeepers, are usually spread over the entire plant. Materials handlers often can be associated with specific departments, reprocess work can likewise be charged to the department that caused the rejected work, and machinery repair definitely can be charged against specific machines. Preventive maintenance, however, is generally an over-all charge.

The following are the typical categories which might be used in a folding-carton plant:

   a. Die-making

   b. Composition

   c. Materials handling

   d. Packing

   e. Inspection

   f. Maintenance

   g. Storekeeping

   h. Shipping and receiving

   i. Shop, clerical

   j. Subsidy of productive workers

   k. Lost time of productive workers

   l. Reprocess and repair

  m. Supervision

   n. Incentive premium pay

3. General Expense

This category should record all administrative and other expenses arising in connection with the factory, except for those included under *period expenses*. The following accounts are typical:

   a. Manager's salary

   b. Social Security and Unemployment Compensation

   c. Overtime and shift differentials

   d. Vacation and holiday pay

   e. Workmen's Compensation insurance

   f. Experimental expenses

4. Period Expense

The following are the only expenses which should be recorded here:

a. Factory rent and taxes

b. Insurance

c. Depreciation

Proper control of the expense account structure—recording the movements of the business, and discerning behind them an accurate set of product costs to show in which product lines (or facilities) the profits and losses are to be found—requires competent record-keeping. There should be no need to *estimate* the expenses in the above-listed accounts. All excuses notwithstanding, the company should modify its clerical procedure to permit the availability of actual figures. Any internal expense should be ascertainable. Management misleads itself with "statements" made on estimates. For example, a small error in the value of a large closing inventory may multiply into a large error in the profit figure. What need not be estimated, should not be estimated. It should be borne in mind that the margin between success and failure in industry is generally very narrow. Any errors in judgment on the part of the sales department in agreeing to a selling price, added to errors in judgment in purchasing materials at unfavorable prices, plus errors in judgment in determining production methods, or in estimating waste allowances, or, say, in setting production standards in the plant, may, through their cumulative effect, completely wipe out an otherwise healthy margin of profit.

If the classifications above cannot be used, some other set should be developed to allow fast managerial action. Just as managerial action on the payroll journal is useless, because it sets out no objective targets, so the lack of expense segregation permits no critical evaluation of the economy of expenditures.

As we get deeper into the subject of costing, it will become clear that the evidence of product costing is of assistance mainly from a sales management angle. For general management purposes, the expenses comprising product costs are brought under control and thus remedial action can be taken before an excess becomes part of the pattern, carried by every order processed through the plant. Just as for factory labor, if the individual period expense segments are profitable, then the overhead segment of the orders processed in that period must likewise be profitable.

General, Administrative and Selling Expenses

This section covers all those expenses which are incurred in the course of the selling activities and the general administration of the business, to be recorded under the following categories:

1. Selling expenses
2. General expenses
3. Period expenses
4. Fixed expenses

1. Selling Expenses

All expenditures connected with or due to the selling of the product should be recorded here. If the business is small, a portion of the owner-manager's salary is usually charged to the selling function. Salesmen's salaries and commissions, advertising, entertaining, traveling expenses, discounts allowed, are all items falling into this category. Some companies place bad debts in this category to impress the salesmen with the importance of a prospect's credit standing. Others feel that this is the function of the credit manager and that such charges should go into the general account. This is a matter of choice.

This selling account should not be loaded with operating charges such as for warehousing, packing or shipping. This would defeat the aims of control and would not provide management with a clear evaluation of the real cost of the active effort to make sales. Typical accounts under this category are:

a. Salesmen's salaries and commissions (includes pro-rata share of general manager, if necessary)
b. Clerical salaries
c. Office expenses
d. Advertising
e. Literature
f. Traveling expenses
g. Entertainment
h. Social Security and Unemployment Compensation
i. Vacation pay

2. General Expenses

This account covers the usually broad range of general expenses and salaries incurred in the management of the enterprise and the conduct of the business. The division between administrative and selling expense is not always clear in certain types of expenditures. If, for example, as is true in smaller plants, the president of the company divides his time between the supervision of the sales organization and other administrative duties, it is not always apparent how much of his salary and traveling expense should be charged to sales. It is not of great importance to know the exact apportionment to be made to each classification. The important thing is to have some rational basis of allocation, in order that expenses *on account of* administration and selling may be determined with a reasonable degree of accuracy and be comparable for different time periods. Typical accounts here are:

    a. Director's fees and expenses
    b. General Management salaries
    c. Clerical salaries
    d. Stationery
    e. Postage and telephone
    f. Traveling expenses
    g. Professional services
    h. Bank service charges
    i. Light and heat
    j. Bad debts
    k. Social Security and Unemployment Compensation
    l. Vacation pay

3. Period Expenses

This category includes only rent, taxes, insurance and depreciation of all buildings, furniture and fixtures used for administrative selling and/or general purposes. The accounts are:

    a. Office rent and taxes
    b. Insurance
    c. Depreciation

4. Fixed Expenses

This category should record only the fixed interest charges payable on borrowed money. These charges include interest on notes, bonds, loans and all other forms of borrowed capital. This category is kept separate because it enters into a determination of the operating profit made on the total capital employed. The accounts are:

    a. Interest on debentures
    b. Interest on bank loans
    c. Interest on notes

Just as in the category of factory expense, expenses in this category must be reported with consistency and accuracy. Obviously that task is simpler here than for plant expenses. Very rarely is there any circumstance which allows these expenses to be directly identified with any of the processes of manufacture, since there is no functional cause and effect relationship between them. Therefore, these expenses must be allocated on logical bases.

The total overhead classifications actually comprise a portion of the P & L statement. Obviously, accounts kept for control purposes should be consistent with the way those accounts are set up on the financial statements. However, not all the income and expense accounts usual to a proper profit-and-loss statement have been listed, because the aim here is to show the various components of total overhead for control and costing purposes rather than to discuss accounting theory. Thus, accounts like Non-Recurring Expenses (a lawsuit was lost; a presentation had to be made) or Non-Operating Income (from rent of company-owned land or buildings, from discounts of accounts payable, from sale of scrap and waste, etc.) have not been discussed. The need for including them, for correctly placing them and consistently recording in them all pertinent expenses, is vital for tracking costs and analyzing profits. The following example is an illustration of the effects of the improper placement of just one such account.

Misclassification of Expenses

The president of a metalworking company showed the following statement with some pride as evidence that his business was doing well:

SALES			
Products	$246,320		
Income from sale of scrap and from rent on property	62,500		
TOTAL		$308,820	100.0%
COST OF PRODUCTS SOLD			
Opening inventory	$643,500		
Direct material purchases	84,250		
Direct labor	47,140		
Manufacturing expense	33,210		
	$808,100		
Deduct: Closing inventory	600,600		
TOTAL COST OF PRODUCTS SOLD		$207,500	67.2%
Gross Profit		101,320	32.8%
General, administrative and selling expenses		68,700	22.2%
NET PROFIT		$32,620	10.6%

The profit on sales was apparently satisfactory to the president, but he failed to see that his profits did not come from manufacturing his metal products.

In the statement above, the profit of one activity was overcompensating for the losses in the other, the "other" being *manufacturing*. Because of the incorrect placement of the non-operating income, this fact was not easily seen. The proper form of statement follows:

SALES	$246,320	100.0%

COST OF PRODUCTS SOLD

Opening inventory	$643,500	
Direct Material purchases	84,250	
Direct labor	47,140	
Manufacturing expense	33,210	
	$808,100	
Deduct: closing inventory	600,600	

TOTAL COST OF PRODUCTS SOLD	$207,500	84.2%
Gross Profit	$ 38,820	15.8%
General, Administrative and Selling Expenses	$ 68,700	27.9%
NET LOSS (From Operating)	($ 29,880)	(12.1%)
Add: Non-operating income	62,500	
FINAL PROFIT FOR PERIOD	$ 32,620	

The president was quite shocked to find that his net profit of 10.6% was in actual fact a net loss of 12.1%. Costing and profit determinations must be based on consistently classified data permitting rapid appraisal, sound pricing policies, and other managerial decisions.

Reporting for Job Costing and Facility Costing

As will be shown in greater detail in a later chapter, it is a waste of time and effort to have two cost systems operating side by side. If one is the machine-hour rate system, then the other can be eliminated. The MHR system determines job order profitability by evaluating the profitability of each production center. If the production centers are consistently recovering their expenses and are profitable, the individual jobs which ran through these centers must likewise be profitable unless large material waste develops.

Labor and overhead costs on an order are arrived at by multiplying the hourly cost of operating each facility involved in the production of a customer's order by the number of hours (or minutes) that the facility is in use for the order. These arithmetic extensions, when totalled for each facility involved in the order, give the order's conversion cost.

To job cost an order (for checking its profitability) it is necessary to have the elapsed time of each operation and the quantity produced in that elapsed time. On the estimate sheet, alongside of each operation, the production standard should be written and then expressed as the allowed time for performing that operation. So long as this time is not exceeded, as would be shown by the actual time tickets, the profit estimated will become a reality. Therefore, the check point of production time tickets is that the standard time estimated be not less than the actual time as shown on the time tickets. Sometimes, a continuous check is provided by the wage incentive system, or the measured daywork system which shows individual productivity and the amount of subsidy monies. In either case, using proper controls, management can take action not necessarily on a particular customer's order, but against a specific operation, or worker, whose low productivity is brought to bear negatively on all customers' orders passing through his or her operation.

Chapter 6

INTRODUCTION TO
MACHINE-HOUR RATES

A machine-hour rate indicates the amount of money that a company spends to operate a machine, work center or production center for one hour. The rate includes all company expenditures, except materials costs namely, direct and indirect production expenses, manufacturing expenses, selling expenses, administrative and general expenses.

Since many of these costs are not incurred by machines, work centers or production centers, as was explained in an earlier chapter, it will be part of the purpose of this Section to show how each of the various expenses is apportioned.

Development of the Rate

The machine-hour rate is a built-up hourly charge constructed from pieces of every expense in the business, except materials cost.

The forms shown in Section 2 are by no means the last word for developing the rates, but since they are the refined result of thousands of machine-hour rate installations, they are considered expedient and convenient. It must be made clear that this data could be assembled in different ways. This fact is not important. What is important is that the information be handled under concepts similar to those presented here.

The forms used in this Section collect the basic data of the previous chapter in a manner suitable for the development of the entire machine-hour rate structure. Basically, the steps required for developing the final rates are these:

1. Develop the production centers by marshalling all the productive facilities and tabulating their data;

2. Determine operating capacity of each center in connection with a sales forecast or other estimate;

58

3. Determine the proper crew and costs of the manpower required to man the centers or facilities;

4. Determine the indirect manufacturing expenses which are required to support the production centers;

5. Allocate the variously classified expenses to each production center upon equitable bases and divide by the operating hours of each center. The result is the overhead component of the machine-hour rate. And adding in the hourly direct labor wages of the crew gives the composite or total MHR.

Company ABC and the XYZ Corporation

So that the reader will be able to understand more fully how machine-hour rates are developed, the procedures for developing them will be given throughout the balance of this Section together with explanations of the rates. As an aid in following the data, the complete case study installations of two companies will be presented.

Company *ABC* is in the corrugated sheet paperbox industry and the *XYZ* Corporation is in the metalworking business.

Besides the data of these two companies, examples of other companies, some of their characteristics, and how they can be treated in the development of the rates will be given.

What Is a Machine-Hour Rate?

The machine-hour rate is a *conversion cost* solely. The term conversion refers to all of the acts that must be done to convert raw materials into a finished product. The term *cost* means those expenditures which the company must make in order to manufacture a product, to sell it, and to collect its sales price. The term *conversion cost*, then, includes all of the company's expenditures except for materials, and it is divided into two parts. One part of the conversion cost shows the cost of productive labor and represents the wages which are paid to those workers who operate the machines or do the handwork operations which immediately change the appearance, shape, or utility, of the raw materials. The second part of the conversion cost shows the overhead, sometimes called burden. This cost includes the wages and salaries paid to those workers who do not perform the converting work but who are necessary to the operation of the company. This classification includes shop truckers and office clerks, and the costs of such things as rent, electricity, and all supplies and services. There are a number of ways of expressing the conversion cost. In the present instance, it is expressed as the machine-hour rate, or the cost of operating a machine or manufacturing process for one hour.

The machine-hour rate is an all-inclusive conversion cost. It encompasses the following:

Productive (direct) labor

Manufacturing (factory) expenses

Delivery expenses

Selling expenses

Administration and general expenses

The data from which the machine-hour rates are determined include:

The Converting Facilities Classification Sheet (CFCS)

The Crew Composition Table (CTT)

The Operating Budget (OB)

The Expense Assignment Worksheet (EAW)

The Summary Sheet

Because the rates should reflect *all* overhead items, it is essential that, before they are developed, adequate data on the items be available. How to gather this information was shown in the previous chapter.

The first step in the process of computing rates is to make a compilation of data to show the true total of company overhead costs. Once this total is obtained, it is broken down to give the overhead segment for each machine or process.

Often overhead costs can be apportioned only by *groups* of machines or processes. In indirect labor, for example, you may find separate supervision or separate materials-handling personnel for a machine, a group of similar machines, or for a process. In such a case, direct charges against the center can be made. However, where maintenance and repair costs cannot normally be charged to any specific machine, these costs have to be handled in any of the following three ways:

1. Direct allocation to machines;

2. Statistical allocation to departments. Here some expenses are divided statistically among the items of equipment within the departments;

3. Plant-wide segregation of over-all indirect expenses. Where expenses are so general and indirect that they cannot even be allocated to any one department, statistical bases have to be developed for apportioning costs among all the machines.

The assembly and preparation of this data to obtain the machine-hour rate is set forth in the chapters which follow.

Before starting to compute machine-hour rates, the reader should do two things. First, he should read these instructions completely through. It is essential that an understanding be had of the entire process before any part is attempted; otherwise some parts will be incorrectly done. Then, when a grasp has been obtained of the whole procedure, the reader should review *in detail* all phases of the estimating procedure.

Chapter 7

HOW TO DEVELOP
THE MHR

Step 1: The Converting Facilities Classification Sheet

The Converting Facilities Classification Sheet, hereinafter referred to as the CFCS, is the first piece of organized data needed in the preparation of machine-hour rates. The CFCS determines and lists the Production Centers in the company—which should correspond to those listed on the estimating sheet. For establishing and developing machine-hour rates, the same Production Centers should be listed consistently for each tabulation.

The CFCS represents an inventory and marshalling of production equipment and of all non-equipment work stations. (An inspection bench for sounding castings with a hammer is a "work station," because no machinery is involved in the operation.) The CFCS does not include non-productive equipment such as scrap-metal balers and tote trucks. The cost of operating non-productive equipment is included in the Operating Budget.

The listing shall include that equipment used to perform only those operations which are the subject of the cost estimate. So that no equipment shall be omitted from the list, the tabulator shall start at a designated point in the plant and proceed from there in a direct line to the end of the plant, listing equipment as it is found, without regard to operation sequence.

The following data are listed in the CFCS. The CFCS tabulations for Company *ABC* and *XYZ* Corporation are shown in Exhibits 7–1 and 7–1a.

61

[1]	[2]	[3]	[4]	[5]	[6]
		Total of All Units in Prod. Center			
Production Center	No. of Units	HP.	Net Working Space	Present Value	Assigned Annual Hours
Printer-Slotter	1	25	840'	$17,000	2000
Partition Slotter	1	6	470'	3,000	1200
Slitter	1	5	400'	2,000	2000
Semi-Auto. Taper	2	5	1100'	8,000	4000
Manual Stitcher	2	1/2	100'	600	1000
Platen Die Cutter	1	3	190'	3,500	2000
Band Saw	1	3	90'	600	500

Exhibit 7–1. The Converting Facilities Classification Sheet
for Company ABC

[1]	[2]	[3]	[4]	[5]	[6]
		Total of All Units in Prod. Center			
Production Center	No. of Units	HP.	Net Working Space	Present Value	Assigned Annual Hours
Punch Press A	1	10	80'	$5.000	2,000
Punch Press B	1	10	110'	5.000	1,700
Drill Press A	1	2	40'	200	1,500
Drill Press B	1	4	40'	150	1,500
Lathe A	1	5	70'	1,800	1,400
Lathe B	1	10	100'	9,200	800
Hand Assembly (8 Positions)	8	0	200'	400	11,200

Exhibit 7–1a. The Converting Facilities Classification Sheet for
XYZ Corporation

1. Production Center (Column Number 1)

A Production Center consists of one or more machines or work stations at which the same operation is performed. These machines or work stations do not have to be located in the same geographical area in the plant. Actually, sometimes they are widely separated for functional reasons or because of poor plant layout. It is still possible for them to be members of the same Production Center. If, for example, a paperbox manufacturing company has two 30″ x 42″ Bobst auto-platen cutters, each located in opposite ends of the plant, they constitute one Production Center having two units. If, however, the company has a 30″ x 42″ and a 42″ x 62″ Bobst auto-platen cutter, each would constitute a different Production Center, each having only one unit.

If in a screw machine shop there are several sizes and types of automatic screw machines, they should be grouped according to capacity by diameter and number of spindles. In a foundry, mold-making would be grouped by hand and machine types, sizes and configurations. In a plastic plant, injection molding would not be combined into one production center with compression molding.

There are several criteria for establishing a Production Center—always keeping in mind that Production Centers determine how the customer's order will be costed. Costing of a Production Center involves the application of its hourly cost of use, determined by the MHR, plus a consideration of the speed with which orders can be processed through the Center.

The criteria for grouping machines which perform the same operation in the same Production Center are:
   a. Machinery capabilities (number of colors that a press can run at one pass, number of auto-feed stamping presses, etc.)
   b. Machinery capacities (sizes, speeds, tonnage, number of spindles, diameters, etc.)
   c. Machinery crew and power requirements (number of workers normally required at center, electrical horsepower, steam and water requirements, etc.)
   d. Machinery type (litho, letterpress, platen, cylinder, injections vs. compression molding, brass vs. aluminum mills, etc.)
   e. Machinery value
   f. Annual assigned hours

In the case of non-equipment Production Centers, or work stations, it is usually not necessary to make any distinctions.

Using the classification of machinery given above, we might group two color presses into one Production Center if their values do not vary greatly, their size and power requirements are fairly close, and the number of operators used are about the same. However, two single-color letterpresses varying in size, age and speed would call for two separate Production Centers, even though, say, the number of operators required might be the same. See Exhibit 7–2.

As a general definition, a production center consists of one or several similar machines, bench positions, assembly lines, or operations where direct labor is performed in the fabrication of a product. The number of production centers established depends upon the degree to which manufacturing processes differ from each other, the number of different end products fabricated within a manufacturing shop or department, the practicability of segregating expenses applicable thereto, and the industry practice in using these centers as estimating factors in orders.

Service Cost Centers: At this point it may be well to define a service cost center and how the costs pertaining thereto are handled in the development of the rates.

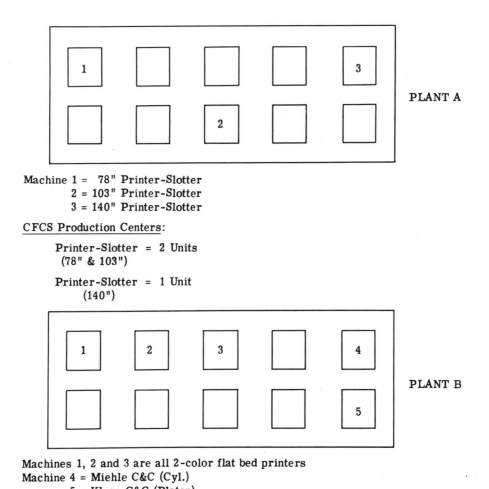

PLANT A

Machine 1 =   78″ Printer-Slotter
          2 = 103″ Printer-Slotter
          3 = 140″ Printer-Slotter

CFCS Production Centers:

    Printer-Slotter = 2 Units
    (78″ & 103″)

    Printer-Slotter = 1 Unit
        (140″)

PLANT B

Machines 1, 2 and 3 are all 2-color flat bed printers
Machine 4 = Miehle C&C (Cyl.)
          5 = Kluge C&C (Platen)

CFCS Production Centers:

    Two-Color Print = 3 Units
    Cyl C&C   = 1 Unit
    Platen C&C   = 1 Unit

Exhibit 7–2. Determinants of Production Center

Among these centers are maintenance shops, tool rooms, power plants, production control departments; they are engaged in activities directly in behalf of the production centers, but do not in themselves perform manufacturing operations. The latter costs are handled through the Operating Budget, as we shall see later on.

We will see as we progress further into MHR development that machinery costs— a function of the machinery value and the depreciation expense—form one of the largest and the most critical cost segments of the overhead portion of the MHR. It is not only critical from the standpoint of consistent order estimation but also from the viewpoint of management's ability to replace machines when they are worn out. Unfortunately, most estimating systems do not make provision for replacement costs, and there are machine-hour rate systems in effect today which fail to include them.

For industries which have substantially high fixed capital investments (machinery), the utilization of which varies considerably because of typically volatile product mixes, the traditional approach to cost accounting will not work, as it will not give management consistent information about the availability of production facilities and will not provide a planned means for keeping the capital structure sound and growing.

2. NUMBER OF UNITS (Column Number 2)

List the total number of units of machinery included in each production center.

3. HORSEPOWER (Column Number 3)

The total horsepower of all the units comprising the production Center is inserted in this column. This includes the ratings of the prime mover motors as well as every electrical device that consumes power. It would include heaters, auxiliary motors for conveyors or for other attachments. Some devices, such as heaters, are generally rated in watts or kilowatts instead of horsepower. To convert watts into horsepower, simply divide the watts by 746. In other words, there are 746 watts in each horsepower. Energy of any other electrical device is converted from kilowatts into horsepower at the ratio of 1 kw. to 1.34 hp. Do not overlook the fact that units operating on air pressure usually come from a compressor which is motor-driven. If a unit has its own compressor, this compressor should be added in. If, however, the air comes from an air line connected to a central compressor, no consideration need be given to this cost at the Production Center, as it will be handled as a general expense item.

4. NET WORKING SPACE (Column Number 4)

For each piece of equipment, the following data should be listed:
1. Floor space occupied, including the necessary work space. The term "work

space" covers the area that the worker needs to do his job comfortably, and the area occupied by materials for the work being processed. If conveyors are used, the space occupied by them and the workers who service them is included. If a conveyor is shared by two Production Centers, then a proportion of the conveyor work space is added to each Center. This column includes the total of the working space of all the units of the Production Center—even if they are 200 feet apart. Aisle space, storage and warehouse areas, offices, and so forth, are not added in this column as these areas are handled in another way later on. EXHIBITS 7–3 and 7–3a show how to calculate net working space.

5. PRESENT VALUE (Column Number 5)

This is one of the two factors that play a major role in consistent and equitable pricing of products, and in the perpetuation of a company's tools of production. It is particularly critical to companies in high fixed-cost industries, because of the large element of depreciation and the heavy costs of replacement.

What is meant by present value, and why is it used instead of book value? Briefly, present value of a machine means its present market value—that value which one of a similar kind has in the open market today. Another way of looking at it is to say that present value is what would have to be paid today in the open mar-

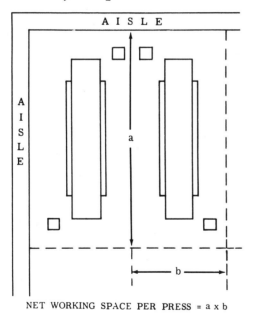

NET WORKING SPACE PER PRESS = a x b

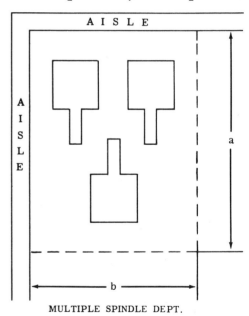

MULTIPLE SPINDLE DEPT.

NET WORKING SPACE PER MACHINE = $\frac{a \times b}{3}$
IF PRODUCTION CENTER HAS 3 UNITS,
NET WORKING SPACE FOR CENTER = a x b

Exhibit 7–3. Determination of Net Working Space for Company ABC

Exhibit 7–3a. Determination of Net Working Space for XYZ Corporation

ket to replace the machine by another in exactly the same condition. This is known as replacement in kind.

Present value is not an easy figure to determine but there are various ways of arriving at an acceptable figure. If you had an offer for the equipment a few years ago, take that figure and add to it the cost of any additions you have made to improve the functioning of this machinery. This practice is used often and serves as an excellent guide. On the other hand, perhaps you had a recent insurance appraisal. Since insured values tend to be overstated, some adjustment may have to be made, but with some care, they can be used.

The original cost or acquisition price should not be used unless the purchase was made very recently. Since a company's equipment is not usually all purchased within the same short period, or a recent period, only newly organized plants will use this figure. If original cost is used as the factor in allocating machinery costs, a 25-year-old machine which cost a large sum of money when it was purchased and which today functions poorly, would automatically inherit a large portion of the expenses to be allocated. Add to that an expected slower speed and that Center adds enough cost to orders to price the company out of its markets. The customer—if he buys the product—is made to pay a cost high enough to support the product's manufacture on modern facilities newly purchased.

On the other hand, the depreciated or book value of equipment is not acceptable either. In the case of a fully depreciated machine, its use would be tantamount to giving the ownership of the machines to the customers for nothing. This practice weakens the company's profit position by allowing the customers to benefit just from accounting arithmetic. Consequently, a depreciation expense even for fully amortized facilities must be included in costs for pricing, even though it may not appear in the accounting books.

It is desirable that the values used represent current replacement cost of the equipment. If such values are not obtainable, the next best value is replacement cost as of a past date, with the cost of subsequent additions restated to that date by application of a percentage representing the difference in the purchasing power of the dollar between that past date and the date of acquisition. The least desirable basis is acquisition cost, since the equipment will have been purchased over an extended period during which the value of money may have fluctuated. Unless all equipment was acquired in the same short period of time, acquisition cost should be avoided.

Look at it this way: Customers should be charged at the rate at which it costs to own and maintain facilities acquired for the benefit of customers. If you went into business today and bought identical equipment in the exact condition it is in today, the book value of that equipment would be what you paid for it—even though somebody had written it off before they had sold out to a used machinery dealer. This value is what the customers' costs should be based upon and what the customers should be charged.

Be sure to include the present values of all devices and attachments, or any additions to the machinery or the work stations.

6. Production Center Annual Hours (Column Number 6)

Perhaps the most difficult schedule to develop in an MHR system is the annual-hours projection, especially when the MHR system is first being set up. Remember that this schedule normally affects the final machine-hour rate more than any other factor. The more accurate your information is here, the more accurate your final rates will be.

The first step in the development of this schedule is to determine the number of paid worker hours in the coming year. These hours normally take in all daily working hours; if the shop is run on Saturdays and Sundays, these days are also considered. Here's how to find total paid hours:

Days in the year		365
Less Sundays	52	
Saturdays	52	104
Total paid days		261
Paid hours per day		8
Total paid hours per year		2,088

This example assumes that all holidays not paid by the company will be worked. If it is the regular practice, however, to shut down for unpaid holidays, these should be deducted, just as Saturdays or Sundays when the plant is shut down. To use easy arithmetic, let's assume that the standard year, after all the above considerations have been allowed for, is 2,000 hours. The task now is to project the number of hours that each production center will be in operation during the coming year. If the company has no past records on workers or machines, the problem becomes more difficult, and a considerable amount of estimating will have to be done. But under the MHR technique, estimating does not lead to serious errors in the long run, because changes can be made easily as you gain experience. Although most shops these days have daily time tickets or other means of time and production reporting, if none of these methods is available, the activity schedule has to be projected from scratch.

Foreman's estimate: After listing all machinery, handwork, and other production centers, the activity scheduler should talk to every production foreman or supervisor. The first, perhaps inevitable, reaction to these talks on expected hours of activity for the coming year will be one of surprise or even mild shock. Questions should be asked about yearly percentages: "What portion of last year was this boring mill kept busy?" "What about the coming year . . . ½, ¼, ¾?" Questions about the far future are unfair, for the future generally is the province of top management and sales forecasters; but it does no harm to ask the foreman about next year, for he might have talked to the sales department recently about an expected activity. Anyhow, the foreman's reaction to questions such as these will give you a check on similar estimates of machine activity that you will get later from the sales department.

It is best to persuade the foreman to think in terms of machine activity rather than products, a record of which he may have seen somewhere else. The questioning process continues until all production supervisors have given their opinions about expected activity for all production centers.

In asking these questions, the inquirer must make certain that the foreman separates machine hours from man hours, and that set-up time is also included in the machine activity hours.

If two men operate a machine for the full standard year, annual hours assigned to the Production Center will be 2,000 and not 4,000. The difference in the machine-hour rate for a one-man and a two-man operation is that the two-man rate is the one-man rate plus the hourly rate of the additional man and the fringe-benefits overhead cost of the additional man. Here's how the two differ:

	Overhead*	Direct Labor	MHR
One-man operation	$12.40	$2.75	$15.15
Two-man operation	$12.90	$5.50	$18.40

* Fringe-benefits cost segment = $0.50

Sales estimate: The next step is to get a similar activity estimate from the sales department. Invariably, the thinking here will be about products rather than operations, and you'll have to convert product-mix estimates into production-center hours of activity. The schedule and its conversion of product-mix percentages and product quantities into hours of production activity will look something like EXHIBIT 7–4.

Top Management's estimate: Finally, the plant owner, without having seen the estimates from production and sales, should make a similar listing.

Then a joint meeting should be held—perhaps under the direction of the controller or the industrial engineering department—to resolve differences. From the meeting a final projection should emerge. This final estimate is by no means absolutely correct, but the participation from three areas of the company will help to reduce the amount of inaccuracy.

If reasonably accurate historical data is available, the projection is much simpler,

Summary of Operational Requirements

Operation	Pieces	Hours Each	Sub-total	Total Hours
Drillpress				3200
--mounting blocks	8000	0.1	800	
--bushings	80000	0.03	2400	
Broach				5600
--mounting blocks	8000	0.7	5600	
Lathe				9900
--rings	11000	0.9	9900	
Grinder				13700
--mounting blocks	8000	0.4	3200	
--rings	11000	0.3	3300	
--rods	64000	0.1	6400	
--bushings	80000	0.01	800	
Screw Machine				3200
--rods	64000	0.05	3200	

Product Mix			Operational Times per Piece in Hours				
Percent of Sales	Product	No. of Pieces	Drill-press	Broach	Lathe	Grinder	Screw Machine
40	Mounting Blocks	8000	0.1	0.7	----	0.4	----
30	Rings	11000	---	---	0.9	0.3	----
20	Rods	64000	---	---	----	0.1	0.05
10	Bushings	80000	0.03	---	----	0.01	----

Exhibit 7–4. Converting Product Mix to Annual Machine Hours

and more accurate. Filled-out daily production tickets from the previous year, and daily time tickets filled out by an operator (showing where he spent his time) can be consulted. A few words of caution here: In checking over daily time tickets, don't give a machine double credit because more than one operator worked on it. In plants where meters are installed on machines to give running time, remember that hours of set-up time must be added to the reading on the meter, for set-up time is considered part of the machine's activity time in the MHR system.

Paperwork for the activity schedule is not very difficult. Data can be posted on a sheet, with machine centers listed vertically and days listed across the top. The total for each center, then, is the horizontal sum of the daily entries. Even though this information is readily available, production supervisors, general management, and sales forecasters should be consulted to spot errors that might have been made in taking figures off various tickets. This subject is covered later in the book under the discussion of testing and correcting the MHR.

Once the list of last year's activity is completed, sales and general management should evaluate the activity figures to anticipate changes during the coming year. Adjustments made now should take into account the modified sales forecast for present products and the anticipated activity for new or changed products. An element of guesswork is still present, but to a much smaller extent than before. Again, remember that with the MHR testing method, incorrectly projected activity levels can be readily adjusted.

Where the machine-hour costing system has been in existence, the cost-recovery statement, which shows actual activity for each production center, can be consulted. The listing is then altered in accordance with next year's forecast, thus completing the projection.

Once the projection of annual activity hours is accepted by every department, the person preparing the data should attempt to balance the hours among the cost centers, to see whether the projection creates bottlenecks and excess machine time. Exhibit 7–5 shows how to balance activity among various production centers.

Bringing the activity of each facility into balance with the others, as can be done in Exhibit 7–5, not only provides a double check on the projection, but also insures that costs will be distributed more evenly.

Some have attempted to determine a whole set of machine-hour rates for every month of operation, or every quarter. This procedure not only is burdensome, but also introduces errors when activity fluctuates from season to season—as it does in all businesses. Exhibit 7–6 shows in chart form how the overhead component of a typical machine-hour rate can fluctuate from month to month. Keep in mind that preparing an annual rate differs from testing new rates and making adjustments because of inaccurate projections.

It's a good idea to accumulate each month the specific activity for each cost center, with a view to correcting projections rather than varying annual rates. For this record, a table similar to Exhibit 7–4 can be made up. Production centers are listed

Operation	Previous Annual Hours	Balance Ratio To Drillpress	New Projection Annual Hours	New Balance Ratio To Drillpress
Drillpress	3200	1.0	5000	1.0
Broach	5600	1.75	7000	1.4
Lathe	9900	3.09	11000	2.2
Grinder	13700	4.28	14000	2.8
Screw Machine	3200	1.0	4000	.8

Exhibit 7–5. Testing the Balance of Annual Machine Hours

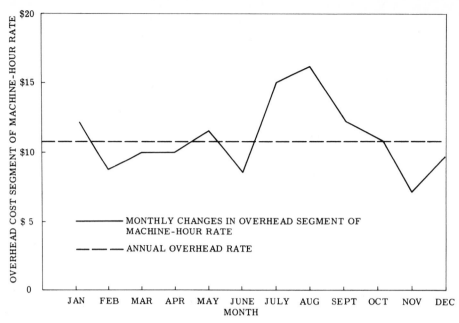

Exhibit 7–6. Monthly Movement of Overhead Portion of a
Machine-Hour Rate

from top to bottom at the left, and the months of the year across the top. Each entry will be the activity of a given center for a particular month. At a glance, you can inspect activity for any center, spot trends, and get evaluations that will help you when you are ready to make out next year's projected-activity sheet. But, again, this subject relates to the MHR testing and correcting procedure covered later in this book.

Problems and Discussion

A cost center, or burden center, or production center, or work center, is a (usually) productive portion of a plant which is treated as a functioning unit for the purpose of applying to it a portion of the overhead expenses. As we indicated before, it may be a single workpoint, such as an inspection station consisting of just one man and his testing devices; it may be a machine or group of similar machines, an assembly line, a group of work-points within a department or located at different points throughout the plant; or it may be a processing department, for example, spray room or plating department.

On Production Centers: Function rather than location distinguishes a production center from any other type of equipment grouping in a plant. A production center has no localized physical boundaries. To classify a center functionally requires more than simply the operational name. Surely we would not want to group into one production center (and list their cost on one line on the estimating sheet) all screw machines. By doing this we run the danger of upsetting the entire MHR concept, which holds to the specific and not the average assignment of costs. Screw machines vary from hand-fed, single-spindle types costing a few thousand dollars to automatic, multiple-spindle types costing many times more. Then, of course, the power requirements are different; so are the space occupancy, the indirect-labor service and maintenance required, the skills and pay of the operators, and the annual hours of use.

Following this reasoning one would not want to place an 85-inch corrugator in the same center as, say, a 68-inch unit, for while the size differences may appear unimportant, the investment costs are considerably different, and it takes nine men to operate the large unit and six to run the smaller one. Lumping them both together in one center would surely defeat the motive of increased profit—the reason for having the larger unit. The same is true of, say, printing presses, where a letterpress of a given size and color capacity could cost one-fifth as much as an offset press of similar size. Nor would platen presses be combined with flat-bed cylinder units.

At times you may find it worthwhile to set up a production center from an operation traditionally classified as indirect. In one radio assembly plant, testing and packing were done right on the assembly line and since the plant paced the line, those operations were measurable. Our opinion is that if an operation can be measured it can be classified as direct, in order to remove one more generality from the allocations. On the cost sheet, then, testing and packing were production centers and each had their own MHR.

Don't be misled by commonly used terms in industry. At a plant producing metal cabinets, there was an activity labelled as a "welding center." Examination showed that all sizes and capacities of spot welders were used, as well as tweezer welders, arc welders and brazers. Now, while no effort should be made to change the location of this welding department if it is situated to minimize internal transportation among the various operations, separation into "cost centers" should certainly be made on the CFCS and on the estimating sheet, to account for the different equipment's relative ownership, maintenance and operating costs.

On Space: Often the question arises as to what becomes of the space in the factory left over after the net working space has been allotted to the various centers. In other words, what becomes of the aisle space, warehousing, shipping, receiving, and clerical space? The answer is quite simple. Since the Net Working Space shown on the CFCS is an allocation factor, it automatically charges to each center its proper share of this other space (see the EAW, Chapter 10). The total space cost represents all of the space costs in the company, and each center carries a portion of the "other" space costs in proportion to its net working space. For the sake of further clarification, assume that all the figures for Net Working Space are doubled: the final space costs for each center would not be affected in the slightest, since the proportions would still remain the same. Allocation factors are concerned with proportionate distribution.

On Present Value: The same is true of the factor of Present Machinery Value.

The higher the value assigned to a center by this factor, the greater will be the percentage of allocatable machinery costs charged against it.

Sometimes arriving at present market values presents some difficulties. In this case many companies consider appropriate the use of original acquisition costs. This method is not sound and should be abandoned. If most of the equipment is old, and if acquisition cost is used for some centers and present market value for others, it is possible for all centers (except handwork stations) to carry the same dollar value under present value. That could mean that similar machinery costs are charged against a drill press and a horizontal boring mill. Since the total amount of the machinery costs remains the same, excessive cost would be charged to the drill press and too little to the boring mill. This would lead to undercosting of parts that made long use of the boring mill, and the artificially higher drill rate would tend to inflate slightly those parts going through the drill press center. Not only does this practice tend to destroy pricing consistency, it makes impossible the job of cost recovery and testing by which the rates are periodically purified and kept current. Actually, the only time that acquisition cost is valid for use as the Present Market Value factor is when a new plant is just starting in business.

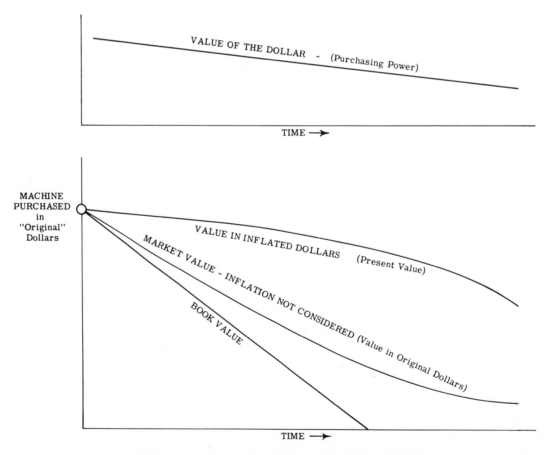

Exhibit 7–7. Effect of Inflation on Purchasing Power

Another typical question is: Why cannot book value be used, since Present Machinery Value is used as an allocation factor and only the relative proportions among the various centers are important? For the answer to this, first see Exhibit 7–7 (the slopes of the curves shown are approximate). The shape of the curves is influenced by the specific period over which the comparison is made, plus the varying market demands for used equipment. We all know cases where a used machine can be sold for as much *or even more* than its original cost, say, eight years earlier. Judged by book value (straight-line depreciation), such a machine would not have enough power to receive a fair share of the machinery costs. As a result, the order passing through that machinery center would be undercosted; the customer would receive the major costs of the ownership of the center for nothing, and the company would lack the mechanism of accumulating replacement monies, to say nothing of the resultant drop in profits it would suffer. The fact that the present value can be a large percentage of the acquisition cost, even after a number of years have passed, is not only a function of the inflationary effect of those years, but is further modified by the demand for the particular machine, its condition and its ability to be adapted to newer devices on the market. Therefore, it is fallacious to make an adjustment for inflation on the acquisition cost and to take that figure as present market value. It won't work.

Chapter 8

HOW TO DEVELOP
THE MHR

Step 2: The Crew Composition Table

In the preparation of machine-hour rates, the Crew Composition Table—hereinafter referred to as the CCT—is the second piece of required organized data. A CCT develops the size of the work force required by each of the Production Centers shown in the CFCS (Converting Facilities Classification Sheet).

Annual scheduled production hours of the Production Centers, together with the direct and indirect labor costs to meet this scheduled production—with allowances for such production interruptions as holidays, vacations and rest periods—are all shown on the CCT.

The CCT separates the various categories of factory labor, charging some directly to the Production Center and some to the factory generally. Excluded are the costs of selling, administration and other non-manufacturing functions which, as we mentioned before, will be included in the Operating Budget.

Exhibits 8–1 and 8–1a show the CCT for company *ABC* and *XYZ* Corporation. The following discussion describes the data listed on the CCT (the Production Centers are the ones described). The numbers correspond to the reference numbers on Exhibit 8–1.

1. Number of Units

In this column, the number of similar machines in each Production Center is indicated. This list should be similar to the one shown on the CFCS (Exhibits 7–1 and 7–1a).

76

2. STANDARD CREW PER UNIT

Shows the number of workers needed to man each production process in the shop.

A standard crew is composed of one or more workers normal to each Production Center. Their titles are inserted below the name of their Center. Thus, in the corrugated container plant, for example, the normal or standard crew for the slitter is one operator, one helper and one bundler. For the platen die-cutter the crew would consist of one operator and one stripper. In some cases, a worker may operate two machines or may service two machines, as in the case of a printing pressman, or a bundler for two semi-automatic tapers. Proper allocation is accomplished by assigning "fractional" people to the facility.

3. WORKER'S HOURLY BASE RATE

This is the average wage of the workers in the group, plus the anticipated increases in the next year. Failure to account for expected increases will lead to unrealistic machine-hour rates. As a worker's wage rate is changed, so will be the costs of fringe benefits, of scheduled production and of idle time.

4. HOURLY PAY RATE PER CENTER

This column shows the total hourly cost of all workers for all units in the Center, with allowance made for anticipated increases in the coming year. For instance, at the semi-automatic taper center, each taping machine will require one operator and one-half helper. Assuming that this equals $2.85 per machine, if there are two machines, or units, in the Center, the total hourly pay rate would be two times $2.85, or $5.70.

5. MAXIMUM ANNUAL CENTER HOURS

This is the total number of hours (one-shift) that the Center could operate if the workers are in attendance for the full year. The maximum one-shift annual hours are usually obtained by deducting from 365 the number of Saturdays and Sundays in the year and then multiplying by 8. This gives 2,088 hours per year. For the purposes of simplicity, as we said before, we shall assume 2,000 annual hours (250 days) to constitute the maximum one-shift paid hours per year.

These hours represent the elapsed annual hours worked by the Center and should not be confused with man-hours. The number of workers in a Center has no bearing on the Center's annual hours, unless workers are assigned to an additional unit in that Center.

Each machine, whether it has one, two, or more operators, cannot work more

Production Center	No. of Units	Std. Crew Per Unit	Workers' Hourly Base Rate	Hrly. Pay Rate Per Center	Maximum Annual Center Hours	FRINGE BENEFIT Rest Period	FRINGE BENEFIT Holidays	FRINGE BENEFIT Vacation	Available Annual Center Hours	SCHEDULED PRODUCTION Hours	SCHEDULED PRODUCTION Cost	Hourly Balance Under	Hourly Balance Over	Transfers	Idle Time	Non-Productive
PRINTER-SLOTTER				$4.70	2000	$587.50	$150.40	$150.40	1811	2000	$9400	189		from Partition Sl.		
Operator	1	1	$2.70													
Helper		1	2.00													
PARTITION SLOTTER				3.90	2000	487.50	124.80	124.80	1811	1200	4680		611	189 to P-S / 189 to P.S.	$908.70	
Operator	1	1	2.20													
Helper		1	1.70													
SLITTER				5.50	2000	687.50	176.00	176.00	1811	2000	11000	189		from Slotter / from Stitcher		
Operator	1	1	2.10													
Helper		1	1.70													
Bundler		1	1.70													
SEMI-AUTO. TAPER				5.70	4000	712.50	182.40	182.40	3622	4000	11400	378		from Stitcher		
Operator	2	1	2.00													
Helper		1/2	1.70													
MANUAL STITCHER				5.70	2000	450.00	115.20	115.20	1811	1000	3600		811	189-1 oper to Slotter / 378 to Tapers / 189 to Die Cut.	$557.10	
Operator	2	1/2	1.90													
Bundler		1/2	1.70													
PLATEN DIE CUTTER				3.60	2000	450.00	115.20	115.20	1811	2000	7200	189		from Stitcher		
Operator	1	1	1.90													
Stripper		1	1.70													
BAND SAW				3.60	2000	450.00	115.20	115.20	1811	500	1800		1311		$4719.60	
Operator	1	1	1.90													
Helper		1	1.70													
SHIPPING CLERK	1	1	3.00	3.00	2000	375.00	96.00	96.00								$5433
TOTALS						$4200	$1075.20	$1075.20			$49080				$6185.40	$5433
Reference in text ⟶	[1]	[2]	[3]	[4]	[5]	[6]	[6]	[6]	[7]	[8]	[8]	[9]	[9]	[10]	[11]	[12]

Exhibit 8–1. The Crew Composition Table for Company ABC

Operation	Standard Crew Rate per Hour	One Unit	No. of Units	Total Crew	Total Annual Hours	Rest Period Hours	Rest Period Cost	Holidays Hours	Holidays Cost	Vacation Hours	Vacation Cost	Available Production Hours	Scheduled Production Hours	Scheduled Production Cost	Overtime Premium Hours	Overtime Premium Cost	Idle Time Prelim.	Idle Time Transfer	Idle Time Adj.	Idle Time Cost	Non-Productive Hours	Non-Productive Cost
Punchpresses	$1.70	1	2	2	4000	250	$425	64	$108.80	64	$108.80	3622	3700	$6290	78	$66.30						
Drillpresses	1.60	1	2	2	4000	250	400	64	102.40	64	102.40	3622	3000	4800				622		$995.20		
Lathe A	2.40	1	1	1	2000	125	300	32	76.80	32	76.80	1811	1400	3360				411		986.40		
Lathe B	3.00	1	1	1	2000	125	375	32	96.00	32	96.00	1811	800	2400				1011		3033.00		
Hand Assembly	2.20	1	8	8	16000	1000	2200	256	563.20	256	563.20	14488	11200	24640				3288		7233.60		
Materials Handling	1.40	1	2	2	4000	250	350	64	89.60	64	89.60										3622	$5070.80
Shipping	2.40	1	1	1	2000	125	300	32	76.80	32	76.80										1811	4346.40
Porter	1.20	1	1	1	2000	125	150	32	38.40	32	38.40										1811	2173.20
Plant Manager	$7000 yr																					7000.00
TOTALS:							$4500		$1152		$1152			$41490		$66.30				$12248.20		$18590.40

Exhibit 8–1a. The Crew Composition Table for XYZ Corporation

than 2,000 regular one-shift hours in a year (unless it is worked on overtime). However, the annual Center hours can be more than this amount, as they represent the total of all the hours worked by all the machines in the Center.

6. FRINGE BENEFITS

These refer to the benefits or rest periods, holidays and vacation time which decrease the available annual Center hours. They must be given consideration for cost purposes and for purposes of an accurate projection of annual hours.

Rest Periods: This column evaluates the time and cost of work stoppages that are authorized for the purpose of relieving fatigue and monotony in repetitive production. For purposes of illustration, 30 minutes per day per worker is assumed. The hours are obtained by multiplying a half-hour by the number of days the workers are available. The cost is obtained by multiplying the rest period hours by the Hourly Pay Rate per Center.

Holidays: This column evaluates the time and cost of paid holidays. For example, four paid 8-hour holidays for the year would represent 32 annual holiday-hours and their cost would be 32 multiplied by the Center's hourly pay rate, as above.

Vacation: This column shows the time and cost of paid vacation time. Costs and hours will vary, because they usually are based on length of service. An average, for the sake of the computations, assumes that each worker has four 8-hour paid vacation days. The cost is calculated the same as the cost of holiday pay.

7. AVAILABLE ANNUAL CENTER HOURS

This column shows us the true availability of the Production Center after the decreases in attendance time caused by the three Fringe Benefits. The figure is obtained by subtracting the total hours shown under Fringe Benefits from the maximum annual Center hours. An interesting observation can be made at this point. In most plants in industry, the Fringe Benefits usually exceed 15% of scheduled production costs. Besides being costly, these benefits decrease the Centers' availability time—the time in which to recover fixed expenses. In developing machine-hour rates, due consideration must be given to the presence of this time loss so that it may be anticipated in the original projection of annual activity.

8. SCHEDULED PRODUCTION

This column shows the time and cost of the scheduled production. The hours scheduled are those projected as assigned annual hours in the CFCS. Keep in mind that the scheduled hours are those which are needed to support the sales aims of the company as outlined on its sales forecast. Scheduled hours are not influenced by the available annual Center hours. This latter figure states the number of Center hours available, while Scheduled Production states the hours needed in the coming 12-month period.

9. HOURLY BALANCE

This column shows the difference between the available and the required Center hours. In the "Under" column is inserted the number of hours that the Center has in excess of the number required.

This step which is done preparatory to balancing the payroll against the projected activities of the company's Production Centers, acts to merge the manpower requirements of the Production Centers with the payroll. Failure to accomplish this can result in payroll excesses or undermanning serious enough to threaten a company's performance during its busy season. If a shortage gets increasingly worse, management will be confronted with the necessity of training people in vital jobs after half a year has passed. Conversely, where such balancing has not been performed and an excess exists, invariably the same workload is distributed over more people, the average work tempo drops to the level where all are kept busy, costs increase and shipments slow down. While this result has its negative impact on operating performance and profits, it also is felt throughout the capital structure: there are less liquid current assets due to higher inventory levels, deceleration of receivables, and decreased cash flow. The task becomes one of transferring workers from the overmanned Centers to the undermanned ones.

10. TRANSFERS

The purpose of this column is to show to what extent the interchange of personnel between Production Centers is accomplished. From this analysis will come the final decision concerning the size and type of the production payroll.

In costing transfers, due consideration must be given to the changing hourly base rates of the men. Some union-management contracts stipulate that when a man is transferred to higher graded work, he shall receive the base rate of that new job.

11. IDLE TIME

This column is used to cost the excess unassigned time of the overmanned Production Centers. If available production hours exceed scheduled production hours, the difference in hours is entered in the Idle Time column. These excess hours, for which there is no scheduled production, can then be applied to other operations. If this transfer is possible, the hours are entered under Idle Time, Transfers, and the cost schedule is adjusted accordingly.

The cost of Idle Time is not to be confused with Lost Time cost, which appears on the Operating Budget.

12. NON-PRODUCTIVE

This column lists the costs of the workers who are not considered part of the regular production force, namely, those who are neither productive workers nor administrative or clerical personnel. These typically include materials handlers, receiving and shipping clerks, foremen, maintenance men, porters, and so forth.

Problems and Discussion

The tabulation of the number of workmen in standard crews required to man the Production Centers is done to find the hourly direct labor cost of each operating unit which comprises part of the machine-hour rate. This tabulation is also needed to find the cost of idle or non-utilized time of the crews, of the fringe benefit segment of their hourly costs, and of indirect supporting labor.

On Crew Rates: Sometimes there are units of a production center which are crewed by workers who, because of length of service, have varying hourly labor rates. In this case, the best procedure to follow is to assign a weighted average rate to the center.

In some industries materials handlers, bundlers, inspectors and the like are permanently assigned to productive operations. Sometimes one of these service people assists two machines in one center or works with machines from different centers. Where these people are directly identifiable with certain operations, then, following the criteria mentioned earlier, they should be listed fractionally under each of the machine units or centers concerned, and should not be listed as indirect labor on the Operating Budget.

On Transfers: Often the size of a center's crew requirements will vary with the needs of the work passing through. Therefore, provision must be made to add or subtract workers from the MHR as required. Adding a worker increases the direct labor portion of the MHR and raises the overhead portion by the inclusion of additional fringe benefit expense. It also may affect the worker balance, and it may increase or decrease idle time in the case of interdepartmental transfers. It may likewise decrease overtime premium, depending on the overbalance and availability of additional workers' hours at regular pay. Of course, subtracting a worker from a crew reverses the above effect.

On Arbitrary Crew Additions: We have been asked about the advisability of arbitrarily placing an extra worker in a crew for cost-estimating purposes just to be "on the safe side." This is a poor practice for several reasons. A worker charged to a center where he does not work artificially inflates the machine-hour rate for that Center and tends to overcost the orders passing through it. If much of the Center is used for the production of orders, this practice will usually price the company out of its markets. This is especially so at centers where the direct labor portion is a large percentage of the MHR, as would be true of handwork stations or operations carrying a relatively low level of machinery costs. Then there are problems of cost tracing, of effectively measuring cost recovery, and of pinpointing machine and Center profitability. Further, the control mechanism of idle time is thrown out of gear, and the reconciling of the manning of the production centers to the payroll becomes subject to distortion.

On Indirect Assignments: Then there are cases of a particular man in a maintenance department taking care of specific equipment. He might be considered a specialist for problems connected with this equipment. Perhaps he spends about half his time taking care of these specific machines, and the rest of the time he performs general work as a member of the maintenance department. The way to handle his costs is to assign one-half of his time and pay in the CCT as a fractional member of the crews operating the equipment he services; the other half of his pay should be budgeted in the Operating Budget as indirect labor to be charged out against all the production centers in the final allocation.

On Working Group Leaders: In assembly line operations and in handwork departments questions frequently arise concerning how non-working group leaders should be charged. Should they be classified with supervision as indirect labor on the Operating Budget, or should they be considered part of the crew? The criteria for these decisions are measurability and identity. Regardless of his job or title, if a particular person can always be identified with the group in which he or she serves, his or her wages and fringe benefits should be charged directly to that group. For example, in a handwork Center consisting of 16 units or 16 operators, the 17th person listed can be the supervisor. If each of the workers receives $1.50 per hour and the supervisor receives $3.00 per hour, the hourly cost of the Center is $27, or an average of $1.69 per operator. If the 16 workers perform a progressive series of 16 different operations, the direct labor portion of the MHR is $27. If 16 duplicate operations are done in the center, the direct labor portion of the rate is $1.69. Including the supervisor as part of the crew satisfies the principle that all costs directly traceable to the operation shall be charged directly thereto.

On Hourly Shortages: Sometimes in preparing a CCT, an estimator finds himself short a few hours in a center. Let's say he finds the Center to be short 70 annual hours, and there are no extra workers whom he can assign to that Center to perform the operation. That means he cannot transfer any manpower to the Center to absorb the deficiency. What happens in such a case?

The answer is simple. If the annual assigned hours are correct and the shortage is real, the solution is to keep the same crew on overtime rather than to commit the payroll to an extra "whole body" that cannot be fully utilized. When this is done, add to the Non-Productive column the cost of just the overtime premium. In this case, it would be 70 times one-half of the hourly pay rate of the center.

On Man-Hours vs. Machine Hours: At times, those preparing the schedule of machine-hour rates fail to remember the difference between man hours and machine hours; so this question occasionally crops up: How can there be the same number of fringe benefit *hours* for each of the production centers (shown in Exhibit 8–1) if the crewing of these centers varies? The answer to this question is that in projecting annual requirements of a Center we are interested in elapsed operating hours and not a sum of man-hours. Naturally, even though the fringe benefit hours may be the same, the fringe benefit *costs* will vary as the hourly pay rate per center varies. Exhibit 8–1a shows variations in both the fringe benefit hours and costs.

On Indirect and Direct Work: Then there are the questions involving what to do when a man spends part of his time on indirect work and part as a one-man production center. This circumstance, of course, should be the concern of both the CCT and the Operating Budget. If, for example, a man is available one year for 2,000 hours, and half the time he runs a small producing unit and the other half he prepares work for other Centers or does general maintenance work, then his time is fully charged by giving his small Production Center 1,000 annual hours, and charging the other 1,000 of his *man-hours* to the crews of other Centers he serves or as indirect labor in the Operating Budget if he is assigned maintenance work—or making any division between these latter two functions in accordance with the actual conditions existing.

On Handwork: Frequently, in industries that have large handwork requirements involving a multitude of operations, there are questions concerning how these different operations are to be classified in the schedule of Production Centers. This dilemma naturally then leads to questions of crewing. The problem arises in companies that have departments like hand decorating or painting; "fancywork" tables where hand glueing, satining and small inserting are done; and inspection tables for final touch-ups of lacquer coating.

The way to tackle the problem is to go back to the company's cost or estimating sheet to see which operations have been made the subject of a separate estimate. The major criterion for dividing such operations into Production Centers is whether or not they are sufficiently different from each other to make it necessary to classify each as a separate Center. This means determining whether each takes widely varying lengths of time to perform per unit piece of product. If one job takes 1 minute per piece and another 20 minutes per piece and these are combined into one Center, the production standard applied to the machine-hour rate will give an average conversion cost. This average puts the manufacturer in the old position of over- or undercosting, depending on whether operational time is low or high for a particular article.

If any of the skilled work Centers utilizes equipment having appreciable value, this is another clue for separation of Centers. Annual assigned hours, of course, is the largest factor in the determination of separate Production Centers.

On Redistributing Operations: In some industries, it is frequently more economical and efficient to break up operations that have formerly been together in one Production Center. For example, inspectors stationed at the outset at one Center might be changed to an inspection pool servicing several Centers, or bundlers reaching the end of an operation might be reassigned to a bundling and tying center. This type of change applies to direct productive work as well. For example, in the folding-carton industry strippers (those who break out the blanks from scored sheets) sometimes tail a cut-and-crease press and, more frequently, work at a stripping center servicing all presses.

Changes are simple to make. A new Center is created and just that space, Machinery, and crew, required to run it are charged to the other Centers. Usually, because of the greater gains in productivity that management expects to get from such a change, the assigned annual hours will be less at the service centers but will continue at the same level at the primary Center.

On Indirect-Direct Ratios: There are those who, even after understanding the concepts of allocation, would like to use a ratio of direct labor for determining their indirect labor; so it is worthwhile repeating statements made differently earlier in the book. Indirect labor does not vary with direct labor. Indirect labor consists of several elements: fringe benefits, unassigned time, unearned time, and lost time of production workers, normally classified indirect workers, and supervisors. Some of these costs are fixed in value irrespective of direct-labor changes. Others may change slightly with changes in direct labor. Fringe benefits vary almost directly with the direct labor dollars. But unassigned, unearned, and lost time of production workers is a function of scheduling, payroll balance and worker effort, and these do not change directly with the amount of direct labor. As a matter of fact, some of these vary inversely with direct labor. For example, as the direct labor payroll increases to higher productivity, the unearned direct labor costs decrease.

The largest influence exerted on indirect labor is the product mix, which in turn is felt as a change in facilities use. In most companies applying indirect labor on the basis of direct labor penalizes and overcosts products which may have high direct labor content, and undercosts those in which direct labor plays a smaller part in the total cost of the product.

Chapter 9

HOW TO DEVELOP
THE MHR

Step 3: The Operating Budget

The Operating Budget, hereinafter referred to as the OB, is the third piece of organized data required in collecting statistics for the development of the machine-hour rate cost-estimating structure. First, you collected information on the nature of each of the Production Centers that the company expects to operate in the coming period. Then, as a second step, you assigned manpower to operate each Center. Now, as the next step in gathering classified facts, you will list the expenses that the company anticipates it will incur in the coming period. This information is tabulated in the OB. The OB represents a projection of expenses in all categories except productive labor, the latter being developed from the Crew Composition Table discussed in the previous chapter.

Costs for Financial Reporting and Pricing

The timing of charges against sales income that is followed for financial reporting purposes may, at times, be inappropriate when cost figures are being assembled to guide pricing of products. Conservatism, established customs, and tax considerations often determine where a specific cost is charged off the books. In some companies fully amortized facilities are still in use, but while in most cases depreciation of such facilities is included in costs computed for pricing purposes, it is not recorded in the accounts. The reason is that the customer should pay for the equipment. A tax advantage will be received by amortization in five years, but the company still has to recover its investment.

Conditions such as these arise most often when assets of substantial value have

86

been depreciated over a period considerably shorter than their useful life. Where equipment is still in use after a normal depreciation period, higher maintenance and repair costs often take the place of depreciation, and book costs are considered satisfactory for pricing purposes. Advertising, sales promotion and research costs are examples of other costs which are sometimes spread over more than one year in computing costs for pricing products but may be treated as period costs for financial reporting purposes.

Budget Form

A budget represents different forms to different people. It is not necessarily a formal system tied into the general books of accounting. Therefore, the exact form of budget is not important, but its substance is. There are probably as many budget forms as there are accounting schools, and each form offers some advantage in traditional cost-accounting systems. The machine-hour rate, however, is not one of these systems. The costs it finds are logical, traceable and provable, and changes due to activity levels, equipment, expenses, crew revisions, product mix, and so forth, are recorded directly without endless and obscure accounting gyrations. For MHR purposes, the OB translates the usual expense accounts into functional classifications, to enable their proper allocation in the composition of the final machine-hour rates.

The OB should use the previous year's expense schedule as a guide. This schedule can then become the budget for the coming period after additions and subtractions have been made. All those changes which the management foresees will happen in the next 12 months should be reflected in this budget. If management expects wage increases within the year, these should be reflected in the CCT and the OB. If the office force is to be enlarged or the amount allocated for advertising decreased, these factors should be anticipated in the OB. If a machine is to be acquired or a Production Center eliminated, the effect of these changes—in terms of power, depreciation costs, and so forth—should be planned for in the OB.

Judgment Essential

A word to the wise at this point: Good judgment must be used in the projection of expenses, and don't season it with too much let's-be-on-the-safe-side reasoning, lest the broth be too rich for customers to digest. Projected expenses must be the realistic, down-to-earth result of the collaboration of key personnel throughout the company who know intimately the caprices of the individual expense items. Healthy budgets do not come out of the ivory tower, but from constructive discussions among all the personnel involved.

Object and Preparation of Budget for MHR

The object of the OB is to estimate in advance a sum of money to finance its operation (planned on the CFCS)—money which the company hopes to recover through its selling prices. By including a correct portion of this budgeted sum in each order and selling the machine activity projected (as determined by the CFCS), the company may be able to recover its full expenses and realize its estimated profit margin. This condition occurs at the end of the period only if the actual expenses do not exceed the budget. A vital point here is that *expenses can and do exceed the budget,* even if they are both equal on paper. This is one of the most controversial points in cost-finding in high fixed-cost industry, and it is one which is constantly overlooked because it is difficult to handle on a formal accounting basis. We'll return to this point later on.

The Operating Budget lists total overhead costs. It is a projection of all manufacturing, selling, delivery, and administrative costs that the company anticipates for the coming 12 months. A shorter period would not take into account the full cycle of production, and projections for a longer time are pointless, because this would duplicate the effect of seasonal fluctuations.

The Operating Budget should be prepared at regular intervals, and the payroll figures it contains should be compared with those developed by the CCT. Differences between the two should be discussed with supervisors concerned and adjustment made, so that figures in the two tables agree. Operating Budgets for Company *ABC* and *XYZ* Corporation are shown in Exhibits 9–1 and 9–1a.

Budget Classifications

In the Operating Budget, budgeted costs are grouped into functional classifications, as follows (only summary costs under each heading are shown; others may be added as needed):

MANUFACTURING COSTS

Space

    Rent
    Real estate taxes
    Depreciation of building
    Maintenance of building
    Light, if segregated from Power
    Insurance on building

Power

    Electricity
    Heat, if not included under Electricity
    Light, if not included in Electricity or Space

Machinery

Depreciation
Maintenance
Rentals
Insurance on Machinery

Fringe Benefits

Social Security taxes paid by the company
Overtime premium
Holiday and vacation pay
Workmen's Compensation insurance
Pension and health plans paid by the company

Indirect labor

Supervisors' pay
Non-productive workers' pay
Idle time of production workers

NON-MANUFACTURING COSTS

Selling

Salesmen's salaries and commissions
Traveling expenses
Warehouse and delivery expenses
Telephone, telegraph expenses
Salesmen's car allowances or expenses
Advertising expenses
Salaries of Sales Office clerks
Sales Office rent, if allocated
Stationery (etc.) costs chargeable to Sales Office

Administration

Executive salaries (except salaries of those whose time is entirely chargeable to a
    function, such as manufacturing or sales)
Office salaries
Office rent
Depreciation of furniture and fixtures
Stationery, postage, etc.
Telephone, telegraph, etc.
General insurance
Interest paid
General taxes, other than taxes on income.

Expense Classifications	Actual Expenses (from books)		Projected (Budgeted) Expenses	
	item	total	total	total (rounded off)
MANUFACTURING COSTS:				
Space:				
Rent	$10,000	$10,000	$10,000	$10,000
Power:				
Electricity	2,900		3,300	
Heat	1,700	4,600	1,700	5,000
Machinery:				
Depreciation	16,500		16,500	
Price-level adjustment for economic depreciation	-0-*	16,500	3,500	20,000
Fringe Benefits:				
Social Security taxes	840		885	
Rest periods	3,920		4,200	
Holiday & Vacation pay	1,910		1,150.40	
Workmen's Compensation Insur.	485		485	
Other	-0-	7,155	1,279.60	8,000
Indirect Labor:				
Non-productive workers pay	6,000		5,433	
Idle time of prod'n workers	-0-*	6,000	6,185.40	12,000
TOTAL MANUFACTURING	COSTS:	$44,255	BUDGET:	$55,000
NON-MANUFACTURING COSTS:				
Selling & Delivery		6,000		8,000
General & Administrative		29,000		32,000
TOTAL NON-MANUFACTURING	COSTS:	35,000	BUDGET:	40,000
TOTAL OVERHEAD COSTS	COSTS:	$79,255	BUDGET:	$95,000

*not allowed in previous year's budget.

Exhibit 9–1. Condensed Operating Budget for Company ABC

Expense Classification	Amount Budgeted
MANUFACTURING COSTS:	
Space:	$8,500
Power:	3,000
Machinery:	10,500
Fringe Benefits: (rest periods, holidays, vacation, overtime premiums)	6,870.30
Indirect Labor:	30,838.60
TOTAL MANUFACTURING COSTS	$59,708.90
NON-MANUFACTURING COSTS:	
Selling:	11,000
Administrative:	17,000
TOTAL NON-MANUFACTURING COSTS	28,000
TOTAL OVERHEAD COSTS	$87,708.90

Exhibit 9–1a. Condensed Operating Budget for XYZ Corporation

After classifying all costs, we total the listings in all the columns. Then these totals should be checked for agreement with the total budget cost. They are later transferred to the Expense Assignment Worksheet developed in the following chapter.

Direct-Indirect Charges

In actual machine-hour rate installations, there are direct and indirect charges for some of the expenses shown. For example, where individual machine records are available, expected repairs on these machines can be charged directly to the Production Centers. This type of record also helps tell when to discard a machine.

Materials handlers serve the plant as a whole and/or they may be assigned specifically to a group of machines. In the former case, their labor should be handled as an over-all indirect labor charge; in the latter case, it should be charged directly to the group of Production Centers served. This is done by means of the Crew Composition Table, through which materials handlers become part of the Center's manpower and thus do not appear a second time in the OB.

The purpose of recasting the expenses for the previous period, in the Operating Budget form, is to insure that all expenses have been accounted for on the projected expense schedule and to provide an estimating guide to the probable changes in those figures.

Some of the amounts budgeted, like rent, are the same as those of the previous period. Some may be altered by an estimate of what is expected to happen; for example, Repairs to Machinery. Some budgeted expenses, like Holiday and Vacation Pay, are developed on and come directly from the CCT without any alteration.

While the total amount of previous period expenses should definitely agree with the same column in the expense schedule, the amount budgeted in the projection column need not agree. This latter sum represents future expectations and may be larger or smaller than the previous actual expenses. When machine-hour rates have been in effect, the differences between these two columns provide an appraisal of the accuracy of budgeting expenses and forecasting activity.

The inclusion of a price-level adjustment under *Machinery Costs:* Machinery, which did not appear on the expense accounts of EXHIBIT 9–1a, is noticed in EXHIBIT 9–1. This item turns us to a consideration of economic depreciation, one of the most important elements of product costing in inflationary economic periods.

Economic Depreciation

Purchased equipment represents heavy capital expenditures in industry. Generally, the cost of owning this equipment is one of the largest single fixed-cost items in the entire cost structure of the converter-manufacturer. By charging customers the equipment's hourly cost management hopes to recover, via its selling prices, all that it costs to own, maintain, and otherwise make their equipment available.

This machinery cost that management hopes to recover is included in the MHR in the charge for depreciation. As each hour of machine activity is "sold" (as part of the product sales price), the company recovers a portion of its depreciation cost. If the machine's expected activity is realized at the end of the year, the company will get back its entire annual depreciation expenses. Ostensibly, if this process continues consistently over the useful life of the facility, management will have recovered its investment. Under this theory, a machine costing $50,000 and having a life expectancy of 10 years, will, in effect, be sold piecemeal to customers at the rate of $5,000 per year. That means that $5,000 of the total annual sales income is derived from selling one-tenth of the "value" of the machine. In ten years the entire machine is "sold" and the capital invested is recovered. But is it really, considering the effects of inflation and the decrease in the dollar's purchasing power? If the above situation took place in the years 1950 to 1960, *the manufacturer would have to pay $104,000 to replace the machine in kind in 1960, not $50,000.*

Technological advances may be so great that an entirely new type of machine, capable of doing much more work of better quality, may be obtained for half the price paid for the old machine. Hence, during the life of the machine, its current replacement value may either rise or fall. If it rises in inflationary periods, the manufacturer has the choice of increasing depreciation charges, so that he "sells" the machine to his customers at the *current market prices,* just as he does his labor and raw materials, or of giving the customers the advantage of his "book" depreciation, which represents the lower prices prevailing ten years back.

If the manufacturer fails to raise the depreciation charge as replacement costs rise (usually an annoyance to those keeping the general books of account), while he may be providing for the recovery of his capital investment in "original" dollars, he is not charging his customers "current value" for the present use of the machine. This practice *will not* lead to a recovery of depreciation charges sufficient to replace the equipment used up in the customer's service.

If there has been neither inflation nor deflation and there was no variation in the dollar's purchasing power, then the temper of the dollar (hardness or softness) would be fairly stable and the accumulation of annual recovered depreciation charges would be a reasonable approach to providing replacement funds. But, even so, *technological depreciation* questions still have to be answered: Will the replacing machines have to be more modern to compete? Will they have more or less productive capacity than the old ones? Will they require more attendance and maintenance than the old ones? What will be the trade-in or salvage value of the depreciated machines?—This salvage value is a variable which reflects how well the machine was cared for.

Chameleon-like Profits

Where profits are based on the difference between total costs and selling prices (not always possible), and some of the costs (principally depreciation expense) are based on a former value of money, the result is a partial artificial inflation of the profit dollars. If there is an additional depreciation based on the present replacement value of the machinery, the profit is reduced to account for the fact that replacement has to be made in "softer" dollars. Without reserve for an increase in the replacement price of equipment, a manufacturer in 1960 is burdened with having to replace a 10-year-old depreciated machine with 48-cent dollars.

Real profits (profits which, because of economic depreciation, are less than profits listed on a profit-and-loss statement) change color depending on when the equipment was bought, the velocity of depreciation, and the degree of technological change occurring in the depreciation period. A dollar of profit on one company's statement is therefore not as green as one on another plant's statement. Profits are inadvertently overstated because of the difference between "original" and "replacement" dollars.

In companies having substantial fixed-capital investments, this accidental overstatement of profits can be serious and can cause an impact in the most unlikely quarters. Profit inflation, unavoidably listed on corporate financial statements, stimulates and accelerates demands for wage increases, which in turn aggravate inflation further. U. S. Steel's net profits were $143 million in 1952 and $301 million in 1958, a doubling of profits. However, if depreciation costs were stated in current dollars, the reported profits would have been cut in half. Liberalizing of the tax authority's depreciation rules regarding accelerated amortization periods is a help, but it does not solve the major portion of the problem.

Price-Level Changes

The real question to be answered by owners and businessmen is whether the amount charged for depreciation should be based on original dollar costs, or adjusted on a varying annual scale, to give effect to the change in the purchasing power of the dollar. Traditionally, profits are determined from matching up costs with income. The man who bought a piece of land for $10,000 in 1950 and sells it in 1960 for $15,000 matches up the cost with the income and figures he has made a profit of $5,000. But *has* he made a profit, considering the 1960 purchasing power of the dollar? The individual who bought 100 shares of stock in a corporation in 1950 for $1,000 and sells them in 1960 for $1,400 may *think* he made a profit of $400 regardless of the fact that $1,400 in 1960 might buy much less than $1,000 bought in 1950. Both men made a profit in physical dollars; but they lost in purchasing power.

The same is true in industry. Since depreciation tax deductions are allowed only on historical cost, a company should have charged its customers in 1960, $2.08 for each dollar of current cost over the original cost in 1950. The only fly in the ointment is that while it should charge this amount in order to reserve a realistic amount for future replacement, it will not be able to claim this sum as an expense. The taxing authorities will recognize the additional recovered sum as part of income; however, the manufacturer will still be ahead on about 50% of this sum.

Fairness to Customers

Is pricing which reflects price-level adjustments fair? In the price of a product, the customer is charged and pays for labor and material in terms of inflated dollars. When he employs people he pays for their services in current dollars. And you can be sure that if a merchant bought an inventory of industrial diamonds years back in a rising market, he would not use his historical cost in arriving at today's selling prices.

There is actually no difference in "selling" or "leasing" the use of productive facilities. When a customer purchases an order from a manufacturer, he leases the use of the plant's facilities for the period during which his order is processed. Why shouldn't the customer pay for that rental in current dollars, as he pays for everything else?

Let's take a specific and simple case of equipment bought for $100,000 with an amortization period of 10 years. EXHIBIT 9–2 shows the difference between unadjusted straight-line depreciation and a depreciation level adjusted for varying price levels. This tabulation shows two types of depreciation: the depreciation on original cost shown on the general books of account, and the economic depreciation in an inflationary period as shown by the last column. There are some who, while agreeing with the concept of making provision in costs for economic depreciation, state that the cost of replacing the depreciated machine at the end of the tenth year would be $200,000 instead of $155,000. This assumes that the same machine is available in its original form, the only change in purchase price to be due to the changing price level. This approach is not practical because it ignores the effect that technological progress has on prices and avoids the strong probability of increased functionality of newer equipment. It is not likely that management could or would replace depreciated equipment with identical equipment.

The Method

Basing depreciation on a fluctuating replacement value would confuse accounting procedures and should not be attempted. However, a reserve can be established to account for the increase in replacement price of machinery. A reserve is simply

Year	Depreciation on Original Cost	Price Level*	Adjustment	Total Depreciation Expenses Charged to Customers
1st	$10,000	110	$1,000	$11,000
2nd	10,000	120	2,000	12,000
3rd	10,000	130	3,000	13,000
4th	10,000	140	4,000	14,000
5th	10,000	150	5,000	15,000
6th	10,000	160	6,000	16,000
7th	10,000	170	7,000	17,000
8th	10,000	180	8,000	18,000
9th	10,000	190	9,000	19,000
10th	10,000	200	10,000	20,000
	$100,000		$55,000	$155,000

*velocity of inflationary movement assumed

Exhibit 9–2. Price-Level Depreciation Chart

a sum which is put aside for a future liability or expense. Economic depreciation qualifies as a possible future expense, but no one really knows to what extent.

An approximation of how much depreciation cost should be increased, to account for price-level adjustments, should be made at the time the Operating Budget is prepared. This is not an easy task. Of course, the best approximation will occur at the time of replacement when the replacement value and the original cost can be compared. But management cannot wait that long; it must recover inflated monies as it goes along. One way of estimating this increase is by reference to various price-level indices (Consumer-Price Index, for one) and by reference to the price of new, fairly similar equipment.

When the depreciation increase is determined, the amount should be transferred to a surplus account and any remnant of the reserve will become part of the current profit. As far as the tax authorities are concerned, both the method of accounting for supplementary depreciation and the type of reserve mentioned above are unacceptable. For tax purposes, the profit should be computed using book depreciation taken on original purchase value.

To add an amount for economic depreciation is perfectly legal, just as it is legal to add a percentage of materials cost for waste. But this added depreciation cannot be considered an expense and taxes must be paid on it, since it is viewed as added income.

Exhibit 9–1 shows such an amount in the projected budget. According to the expenses shown on the general books of account, sales will over-recover expenses. This over-recovery (all other things being equal) results from the presence of an "expense" for added depreciation which is not shown as an expense on the books. As suggested above, this sum can be transferred to a reserve account, or it can be invested in outside securities which seem to offer a hedge against further inflation. This decision would, of course, depend on the time and the forecasted price-level increments.

Rapidly expanding and progressive plants find difficulty in matching the health of their capital architecture with operating effectiveness because of their failure to consider, and include in their costing, the element of economic depreciation. Especially in the foreseeable future, the compounding nature of this element will take its toll among those who cling to traditional methods.

Flexible Budgets

Naturally, all plants do not budget expenses in the same way. A budget is a reflection of the company's way of doing business. In fact, the budget can be considered one reflection of the composite personality of the many people who shape it.

Companies elect to incur expenses for various reasons and out of different motives. They may have objective reasons for starting or continuing an expense, or they may be prompted by habit or intuition.

Basically, there are those expenses which change with volume, sales, and other activities relating to the management of the company, and those which occur due to the passage of time. Some, like productive labor, are directly variable. Others will vary in step-like fashion with volume or output, as will supervision; and others vary directly with sales or management activity, as do depreciation and rent. Respectively, these expenses are called variable, semi-variable and fixed. The variable costs are sometimes called volume costs and the fixed costs can be termed time or standby costs. With the separation of these costs, MHR can be developed for out-of-pocket as well as full costs.

Obviously, the expenses shown on any Operating Budget are valid only within a certain range of activity: more or fewer funds would be necessary depending on the specific level of activity at which the plant was being operated. However, because of the nature of the variation of certain groups of expenses, the total budget cannot be altered by direct percentages. One could not summarily "mark up" the total budget by the percentage change. Change in the total budgeted amount should change by the additive amounts of the individual expense changes. The greater the element of variable expense in the budget, the closer the change in the total budgeted amount will approach the percentage of change, and vice versa.

Consider also, that each semi-variable has a fixed as well as a variable expense portion. These factors demand that the Operating Budget be designed to suit the expected level of activity by evaluating how the movement of each expense will be affected by the changed activity. This is the nature of flexible budgets.

In EXHIBIT 9–3 a simple condensed budget shows how this idea works (with "activity" based on productive labor):

Notice that total expenses do not follow increases in activity. A traditional or fixed budget would produce $1,600,000 as total expense for the 80% activity level, if 40% was the starting base of calculation. Including such an inflated (and non-

Expense Classification	ACTIVITY LEVEL		
	40 percent	60 percent	80 percent
Variable expenses	$400,000	$600,000	$800,000
Semi-variable expenses	100,000	120,000	130,000
Fixed expenses	300,000	300,000	300,000
TOTAL EXPENSES	$800,000	$1,020,000	$1,230,000

Exhibit 9–3. Condensed Flexible Budget Based on Direct Labor

incurred) sum would price the company out of its markets. As a matter of fact, giving credence to this type of "budgeting" is tantamount to denying the existence of economies at the upper activity levels.

A further insight into the nature of expense movement with activity variances is shown in the condensed profit-and-loss statement of Exhibit 9–4 (with "activity" based on sales volume).

Note that the fixed and variable segments have been separated in some of the major expense categories. Also, note that the variable portion does not vary directly with activity because the activity has been stated in terms of sales. Consequently the dominant influence of product mix comes into play. If the double sales volume was sold at a different product mix than was represented by the profit-and-loss tabulation, the 80% expense figures could be different from those shown: Direct Materials cost might be half the amount shown; Productive Labor might cost more than double. The amount of variable-expense increase (whether in wholly variable items or partially variable ones) is related directly to the activity increase (if measured in sales) conditioned solely by the specific product mix.

Flexible Budget Formulation

It is practical to assign the expenses for various levels of activity by formula rather than by estimate. All that is needed to accomplish this is the analysis of past records that show the various expenses that occurred at the different activity levels. For example, let us develop a formula so that we can budget factory supervision properly at any activity level. Let us also try another activity base: man-hours, which would relate well to the supervision loading required.

In our example, assume that for normal volume one general foreman at $600 per month and four assistant foremen, at $300 per month each, are required. When activity drops to 75% of normal volume, one of the assistant foremen can be transferred to other work and a second assistant foreman can divide his time between this department and other work. Further reduction in supervision can similarly be made at lower levels of production. The normal organization can carry up to 125% of normal volume, at which point it will be necessary to add a second shift in one section, and another assistant foreman. This information is expressed in graphic form in Exhibit 9–5.

The line Probable Actual Expense appears as a series of steps. It shows the amount which probably will be expended on the general foreman and his assistants for the range of activity shown. As a practical matter, the budget should not be established coincident with these steps, because the formula for expressing the relationship between activity and budget allowance would be too complex for easy use.

Budgeted Expense is expressed as a straight line passing through the expected

| | ACTIVITY LEVEL | | | | | |
| | 40% | | | 80% | | |
	Total	Variable	Fixed	Total	Variable	Fixed
SALES	$3,000,000	----	----	$6,000,000	----	----
Direct Material	1,000,000	$1,000,000		2,100,000	$2,100,000	
Productive Labor	700,000	700,000		1,100,000	1,100,000	
Manufacturing Overhead	800,000	150,000	$650,000	900,000	250,000	$650,000
Administrative Expenses	300,000	150,000	150,000	375,000	225,000	150,000
Selling Expenses	300,000	200,000	100,000	475,000	375,000	100,000
TOTALS	$3,100,000	$2,200,000	$900,000	$4,950,000	$4,050,000	$900,000
NET PROFIT OR (LOSS) before income taxes	($100,000)			$1,050,000		

Exhibit 9–4. Condensed Flexible Budget Based on Sales

cost at normal volume, and having a slope conforming as closely as possible with the slope indicated by the step line. The point at which the Budgeted Expense line intersects the vertical axis, at zero activity, represents the minimum cost, and the slope of the line indicates the rate at which the budget will increase per unit of man-hour or other measure of activity.

The budget formula by which the expense of factory supervision is determined for any level of activity is shown at the bottom of Exhibit 9–5.

This type of calculation for various activity levels should be done in projecting a Crew Composition Table.

Electricity

Let us examine the semi-variable expense for Electricity, which varies differently than factory supervision. This type of expense increases from a fixed minimum at zero activity in direct proportion to the volume. Such expenses are often budgeted by analyzing past experience. The following example is based on the cost of purchased electricity for which there is a minimum charge or fixed demand:

These data appear on the graph of Exhibit 9–6 in scatter-chart fashion, by numbered circles. This information is derived from the table at the bottom of the chart.

The Budgeted Expense line is drawn to approximate the slope or trend indicated by the plotted points. This is the flexible budget line. The amount of expense ($1,000) indicated by the point at which this line intersects the vertical zero production line is considered the fixed portion of the cost of electricity. A "standard expense" line, which would not consider the fixed and variable portions of the expense, is shown in a dotted line. As in a break-even chart, the lower wedge would represent the area of undercharging customers (loss); the upper wedge, overcharging—if "standard expense" were used as the amount to budget for the cost of electricity.

The budget formula by which the expense of electricity is determined is shown at the bottom of Exhibit 9–6.

Exhibit 9–7 shows a comparison between a "standard" expense and a total flexible budget for four items of varying "fixedness" and variability: Depreciation, Factory Supplies, Supervision and Electricity. Notice the size of the undercharge wedge. Again, and it bears repeating, if customers were charged according to a direct proportion between activity and expense for all activity below normal, the company would not recover its full cost.

Depreciation

Some of the following reasons are usually given for basing depreciation on historical cost. Only the first one could be considered good:

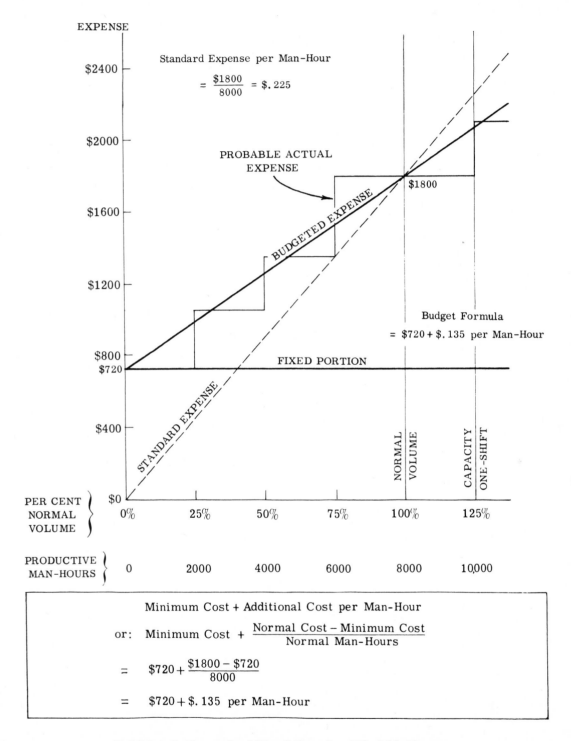

Exhibit 9–5. Example of "Step" Type Semi-Variable Expense:
Supervision

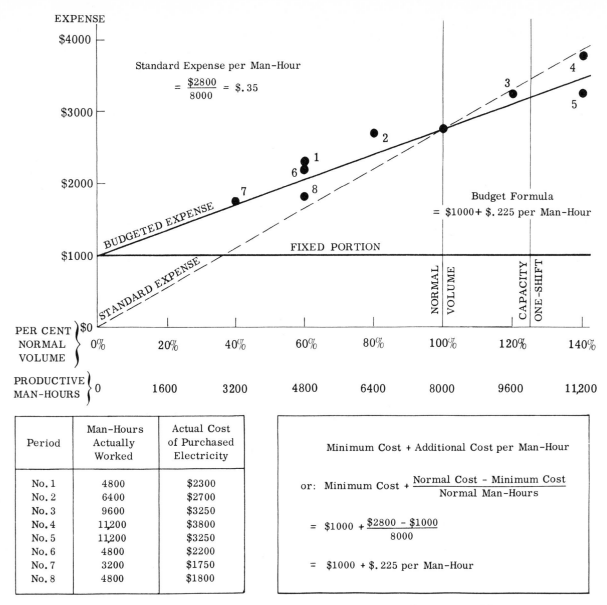

Exhibit 9–6. Example of "Straight-Line" Type of Semi-Variable
Expense: Electricity

1. Depreciation constitutes a relatively small portion of total product costs in some companies (naturally, we are not considering converting industries, where heavy investments in machinery exist) and any changes in product costing resulting from restatement of depreciation on a current cost basis would not be significant.

2. Others feel that, because the competition does not use costs containing depreciation allowances, it would price their own products off the market.

3. Still others wrongly believe that there is no practical method to ascertain depreciation in terms of current price levels and consequently prefer to base their costs on historical data.

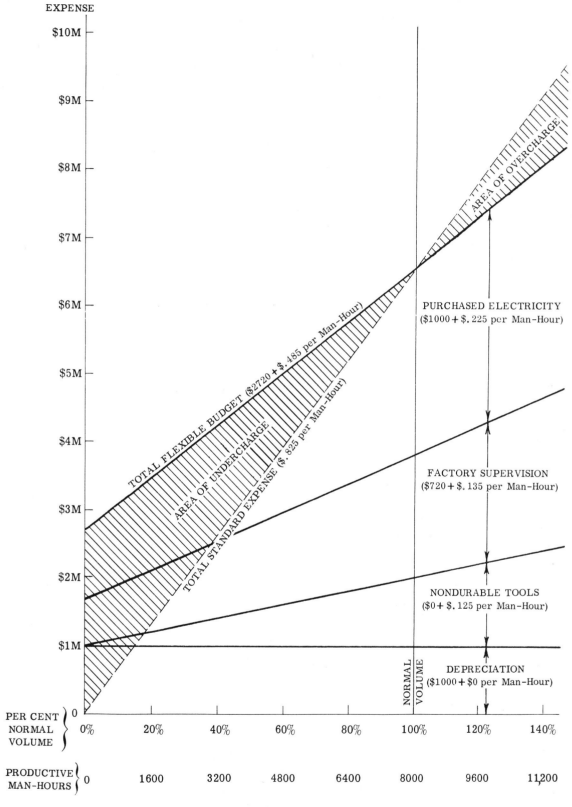

EXPENSE

$10M

$9M

$8M

$7M

$6M

$5M

$4M

$3M

$2M

$1M

0

AREA OF OVERCHARGE

TOTAL FLEXIBLE BUDGET ($2720 + $.485 per Man-Hour)

AREA OF UNDERCHARGE

TOTAL STANDARD EXPENSE ($.825 per Man-Hour)

PURCHASED ELECTRICITY
($1000 + $.225 per Man-Hour)

FACTORY SUPERVISION
($720 + $.135 per Man-Hour)

NONDURABLE TOOLS
($0 + $.125 per Man-Hour)

NORMAL VOLUME

DEPRECIATION
($1000 + $0 per Man-Hour)

PER CENT
NORMAL
VOLUME

0%   20%   40%   60%   80%   100%   120%   140%

PRODUCTIVE
MAN-HOURS

0   1600   3200   4800   6400   8000   9600   11,200

Exhibit 9–7. Development of Total Departmental Flexible Budget in
Relation to Productive Activity

On the other hand, companies that do state depreciation in terms of current price levels for the purpose of calculating their product prices, use mainly the current replacement cost of depreciable assets, calculated for insurance purposes, as a base. The fallacy here is that usually sound insurable values tend to be overstated.

Other companies prefer to use as a basis the cost of their plant and equipment, determined on a current basis each month by applying the U.S. Department of Labor construction costs index to the number of asset dollars invested in each year, as shown by the investment ledger. Product costs are affected in two ways by the use of these current figures:

(a) Some overhead costs are allocated on the basis of invested capital. Historical costs would result in inequitable distribution, because departments having recently acquired equipment would be overcharged. Perhaps invested capital is an important basis for cost distribution in an industry where use of the resulting figures is not limited to pricing; however, applying this concept to the investment ledger instead of to individual centers (property ledger) tends to average out the economic depreciation of a specific machine—especially where assets were acquired at different intervals over a long period of time.

(b) Product costs containing depreciation at current price levels would be those that management would use in pricing.

To use current or replacement costs for pricing purposes does not necessarily imply that any change should be made in accepted methods of computing product costs for charging inventory and cost of goods sold; that is, for tax purposes, unadjusted depreciation expenses (as shown on the books) are included in inventory.

Problems and Discussion

Manufacturers must constantly guard against cost inconsistencies because they appear to be "convenient" or "logical." At almost every turn in the cost-finding road, there are temptations to follow some rule-of-thumb procedure. As we mentioned earlier in this book, costs are born differently and develop according to their own peculiar traits. Since costs do not come into being already allocated "by product," they cannot be allocated directly to the product. They have to be assigned in another way. The cost of owning, maintaining and operating facilities is the highest cost encountered by converting industries. The producing machine becomes the point of meeting between that large expense and the orders which justify it. All expenses properly allocated to the machinery thus have cost meaning for each order or product.

On Allocation Variances: Allocating a group of expenses to machines or production centers by different methods and on different bases can produce startlingly different results. A variation in one allocation method of a manufacturer of electro-mechanical devices doing a $15 million business annually was enough to produce a 5% decrease in selling prices coexistent with a 2% increase due to the particular product mix. This 3% net underpricing cost the company $450,000 in profits.

Such allocation inconsistencies can start long before final costs are assigned to the Production Centers. They can start in the classifying of the converting facilities (CFCS); they can start or be carried along in the CCT, where the technique of assigning manpower for different levels of operation is considered, and there are ample opportunities for budgeting inconsistencies to emerge in the OB.

The OB, unless policed, is a fertile area for rules of thumb. Its preparation should be policed and the final product should be subject to periodic review. Experience has revealed that changing depreciation methods, ambiguous activity interpretations and the like, have actually robbed companies of a large portion of their rightful markets and profits. Consider that a misapplication of cost that results in just a one percent error in pricing in a company doing a $20 million business annually can mean a loss of $200,000 in profits.

On Capacity: One of the largest points of confusion in flexible budgeting (also discussed in Chapter 10) is the idea or notion of capacity. First, let's review some of the common definitions of this term. In this book, we call it *activity* and apply it to individual production centers in recognition of the fact that all centers cannot be equally active. To assume that all centers are equally active would mean that a perfect time balance exists among all pieces of equipment, not a practical assumption.

Then there are terms such as "normal capacity," "practical capacity," "maximum capacity." Sometimes the phrase "operating level" is used in place of the word capacity. The problem is that a different concept comes into play with each expression. Confusion is further compounded by questions of by what unit capacity is measured, and whether the term applies to the entire business, product lines, or operations.

To some companies, normal capacity means an average utilization of plant and equipment based on expected sales orders. But, what is "average utilization"?

To others it means the volume at which the plant is equipped to operate, or the maximum capacity attainable. Thus, even with the same capacity framework, you have not only different meanings but different implementations of those meanings.

Some companies measure their capacity in sales dollars; others in number of units or weight sold. Still others do it by maximum man-hours, or by turnover of working capital. Bewildering, isn't it?

The concept of activity and capacity is bewildering even to those who have seriously thought about it. Activity in the corrugated container company (*ABC* in our example) can be measured by sales volume, by man-hours, by machine-hours, by square footage of board converted, by tons of board processed, by boxes sold, by number of people on the payroll, by space utilization, by investment in inventory, and by turnover of working capital. Selecting a proper basis for activity requires using at least two of these bases. One base is not a sufficiently weighted yardstick; to use just one of these factors would be to measure autonomous activity and assume that the activity is not related to the company as a whole.

For example, the use of sales volume as the sole measurement of activity can be dangerously misleading. Obviously, as the product mix shifts, the same level of sales volume can cause wide variations in man-hours, and in machine-hours. This in turn affects the velocity of expense recovery. Depending on the product mix, the same level of sales can lightly or heavily load the plant, the office operations, and the estimating. The same level of sales can involve widely varying amounts of board, makeready times, and so forth. In the financial area, due to the material cost content in the product mix sold, the same level of sales can place light or normal requirements on the inventory, or it can seriously weaken the capital architecture because of the large amounts of capital that must remain in inventory to support the specific needs of the mix being processed.

In one folding carton plant, by reviewing past years' statistics, it was proved that in terms of the factors mentioned above, $5,000,000 in sales was at one time 55% of maximum activity on the same base. Obviously, sales volume was a fallacious base. But there were other factors at play: In the first place, where the products were manufactured using only 55% of the available one-shift machine hours, the element of make-ready time was high, and the mix was rich with high-quality cartons and required a high level of capital support in inventory. This was straining the working capital position of the company and allowing creditors to have an excessive stake in the company. In other words, the activity of using only 55% of the available machine-hours had caused the *capital facility* to exceed its capacity.

When measuring activity one must consider the impact in several areas of the company. Activity-level budgeting should be related to profit-generating conditions. Some corrugated container plants still use square footage as a measure of activity when, depending on the type, the same size container can be much different in labor and overhead cost from another. Other plants budget activity by machine-hours without considering that this rate represents a specific machine and a given level of expense recovery, and therefore is related to profits.

Profit-making in the converting industries depends largely on the speed and consistency with which fixed-expense recovery is accomplished. The largest portion of this recovery is devoted to the uncontrollable element incurred "by machine." Once management recovers this sum, it can adjust other expenses to get the optimum amount of profit from various sales volumes. Therefore, the concept of expense recovery as a measure of activity or capacity is valid. Instead of budgeting to a certain sales volume and calling it X percent, the budget can be designed to support a given amount of expense recovery.

On Recovery and Sales Variances: How fixed-expense recovery and sales varied in one plant over a six-year period is shown below:

Sales in the Period	Fixed-Expense Recovery Produced by Mix of Sales
$3,500,000	$625,000
$3,600,000	$480,000
$5,400,000	$520,000
$5,650,000	$355,000

Of course, as was mentioned earlier, the capital impact must be considered, because in the drive for increased expense recovery, the capital structure can be seriously weakened. This is the tragedy of companies that cannot utilize their fullest capacity in production because of the lack of capital strength and/or cannot utilize their capital to the fullest and remain therefore with large sums of idle capital.

More is said about capacity and activity in Section 4.

On Depreciation Methods: Another point of confusion in costing budgeting is the question of which depreciation method to use. Three methods in common use are described below:

1. *Straight-Line Method:* This method is popular because it is convenient, being based on the proposition that if a machine has an estimated life of n years, its value should be written down 1/n each year. Accordingly, successive values at the end of each year of use would fall on a straight line beginning at first cost and terminating at zero. A machine purchased for $30,000 and having an expected life of 10 years would depreciate $3,000 each year. After 4 years of use, it would have an estimated book value of $18,000. Some state that after a machine has completed its estimated life, it still has a scrap value and that this value should be included in estimating the annual depreciation. It is doubtful whether this refinement is consistent with the degree of accuracy with which the useful life of the machine can be predicted in the first place.

2. *Diminishing Balance Method:* This method is based on the theory that machines wear out faster toward the latter years of their useful life than in their earlier years and that, hence, repairs and maintenance costs in the earlier years are comparatively light. Under this concept, greater depreciation is charged off in the earlier years and less in the late years, in order that the sum of depreciation, maintenance and repairs shall be uniform throughout the useful life of the equipment. This is accomplished by charging off a constant percentage each year on the book value or remaining value. If a machine is valued at $10,000 when acquired, and is estimated to have a scrap value of $2,000 at the end of 10 years, the depreciation written off at the end of the first year will be some percentage of $10,000 and, in the

tenth year, the same percentage but on some value which is slightly above $2,000. The particular percentage which will determine the write-off to be established each year—such that by its application to successive book values, it will reduce $10,000 to $2,000 in 10 years—is found in the following formula:

$$N = 1 - \sqrt[n]{\frac{S}{P}}$$

N = the constant percentage to be written off each year
P = the initial book value of the investment
S = the estimated scrap value at the end of n years
n = the years of useful life in the equipment

In this formula, some scrap value above zero must be assumed; otherwise this formula is mathematically meaningless.

3. *The Sum-of-the-Digits Method* (Exhibit 9–8).

The depreciation method selected does not solve the problem of economic depreciation; it simply shifts the charging off of depreciation to periods that ostensibly will give the taxpaying manufacturer greater advantages. The factor in a depreciation method that gives some relief from the effects of inflation is an accelerated "life" for the machine that allows the manufacturer a shorter amortization period.

Let's discuss what practical differences, if any, result from the use of a high or low rate of depreciation.

Conservative management tends to use high rates of depreciation resulting in an early "write-down" of capital assets for the sake of safety. On the other hand, high depreciation means high cost estimates which may be misleading, particularly if they lead a manufacturer to believe that certain orders cannot be taken at a profit, whereas a more reasonable depreciation allowance would indicate that those orders could be accepted at a profit. High depreciations are generally favored because of the consequent lower income taxes.

There is another important factor in deciding on a depreciation method. Ownership of assets often resides in two classes of security interests: the stockholders and the bondholders. Stockholders are interested in obtaining maximum dividend returns and therefore favor a low depreciation charge. Bondholders, on the other hand, are not interested in dividends but in maintaining the value of the fixed assets which are pledged through mortgage as security for the bonds. Bondholders prefer a high rate of depreciation, because it tends to maintain the value of the fixed assets.

3. The Sum-of-the-Digits Method: When using this method, the depreciation applicable in a specific year may be defined as:

Original Cost x Remaining Years of Machine's Agreed-Upon Life
——
Sum-of-the-Digits of the Total Number of Years in Machine's Agreed-Upon Life

or:

$$D_x = \frac{A\ (n - x + 1)}{n\left(\frac{n + 1}{2}\right)}$$

where:

n = agreed-upon total years in asset's life

x = year in machine's life at which depreciation is to be figured

A = original cost

D_x = annual depreciation in year x

Or putting it another way, divide the original cost by the "sum-of-the-digits" $n\left(\frac{n + 1}{2}\right)$ or, $1 + 2 + 3 + 4 + 5 = 15$ and multiply by the remaining years in the machine's life $(n - x + 1)$.

To illustrate, it is desired to determine the depreciation in the first year of a machine's life that has a useful life of 5 years and has an original cost of $10,000.

$$D_1 = \frac{\$10,000}{15} \ x \ 5 = \$3.333$$

Following this formula, the depreciation for the five years of the machine's life is:

1st year	=	$3.333
2nd year	=	$2.667
3rd year	=	$2.000
4th year	=	$1.333
5th year	=	$ 667
		$10.000

Exhibit 9-8. Example of Calculation of Sum-of-the-Digits
Depreciation Method

Chapter 10

HOW TO DEVELOP THE MHR

Step 4: The Expense Assignment Worksheet

The previous three major steps in organizing the basic data from which to establish machine-hour rates have been the Converting Facilities Classification Sheet, the Crew Composition Table, and the Operating Budget. These data represent, in essence, a marshalling of the mechanical and human facilities of manufacturing and the means for financially supporting that effort.

From these three tabulations we are now able to allocate to each Production Center its annual overhead costs so that they reflect the Center's individual operating characteristics. The purpose of the Expense Assignment Worksheet is to build up an annual overhead cost for each Production Center.

Costs vs. Allocation Factors

The EAW develops the overhead portion of the annual Production Center cost by allocating the projected expenses to the various machines and processes. It is essential that the allocation factors selected bear logical and equitable relationship to the overhead costs being apportioned. Thus, if the expense of electricity is to be distributed among various Production Centers, one would sooner select the number of hours the equipment operates rather than the space it occupies as, obviously, running hours are more closely identified with electricity cost than is space occupancy.

Let's improve further on the factor for allocating electricity to get an even more equitable basis for the expense assignment. Since all machinery uses motors of different horsepower and contains other electrical devices which use electricity, the amount of electricity each piece consumes per hour will be highly variable.

Consequently, a proper allocation factor must consider *both running hours* and hourly *rate of consumption*. This factor is reached by multiplying the two together and getting *horsepower-hours*. (This happens to be the usual basis used for apportioning electricity expense, but it is not necessarily the most valid for all situations.)

In a similar manner, proper bases are selected for all other budgeted expenses. It must be stressed that *not all companies will use necessarily the same allocation factor for each expense.* The choice depends largely on the operating "personality" of the company, and the type of product mix emphasized. In a test of several companies it was found that the use of the same data allocated on different bases was enough to cause an error in costing of approximately 15% either way of the equitable cost level. This means that severe underpricing and overpricing could be produced by the same allocation factors. Then, usually customers begin limiting their orders to the underpriced items, while the overpriced items are left gathering dust in the manufacturer's warehouse. The facilities used in producing these latter articles consequently also remain idle.

While the machine-hour method is by far the most equitable way to allocate overhead costs to the product, experience and judgment must be used in the allocation of some of these critical determinants; otherwise the system will be an MHR in name only.

The Operating Budget shown in Chapter 9 lists the classified expenses which are expected to occur in a future 12-month period. These expenses have to be apportioned to each of the Production Centers so that, when the actual activity is reasonably close to the expected activity, the selling price will recover all of these costs. Such recovery depends on two major steps in the MHR procedure: (1) the projection of annual activity, and (2) the method by which the costs are apportioned to each Center. To a lesser extent, it depends on the accuracy of the expense budget.

Allocating Expenses to Production Centers

Now, means must be found to connect the budgeted expenses indicated in the Operating Budget (OB) with the manufacturing centers. This is the function of the allocation factors.

Before going on to an actual development of an EAW, it may be helpful to consider the matter in condensed form. EXHIBIT 10–1 shows how four budgeted manufacturing expenses are apportioned to three Production Centers. This exhibit shows in simplified form the technique of developing the annual cost of a Production Center.

The Center costs are based on specific allocation factors. The allocation of POWER COSTS is based on the expected annual *horsepower-hours;* SPACE COSTS on *space occupied;* MACHINERY COSTS on *value;* and INDIRECT LABOR COSTS on *annual direct labor costs.*

Suppose, however, that it is deemed more practical to allocate the indirect labor costs on the base of assigned annual hours, instead of on annual direct labor cost. How will the costs assigned to each Center change? Following the technique shown in EXHIBIT 10–1, the indirect-labor costs at Printing will become $2,400 instead of $2,180; at Cut and Crease $3,200 will replace the $2,545; and at Glue the indirect labor costs will be $2,400 instead of $3,275. While the total to be allocated and the total actually allocated remains at $24,300, the amounts assigned to each Production Center do change.

If the change in basis, as described above, is inequitable for the particular carton company involved, then the Printing operation will tend to overprice the orders and the Cut-and-Crease and Glue operations will underprice the products. As a result, the company will be in the unenviable position of being victimized by its own product mix.

Allocation factors must stand the test of equity to the company and must reflect

---

Manufacturing-Expense
Budget:

POWER	$ 400.00
SPACE	900.00
MACHINERY	15,000.00
IND. LABOR	8,000.00
Total	$24,300.00

PRINTING:

Horsepower: 12

Space: 800 sq. ft.	8/22 × $900.	= $ 327.
Value: $20,000	20/65 × $15,000.	= 4,615.
Assigned Annual Hours: 1,200		
Annual Direct Labor Cost: $4,800.	48/176 × $8,000.	= 2,180.
Horsepower-Hours: 14,400	14.4/40.4 × $400.	= 143.
		$ 7,265.

CUT & CREASE:

Horsepower: 15

Space: 800 sq. ft.	8/22 × $900.	$ 327.
Value: $15,000.	15/65 × $15,000.	3,462.
Assigned Annual Hours: 1,600		
Annual Direct Labor Cost: $5,600.	56/176 × $8,000.	= 2,545.
Horsepower-Hours: 14,000	14/40.4 × $400.	= 138.
		$ 6,472.

GLUE:

Horsepower: 10

Space: 600 sq. ft.	6/32 × $900.	= $ 246.
Value: $30,000.	30/65 × $15,000.	= 6,923.
Assigned Annual Hours: 1,200		
Annual Direct Labor Cost: $7,200.	72/176 × $8,000.	= 3,275.
Horsepower-Hours: 12,000	12/40.4 × $400.	= 119.
		$10,563.
	Total	$24,300.

Exhibit 10–1. Allocation of Budgeted Expenses to Production Centers

the company's way of doing business. Using standard allocation factors without thoroughly analyzing the company's operating characteristics denies the full benefits of machine-hour rate cost-estimating.

EXHIBIT 10–2 shows the valid allocation factors actually in use in five companies in the corrugated container and folding carton industries. Each of these five companies used a set of allocation factors vastly different from the others', and each attained full expense recovery from its estimates. As you can see, the possible variations in selecting proper bases are almost endless. From an actual test at an educational seminar for a manufacturing group, interchangeability of the factors led to cost differences as high as 55% in the overhead portion of the machine-hour rate. The test was made by applying the allocation factors of Company D to the data of Company A, and so on.

Development of the EAW (for Full Costs)

The format of the EAW is quite similar regardless of the specific allocation factors used. There are two principal elements of this worksheet: ALLOCATION FACTORS and MANUFACTURING COSTS. The Manufacturing Costs (the totals for each category) come from the Operating Budget. The Allocation Factors are then used, to apportion the Manufacturing Costs to each of the Production Centers on the basis of the allocation factors shown beneath each expense category. EXHIBITS 10–3 and 10–3a show the EAW for Company *ABC* and *XYZ* Corporation.

Let's be more specific and discuss each column on the EAW. In this particular example, four pieces of allocation factor data come directly from the Converting Facilities Classification Sheet. These are the names of the Production Center, Assigned Annual Hours, Working Space Occupied and Machinery Value. These data come directly from columns 1, 6, 4 and 5 of the CFCS. To get column 4 of the EAW, it is first necessary to multiply columns 3 and 6 of the CFCS. Column 5 of the EAW comes from the Crew Composition Table. The CCT corresponding to these EAW's may be found in EXHIBITS 8–1 and 8–1a of Chapter 8.

The totals of columns 6, 7, 8, 9, 10, 11, 12 and 13 of this EAW are taken from the corresponding totals of the Operating Budget.

Allocation Factors Selected

The Allocation Factors used to distribute these totals among the Production Centers, as shown on the EAW, are:

> *Occupancy* to apportion *Space Costs*
> *Hp-Hrs.* to apportion *Power Costs*
> *Value* to apportion *Machinery Costs*
> *Annual Hrs.* to apportion *Indirect Labor Costs*
> *D. L. $* to apportion *Fringe Benefit Costs*
> *Mfg. Cost* to apportion *Non-Mfg. Costs*

	SPACE COSTS	POWER COSTS	MACHINERY COSTS	IND. LABOR COSTS	FRINGE BEN. COSTS	NON-MANUFACT. COSTS
Company A	Standard Crew	Horsepower-Hours	Annual Maintenance Costs	Direct-Labor $	Direct-Labor Hours	Total Manufacturing Costs
Company B	Net Space Occupied	Direct-Labor Hours	Book Value	Annual Hours	Annual Hours	Sales Value
Company C	Gross Space and Share of Warehouse	Square feet Produced	Present Replacement Value	Ratio of Supervision to Direct labor	Direct-Labor $	Gross Space Occupied
Company D	Net Space Occupied	Speed of Combiner	Depreciation Reserve	Number in Standard Crew	Annual Hours	Sold Footage
Company E	Net Space Occupied	Horsepower Only	Sound Insurable Value	Direct-Labor $	Direct-Labor $	Cost of Goods Sold

Exhibit 10–2. Valid Allocation Factors for Five Different Companies

EXPENSE ASSIGNMENT WORKSHEET — X-PERCENT CAPACITY LEVEL

| | ALLOCATION FACTORS | | | | | MANUFACTURING COSTS | | | | | | | |
	Assigned Annual Hours [1]	Working Space Occup. [2]	Mach'y Value [3]	Hp-Hours [4]	Direct-Labor Budget [5]	SPACE [6]	POWER [7]	MACH'Y [8]	INDIRECT LABOR [9]	FRINGE BENEFITS [10]	TOTALS: MFG. COST [11]	NON-MFG. COSTS [12]	TOTAL COSTS [13]
Printer Slotter	2,000	840	$17,000	50,000	$ 9,400	$2,633	$2,626	$9,797	$1,890	$1,532	$18,478	$13,439	$31,917
Partition Slotter	1,200	470	3,000	7,200	4,680	1,474	378	1,729	1,133	763	5,477	3,982	9,459
Slitter	2,000	400	2,000	10,000	11,000	1,254	525	1,153	1,890	1,793	6,615	4,810	11,425
Semi-Auto. Taper	4,000	1,100	8,000	20,000	11,400	3,448	1,050	4,611	3,780	1,858	14,747	10,726	25,473
Manual Stitcher	1,000	100	600	500	3,600	313	27	346	945	587	2,218	1,614	3,832
Platen Die Cutter	2,000	190	3,500	6,000	7,200	596	315	2,018	1,890	1,174	5,993	4,358	10,351
Band Saw	500	90	600	1,500	1,800	282	79	346	472	293	1,472	1,071	2,543
TOTALS	12,700	3,190	$34,700	95,200	$49,080	$10,000	$5,000	$20,000	$12,000	$8,000	$55,000	$40,000	$95,000
	From Col. 6 CFCS	From Col. 4 CFCS	From Col. 5 CFCS	Columns 3 × 6 of CFCS	From CCT					D.L. $	MFG. COST		

ALLOCATION FACTORS → OCCUPANCY | HP-HRS | VALUE | ANN.HRS.

Exhibit 10–3. Expense Assignment Worksheet for Company ABC (Corrugated Sheet Plant)

EXPENSE ASSIGNMENT WORKSHEET — X-PERCENT CAPACITY LEVEL

| | ALLOCATION FACTORS | | | | | MANUFACTURING COSTS | | | | | | | |
PRODUCTION CENTER	Assigned Annual Hours	Working Space Occupied	Mach'y Value	Hp-Hours	Direct-Labor Budget	SPACE	POWER	MACH'Y	FRINGE BENEFITS	INDIRECT LABOR	TOTALS: MFG. COST	NON-MFG. COSTS	TOTAL COSTS
Punchpresses	3700	190	$10,000	37,000	$6,290	$2,523.40	$1,820.15	$4,828.00	$1,041.60	$5,676.80	$15,889.95	$7,451.10	$23,341.05
Drillpresses	3000	80	350	9,000	4,800	1,062.70	442.40	168.88	794.85	4,602.60	7,071.43	3,315.80	10,387.23
Lathe A	1400	70	1,800	7,000	3,360	929.90	344.15	869.00	556.35	2,148.20	4,847.60	2,273.10	7,120.70
Lathe B	800	100	9,200	8,000	2,400	1,328.00	393.30	4,441.00	397.40	1,227.50	7,787.20	3,652.00	11,439.20
Hand Assembly	11,200	200	400	0	24,640	2,656.00	0	193.12	4,080.10	17,183.40	24,112.72	11,308.00	35,420.72
TOTALS	20,100	640	$21,750	61,000	$41,490	$8,500.00	$3,000.00	$10,500.00	$6,870.30	$30,838.60	$59,708.90	$28,000.00	$87,708.90

ALLOCATION RATIOS:

$$\frac{\text{Space Cost}}{\text{Occupancy}} = \frac{\$8,500}{640} = 13.28$$

$$\frac{\text{Power Costs}}{\text{Hp-Hrs}} = \frac{\$3,000}{61,000} = .0492$$

$$\frac{\text{Mach Cost}}{\text{Mach Value}} = \frac{\$10,500}{\$21,750} = .4828$$

$$\frac{\text{F.B. Cost}}{\text{D.L. Cost}} = \frac{\$6,870}{\$41,490} = .165$$

$$\frac{\text{I.L. Cost}}{\text{Ann. Hrs.}} = \frac{\$30,838}{\$20,100} = 1.534$$

$$\frac{\text{Non-Mfg Cost}}{\text{Mfg Cost}} = \frac{\$28,000}{\$59,708} = .469$$

Exhibit 10–3a. Expense Assignment Worksheet for XYZ Corporation (Metalworking Plant)

It is worth repeating that each situation calls for a critical examination of the allocation factors. Failure to examine them carefully can result in wide differences in the MHR.

Column 11 of the EAW is the crossfooting of columns 6, 7, 8, 9, and 10 for each Center.

Column 13 is the total of columns 11 and 12. This figure represents the total annual *overhead* cost of operating each Production Center under the allocation factors selected.

Not All Similar Plants Use Same Allocation Factors

Not all plants should use the same allocation factors even though they may have the same Production Centers, crew, and space. As we have said repeatedly, each company acquires its own economic "personality" composed of the influences of the many human personalities who have molded it over the years. The *way of doing business* is conditioned by the market; by the habits of workers and management; by the capabilities of the equipment and the factory housing; and by the tastes, wishes and habits of customers. Failure to reflect these specifics in the MHR can lead to costly errors.

Exhibit 10–4 shows an EAW for another corrugated sheet plant having the same physical and financial characteristics as the plant shown in Exhibit 10–3. It has the same Production Centers, crew, space, etc. In addition, both companies operate on a projected budget of $95,000. However, the allocation factors in this exhibit are entirely different from those in Exhibit 10–3. And, again, this difference is due to the specific needs of these plants.

Total annual overhead costs are shown in column 13 and are similar to those shown in Exhibit 10–3. The company-wide totals ($95,000) are the same. But how about the individual Production Centers? How different are they?

Let's see:

	Exhibit 10–3 Column 13	Exhibit 10–4 Column 13
Printer-Slotter	$31,917	$19,394
Partition Slotter	9,459	11,006
Slitter	11,425	12,730
Semiautomatic Taper	25,473	35,390
Manual Stitcher	3,832	4,473
Platen Die Cutter	10,351	8,379
Band Saw	2,543	3,628
TOTALS	$95,000	$95,000

This example shows that the annual overhead cost for the Printer-Slotter in the company discussed in Exhibit 10–3 is 65% higher than for the same Center in the

EXPENSE ASSIGNMENT WORKSHEET — Y-PERCENT CAPACITY LEVEL

PRODUCTION CENTER	ALLOCATION FACTORS					MANUFACTURING COSTS						NON-MFG. COSTS	TOTAL COSTS
	Space Occup.	Std. Crew	D.L. Hrs.	Book Value	D.L. Budget	SPACE	POWER	MACH'Y	INDIRECT LABOR	FRINGE BENEFITS	TOTALS: MFG. COST		
Printer Slotter	840	2	4,000	$5,500	$9,400	$1,250	$637	$3,653	$2,300	$1,020	$8,860	$10,534	$19,394
Partition Slotter	470	2	2,400	2,600	4,680	1,250	382	1,726	1,144	611	5,113	5,893	11,006
Slitter	400	3	6,000	1,000	11,000	1,875	955	665	2,690	1,529	7,714	5,016	12,730
Semi-Auto. Taper	1,100	3	12,000	18,000	11,400	1,875	1,912	11,964	2,788	3,057	21,596	13,794	35,390
Manual Stitcher	100	2	2,000	400	3,600	1,250	318	266	878	509	3,221	1,252	4,473
Platen Die Cutter	190	2	4,000	2,000	7,200	1,250	637	1,327	1,761	1,020	5,995	2,384	8,379
Band Saw	90	2	1,000	600	1,800	1,250	159	399	439	254	2,501	1,127	3,628
TOTALS	3,190	16	31,400	$30,100	$49,080	$10,000	$5,000	$20,000	$12,000	$8,000	$55,000	$40,000	$95,000
ALLOCATION FACTORS →		Std. Crew	D.L. Hrs.	Book Value		Std. Crew	D.L. Hrs.	Book Value	D.L. Budget	D.L. Hours		Occupancy	

Exhibit 10—4. Expense Assignment Worksheet with Different Allocation Factors (Corrugated Sheet Plant)

EXPENSE ASSIGNMENT WORKSHEET—Z-PERCENT CAPACITY LEVEL

PRODUCTION CENTER	Units	ALLOCATION FACTORS					MANUFACTURING COSTS						NON-MFG. COSTS	TOTAL COSTS
		Space Occup.	Hp-Hours	Annual Deprec. & Maint. Costs	D.L. $	Annual Hours	SPACE	POWER	MACH'Y	INDIRECT LABOR	FRINGE BENEFITS	TOTALS: MFG. COST		
COMPANY A:														
Single Scorer	1	160	1,600	$ 200	$1,760	1,600	$137	$28	$233	$429	$86	$913	$1,705	$2,618
Corner Cut	1	60	1,400	100	1,540	1,400	51	25	117	375	75	643	1,201	1,844
S. Stay	2	400	9,300	400	4,030	3,100	342	164	467	830	196	1,999	3,731	5,730
Strip. Frames	3	330	8,100	300	9,360	3,600	282	143	350	964	454	2,193	4,094	6,287
S. & S. "B"	1	220	2,250	800	3,900	1,500	188	40	933	402	189	1,752	3,269	5,021
TOTALS		1,170	22,650	$1,800	$20,590	11,200	$1,000	$400	$2,100	$3,000	$1,000	$7,500	$14,000	$21,500
				ALLOCATION FACTORS → Occup.			→ Occup.	Hp-Hrs. →	Dep. & Maint. →	Annual Hours →	D.L. $ →		Mfg. Costs →	
COMPANY B:														
Double Scorer	1	210	3,600	$ 400	$2,880	1,800	$281	$74	$514	$398	$131	$1,398	$1,116	$2,514
Corner Cut.	2	120	7,200	200	3,960	3,600	160	148	256	796	180	1,540	1,229	2,769
S. Stay	1	200	1,800	200	1,560	1,200	267	37	256	265	71	896	715	1,611
Quad. Stayer	3	420	27,000	2,100	13,200	6,000	563	555	2,696	1,325	597	5,736	4,576	10,312
S. & S. "B"	1	220	2,250	800	3,900	1,500	294	46	1,029	332	177	1,878	1,499	3,377
Stokesfeed "HNS"	2	400	36,000	3,700	9,800	4,000	535	740	4,749	884	444	7,352	5,865	13,217
TOTALS		1,570	77,850	$7,400	$35,300	18,100	$2,100	$1,600	$9,500	$4,000	$1,600	$18,800	$15,000	$33,800
				ALLOCATION FACTORS → Occup.			→ Occup.	Hp-Hrs. →	Dep. & Maint. →	Annual Hours →	D.L. $ →		Mfg. Costs →	

Exhibit 10–5. Expense Assignment Worksheets for Two Plants with Identical Production Center (Setup Box Plants)

company of Exhibit 10–4. The Semiautomatic Taper is also 39% higher in the company of Exhibit 10–4. Obviously, if the company of Exhibit 10–3 used the allocation factors shown in Exhibit 10–4, the errors would amount to double the differences shown in the above tabulation.

At first glance, questions of competitive strength might be provoked by the tabulation of such differences, but this need not be the case. If each of the two companies above has production standards that compensate for the differences in annual overhead costs, both companies could produce the same *order* or product cost. We shall discuss this influence on order cost and its use in the MHR system later in this book.

Different Plants May Use Same Set of Allocation Factors

Exhibit 10–5 shows another variation of the E.A.W. Here are tabulated the annual overhead costs for the Production Centers of two set up box plants. The purpose of the comparison of these two plants is to show that an identical Production Center in two different companies will have a different annual overhead cost, *even if the allocation factors are the same in both companies.*

At both Company *A* and Company *B*, the same S & S Model "B" hand-fed wrapper is used. In both companies, this wrapper has the same book and market value, the same space occupancy, depreciation and maintenance costs, crew, and so forth. Yet, in Company *A*, the annual overhead cost for the Model "B" wrapper is 49% higher than it is in Company *B*.

It is important to realize, in establishing a Production Center's annual overhead cost for purposes of the MHR, that individual machines, processes or Centers do not possess absolute operating costs. Their costs are always relative to the activities and the characteristics of the operating environment into which they are introduced. Machines do not possess fixed economic identities. In some companies they may be called upon to pull a greater share of the economic load than in others. Thus, industry-wide averages of machine-hour rates are not particularly significant; moreover, they can vary widely and yet remain valid.

It will be noticed that the activity or capacity levels for the three Expense Assignment Worksheet exhibits have not been stated, other than to mention the X percent, Y percent, and Z percent capacity levels. Capacity level is a most important consideration because, as a company's activity grows, the company is able to recover its fixed expenses faster. If faster recovery is used to reduce the MHR, the resultant increase in business may more than offset the reduced rate.

Differences in MHR due to changes in activity levels will be discussed after composite machine-hour rates.

Chapter 11

HOW TO DEVELOP
THE MHR

Step 5: The MHR Summary Sheet

In the previous chapter we developed annual overhead costs for the Production Centers after first allocating to each of these Centers the budgeted costs on bases selected as equitable for the specific plant. In this chapter, we show how the hourly costs for each Center are calculated to include the Manufacturing, Non-Manufacturing and Direct Labor segments.

Composite Rates

EXHIBIT 11–1 shows an MHR Summary Sheet for Company *ABC*, listed in EXHIBIT 10–3 of the previous chapter. EXHIBIT 11–1a is a summary sheet for the XYZ Corporation, listed in EXHIBIT 10–3a. The method for arriving at these rates is very simple. The two elements of annual overhead costs, as expressed on the EAW in columns 11 and 12, are individually divided by the projected annual hours to obtain these costs on an hourly basis. The hourly direct labor costs are taken from the Crew Composition Table, but with this change: Column 4 of the CCT gives the hourly pay rate per Center rather than per machine. The reason for this is to find the total fringe benefit and idle time costs to be charged to these Centers, and to be listed in the Operating Budget. However, for cost-estimating purposes, it is necessary to have the hourly costs *per machine*, or the MACHINE-HOUR RATE, since the same piece of material cannot be processed on more than one machine simultaneously. Therefore, in the case of the corrugated plant, since the Semi-automatic Taper and Manual Stitcher Production Center contain two units each, column 4 of the CCT is divided by two to find the hourly costs per machine, and this figure is inserted in column 4 of the MHR Summary Sheet.

120

Corrugated Sheet Plant

X% Capacity Level

OPERATION	[1] ASSIGNED ANNUAL HOURS	[2] HOURLY COSTS OVERHEAD MFG.	[3] NON-MFG.	[4] DIRECT LABOR	[5] COMPOSITE MHR
Printer-Slotter	2000	$9.24	$6.72	$4.70	$20.66
Partition Slotter	1200	4.56	3.32	3.90	11.78
Slitter	2000	3.31	2.40	5.50	11.21
Semi-Auto Taper	4000	3.69	2.68	2.85	9.22
Manual Stitcher	1000	2.22	1.61	1.80	5.63
Platen Die Cutter	2000	3.00	2.18	3.60	8.78
Band Saw	500	2.94	2.14	3.60	8.68
	↑ From EAW: Col. 1	↑ From EAW: Col. 11 / Col. 1	↑ From EAW: Col. 12 / Col. 1	↑ From CCT	↑ Columns 2+3+4

Exhibit 11–1. MHR Summary Sheet for Company ABC

OPERATION	Assigned Annual Hours	HOURLY COSTS Overhead Mfg.	Non-Mfg.	Direct Labor	COMPOSITE M.H.R.
Punchpresses	3700	$4.29	$2.02	$1.70	$8.01
Drillpresses	3000	2.36	1.10	1.60	5.06
Lathe A	1400	3.46	1.62	2.40	7.48
Lathe B	800	9.73	4.57	3.00	17.30
Hand Assembly	11200	2.15	1.01	2.20	5.36

Exhibit 11–1a. MHR Summary Sheet for XYZ Corporation

Other Plant Examples of Summary Sheets

EXHIBIT 11–2 shows the Summary Sheet for another corrugated sheet plant having the same Production Centers, over-all expenses, and activity as the plant discussed above. This plant uses different allocation bases for its overhead expenses to support its specific needs and its product mix. The data of one plant can be dangerous for another and may undermine prices as well as the life of the business. Improper allocation bases (like arbitrary price-cutting) may create inadvertent unhealthy competition which does not permit the man with proper costs to recover the investment he has in his plant.

EXHIBIT 11–3 illustrates the difference in cost that the incorrect interchange of these rates would cause on a run of 50,000 regular slotted containers, 18″ x 14″ x 20″ (blank size approximately 65″ x 35″), the operation involving just the Printer-Slotter and Semiautomatic Taper (approximately 800,000 square feet).

EXHIBIT 11–4 shows how these MHR differences would show up for the two setup box plants shown on EXHIBIT 10–5 of the previous chapter. As it may be recalled, the same operation is being performed in each of the plants, and although the allocation factors are the same, the total annual costs vary. In EXHIBIT 11–4, we see that Company *A*'s MHR for the S & S Model "B" machine wrapper is $5.95, and in Company *B* it is $4.85. There are also differences in other similar operations: Corner Cutting and Single Staying in Company *A* carries total composite rates of $2.42 and $3.14, respectively, while those rates in Company *B* are $1. 87 and $2.65.

This is a clear-cut example of the operating differences in these companies in terms of variations in other Production Centers, in the crews assigned, in the indirect expenses incurred and in the activity anticipated.

Activity-Capacity Levels

At the early stages of growth a company may find that its fixed sunk costs, such as depreciation, are not fully utilized. The same condition may be true of some of the fixed costs requiring current outlay, as salaries. Certainly, if a company is in business, even if it is only starting out, it requires administrative manning. When capacity is mentioned in these terms, it refers to the maximum volume those fixed costs are capable of supporting before duplication of equipment and/or persons is required.

If a company rises from $1,400,000 to $2,000,000 in annual sales, which of its fixed cost will change? This is a matter of flexible budgeting, and the budgetary levels should be reflected, via the EAW, into the final rates. In the above-mentioned sales rise, if the product mix does not require a duplication of facilities, then the only fixed costs to be examined are those involving salaries. To develop budgets for various operating levels, it is necessary to identify the fixed and variable components of each expense, to see by how much the variable segment will rise with volume, and whether or not new fixed costs will be added. Thus, if a sales increase is anticipated, will the president's salary be changed? Will he need an administrative assistant? Will a sales manager be required to relieve the executives presently handling that function? Should more be provided for advertising? Does this call for an assistant to the plant manager? Should the company now install a scheduling system? Should it add a sample maker?

The MHR Summary Sheets shown in this chapter are simply the mechanical

Corrugated Sheet Plant

Y% Capacity Level

OPERATION	[1] ASSIGNED ANNUAL HOURS	[2] HOURLY COSTS OVERHEAD MFG.	[3] NON-MFG.	[4] DIRECT LABOR	[5] COMPOSITE MHR
Printer-Slotter	2000	$4.43	$5.28	$4.70	$14.41
Partition Slotter	1200	4.26	4.91	3.90	13.07
Slitter	2000	3.86	2.51	5.50	11.87
Semi-Auto Taper	4000	5.40	3.45	2.85	11.70
Manual Stitcher	1000	3.22	1.25	1.80	6.27
Platen Die Cutter	2000	3.00	1.19	3.60	7.79
Band Saw	500	5.00	2.25	3.60	10.85

Exhibit 11–2. MHR Summary Sheet with Different Allocation Factors

		Plant of Exhibit 1				Plant of Exhibit 2		
Conversion Costs:								
Printer-Slotter								
Setup	.4 Hours	×	$20.66	=	$ 8.26	×	$14.41	=	$ 5.76
Run	9 Hours	×	20.66	=	185.94	×	14.41	=	129.69
Semi-Auto. Taper								
Setup	.1 Hours	×	$ 9.22	=	.92	×	$11.70	=	1.17
Run	51 Hours	×	9.22	=	470.22	×	11.70	=	596.70
TOTAL CONVERSION COSTS					$665.34				$733.32

Exhibit 11–3. Effect on MHR Interchange

follow-through for the EAW and show its arithmetic steps. In practice, as will be shown in a later chapter, separate EAW's must be constructed for each activity or capacity level, and then means must be developed to separate the fixed and variable components of the MHR for purposes of direct costing.

Summary of Rate Determination

Now that the Summary Sheet has spelled out the final or composite machine-hour rate, it will be worthwhile to summarize all that has been explained up to this point.

In our task of predetermining the overhead component of the machine-hour rate, the apportioned expenses were brought to the door of each Production Center, and those expenses which were determined to be the direct responsibility of a Production Center were charged directly thereto.

These elements, applied to the production going through each Center, most nearly represents the costs and expenses incurred by the individual units of production. The MHR is designed to recover all of the costs incurred in making the product unit, provided that future experience coincides closely with the projections made.

As we saw, it was first necessary to accumulate, identify and classify all primary expenses into functional groups. That is, we had to place expenses in certain cate-

SETUP BOX COMPANIES A & B

Z % Capacity Level

OPERATION	[1] ASSIGNED ANNUAL HOURS	[2] OVERHEAD MFG.	[3] OVERHEAD NON-MFG.	[4] DIRECT LABOR	[5] COMPOSITE MHR
Company A:					
Single Scorer	1600	$ .57	$1.07	$1.10	$2.74
Corner Cutter	1400	.46	.86	1.10	2.42
Single Staying	3100	.64	1.20	1.30	3.14
Stripping Frames	3600	.61	1.14	2.68	4.43
S & S "B"	1500	1.17	2.18	2.60	5.95
Company B:					
Double Scorer	1800	.78	.56	1.60	2.94
Corner Cutter	3600	.43	.34	1.10	1.87
Single Staying	1200	.75	.60	1.30	2.65
Quad. Staying	6000	.96	.76	2.20	3.92
S & S "B"	1500	1.25	1.00	2.60	4.85
Stokesfeed "HNS"	4000	1.84	1.47	2.45	5.76

Column headers [2] and [3] fall under HOURLY COSTS / OVERHEAD.

Exhibit 11–4. MHR Summary Sheet for EAWs of Exhibit 10–5

gories to see which ones would vary with production and which ones would not. Then we had to establish Production Centers and assign all producing equipment to those centers which played any part in the manufacturing of the articles. After this, we had to provide for the manning of these centers in accordance with the production planned and, then, using past expenses as a guide, we had to project a schedule of expenses (budget) that would indicate the amount of money necessary to obtain the planned production.

The resulting machine-hour rate is the hourly rate at which all expenses in the company, except materials, are incurred at the various production centers. Therefore, the product which occupies the resources of the facility, or Production Center, for four hours, should be charged 8 times the amount allocated to the product which is in process at that facility 30 minutes.

Chapter 12

HOW TO DEVELOP
THE MHR

Additional Considerations

The method of expense classification, grouping and allocation shown in the previous five-step development is valid only for the examples given. They cannot be summarily applied to all companies. For example, in the furnace industries a relining expense can be charged directly to the product without any allocations. Take the estimated relining cost, the number of tons processed before a new lining is required (lining life), and divide the former by the latter to get the relining expense per ton. But this technique cannot be used for the rebearing expense on an 80-foot planer, because the large variety of products passing through such a planer makes a direct charge to any one product impossible.

When it comes to the allocation of the classified expenses to the individual production centers, there are situations where the use of certain allocation bases, or factors, will be more equitable than others. Each situation demands careful analysis based on its cause and effect relationships.

Assigning Service Expenses

One phase of cost allocation has annoyed accountants and puzzled businessmen for quite some time: the matter of distributing service department expenses to the Production Centers. Sometimes the procedure has called for making an assignment of some service department expenses to other service departments before allocating them to Production Centers. To say the least, the procedure is confusing to most businessmen who are trying to use cost-finding as an objective tool. And accountants have no easy time chasing themselves in mathematical circles in an effort to achieve a degree of number rationality. Nor is explaining the procedure to top management an enviable task; even if it is comprehended, managerial action to implement the resulting figures is seldom forthcoming.

Because of the great variable of the market, because of product mix which cannot be accurately forecasted because of machinery utilization with elements of volatility as a function of the product mix, because of the changing expense level and purchasing power of the dollar, the paperwork involved in making the assumptions necessary for assigning service expenses is not worth the effort.

Where an expense is directly incurred by a product, as in the above case of the furnace relining, or by a Production Center, as a repair on a machine, it should be charged directly. Foremen, cranemen, cafeteria, time-and-motion study, medical facilities, engineering, toolroom—all are services which, unless directly attributable to a Production Center, should be charged on a plant-wide basis. Interdepartmental distributions result in a confused mixture of expenses, and for management's purposes it is enough to know the existence and magnitude of the service department expenses.

Other Expenses

There are other expenses usually incurred in industry which have not been listed on the parallel five-step examples of Company *ABC* and *XYZ* Corporation. They were purposely left out in order not to cloud the basic concepts. Also, attention should be called to the fact that certain industries, even companies within specific industries, have characteristics that should be reflected in the bases used to allocate several of their expenses.

Distribution Costs: In some industries expenses vary according to certain characteristics of the product, and are not greatly affected by customer characteristics. Other expenses vary primarily due to certain customer characteristics. Usually these considerations manifest themselves when distribution costs are up for discussion and allocation, since, obviously, it must be determined whether some costs are to be allocated to products or directly to customers.

Allocating costs directly to a *customer* means that the selling of the finished product to a specific customer incurs an expense directly attributable to him and the act of his being sold the product by the company. This usually occurs in some segments of the clothing and sportwear industries where the manufacturer does a private label business with a number of special customers. These customers typically request exclusive use of some styles and designs and ask the company to lower prices on a few items that the distributor could use as price "leaders." This practice calls for a reallocation of some expenses because of the greater load the regularly priced items will have to carry.

Shipping and Delivery Expenses: In some companies that have a more or less constant radius of delivery, *shipping* can be included as an over-all charge by listing its expenses in the Operating Budget. In those instances where production standards have been established, based on the number of unit-miles or ton-miles, the shipping effort can be set up as a Production Center and treated as any other center on the CFCS. Normally, the shipping function is thought of as indirect labor and typically is excluded from listing as a Production Center. This is not the case where the company has performed work measurement and has adequate work standards.

Any expense that can be identified directly with the product, or work center, should not be placed in the OB. For example, some companies set up a schedule of extra charges, to be added to the final total cost developed on the estimate sheet, for costing extraordinary delivery charges. On the other hand, one manufacturer of tin cans excluded shipping and delivery expenses from the final MHR and instead charged these expenses according to the mileage traveled and the volume units of the cans shipped. This solution was based on the proposition that it costs more per container to ship a truckload of large containers than a truckload of small containers. In the former case, of course, the primary commodity being shipped is air. After some experience with the actual costs of shipping, the above-mentioned tin can manufacturer developed a schedule equating cubic container volume with radii that showed the most economical radius of delivery. This schedule allowed the company to sell and deliver containers to points four times more distant than it ordinarily thought feasible. Whereas, 400 miles had been the maximum distance their deliveries would penetrate, afterwards, they sold and delivered very small containers halfway across the country at the same cost per container that it cost them to make local deliveries of the larger units.

Advertising Expenses: There are also expenses which relate specifically to a product. Take advertising, for example. There are companies that advertise one or more specific product lines which do not comprise their entire product mix. Since the advertising expense is incurred clearly and specifically for a particular class of products, the company should, therefore, allocate it directly thereto, instead of making each product carry a share of this expense. Besides a fairness of expense burden, management gains the opportunity of determining whether the advertising expense is paying off. In this instance advertising expenses are added after total costs are determined.

Storage Costs: There are also the expenses of the investments in finished goods, and in the storage costs of finished products, which the manufacturer has to incur for certain customers, or even for specific product lines. This condition arises in the packaging industries where, for economy of run, the manufacturer must make a large quantity of packages to be fed to the packager as the latter has the filler ready; yet the manufacturer does not have the space in his plant to accommodate the packages. This is true in food packaging that is seasonal in nature or that depends on crop harvesting. But it is likewise true in other seasonal businesses. For these conditions, the manufacturer must make specific expense allocations, which, incidentally, also give him the opportunity to evaluate customer, product and even territory profitability.

Instead of being treated as an over-all charge, receiving and storage service expenses may be distributed to production centers on the basis of the tonnage handled for each class of materials affecting each group of machines. This method is equitable where these departments feed different production centers with different types of materials. Plants that make products involving more than one type of material find that, unless there are clear-cut differences in time and effort, it does not pay to make this separation.

Production-Line Centers: Sometimes, allocation of expenses should not be direct, because the paperwork may be prohibitively complex and expensive. In one plant, making heavy and bulky products, all similar production tools could not be located together, because such a system would boost excessively the internal transportation of the product from one tool center to another. Most of the parts had to be produced on progressive production lines, and, because of the vast number of parts being made, the number of Production Centers ran into the hundreds. A solution was found in establishing Centers for each production line instead of by type of tool. The relative cost of operating each machine was found, on a weighted basis, and, on this scale, the relative cost of producing each product was determined. Total overhead was thus applied by products according to the relative cost scale.

Some Special Industry Cases

Meat Packing: One of the most complex industries in regard to product mix, and its effect on costing, is meat packing. Here the variety of what is and what can be produced seems to be limitless. The large packing houses slaughter all kinds of animals and then do the curing and smoking—some carrying into the operations of canning and packaging. Some of the larger packers control or operate plants that tan hides, make soap and drugs. Some go into the production of edible fats, ice cream, and so forth. And it is usual for these larger firms to have a wide distribution organization.

The smaller packers may engage in any of the above activities in varying degrees, depending upon the specie of animal slaughtered, the type of process performed, or their market. Some sell to each other; others sell to hotels and wholesalers.

The more of these efforts a packer is involved in, the more acute his cost-finding problem becomes. For regardless of which or how many operations he does, he must keep competitive with those packers who do some of what he does. If a packer slaughters, cures and smokes *and* makes sausage, he must be competitive with a packer who does nothing else but make sausage. If a packer cures, smokes and cans, he must first find out whether he makes the most profit from fresh, boiled or baked meat, and he must be able to compete against the packer who specializes in these items.

And, unusual as it may sound, the meat packing industry has its special "make or buy" problems. This problem typically not only confronts the packer who does not do his own slaughtering, but slaughterers as well, because of the added problem of moving surplus products. The dilemma is characteristic of this industry, which, like so many others, believes that increased volume will be a panacea to the problems of recovering overhead expenses. It is really not so, because, inevitably, the result is overbuying to support sales made at lower prices in order to move surplus stocks.

Unlike most other industries, the meat packing industry sets up Production Centers by product instead of by operation, because the product—whether beef, processed pork, sausage, or inedible—has individual characteristics which cause overhead expenses to vary. Exhibit 12–1 shows the product Centers and the comparative weight each exerts on labor, sales poundage, sales dollars, machinery values, and occupancy.

PRODUCT (Dep't of Production Center)	Space Occupied	Investment Values		Dollars Sold	Pounds Sold	Direct Labor
		Equipment	Building			
Fresh Pork	25	27	30	29	26	33
Processed Pork	23	19	23	19	13	16
Sausage	11	15	9	11	8	17
Lard	8	18	9	6	14	3
Beef	26	13	23	32	26	28
Inedibles	7	8	6	3	13	3
TOTALS	100%	100%	100%	100%	100%	100%

Exhibit 12–1. Percentage Comparison of Different Allocation Factors in Meat Packing

Establishing Centers by product permits the allocation of repairs and maintenance to be charged directly to the product department. However, the problem of allocating refrigeration, water, sewage, power and light is not easy. Were this another industry, the problem would be solved, usually, by combining these expenses in the power grouping. In meat packing, though, these utilities can almost be thought of as direct materials. However, a little careful inquiry into the nature of the expenses, and what functions they perform, leads to a factor of refrigerated space, or the temperatures required in the product Center, for allocating refrigeration costs; gallons of water for the water cost (from water meters in each department); electrical power, as usual, by horsepower-hours; lighting costs by square footage, and so forth. In practice, all of these expenses are combined and result in a unit cost per pound, per package, or per head.

These represent only a few of the costing problems in the meat packing industry. When it comes to order-filling involving different weights, units and types, the problem gets so complex that it becomes difficult for management and the sales department to use the cost figures. Most importantly, it becomes difficult for the salesmen to explain the derivations of quotations to customers, who would be inclined to make comparisons with similar products. When this condition exists, it is good business not to carry the cost refinement too far.

Milk Products: The milk products industry is another example of the problem of overhead allocation. First, of course, there is the variability of the milk supply. More milk is available in the early part of the summer. And though this circumstance affects only the raw material, it leads to many problems in production which must be reflected in the costing system. Milk is processed into table cream, ice cream, condensed milk, cheese, butter and several other products. Facility costs are quite high and require technically skilled and relatively highly-paid workers. During the time when the milk supply is plentiful, all the men and facilities are busy. However, during the winter, production is low; consequently, workers are kept at about the same level all year round and during the slow season are assigned a variety of jobs to keep them busy.

This doesn't hurt the small plant owner the way it does the larger enterprises, which have wider marketing facilities as well as more extensive manufacturing facilities. In the larger companies, during the slack periods skilled workers are assigned tasks unrelated to the tasks they were hired for. These tasks carry inflated labor costs out of proportion to the actual value of the work, which is usually paid for at lower rates in the peak periods. This leads to overcosting the product in the period in which the work was performed, this practice giving a misleading figure to management. Yet, it can be argued, this is the actual cost. True, but this statement doesn't go far enough. Management should receive information based on conditions as they *could be* if all men were utilized properly. It could, thus, make better decisions in regard to marketing steps or expansions.

The MHR system in this industry should make provision for unearned labor (not the fault of the workers), and companies should use only the full direct labor of skilled workers in their machine-hour rates—with the lower figure charged out in the OB. In this way, management can determine the real magnitude of its processing operations, thus can decide better whether to buy a machine, what its capacity should be, and so forth.

Forging Industries: Forging plants have certain definite requirements which must be supported by the cost-estimating system and the specific bases used to allocate expenses. For example, certain facilities use various supplies in direct proportion to the time they operate, a condition which would require a direct expense allocation to the facility instead of to a general indirect material category. This is true of the expense of steel shot, used in blasting scale and rust from the forgings, and of the expenses of the ordering and storage effort for this type of "indirect material."

In this case, the indirect material expense is excluded from the OB and charged to the total product cost from a chart relating steel shot cost to the number of blasting hours. (Note: This same practice may be followed in any other industry which consumes material directly proportionate to facility hours, viz.: glue cost at glueing centers, certain ink costs at printing centers, etc.)

Paint Industry: This industry also has features of operation which subject certain of the previously classified service expenses to more sensible allocation. Let's just talk about receiving and shipping expenses, which the five-step procedure charged as an over-all indirect charge, and fuel oil and gas, an expense which normally was allocated on either a power consumption or occupancy basis.

By classifying raw materials into types of materials, and accumulating records on time costs for receiving, it is practical to charge these expenses directly to the product on the basis of each pound of raw material received. Shipping expenses are, then, allocated on the basis of labor time to the different sizes of containers. Fuel oil is used at the emulsion production center for either the supplying of power for processing or for heating the production space. Knowledge of the output of the emulsion plant allows this expense to be allocated directly to the gallons of product produced.

Since almost all of the gas consumed is usually used by the varnish department, this expense can be likewise allocated to the gallons of product produced. The various paint products are classified according to the times on the fires, and a gas cost is computed which is then allocated to all of the products in relation to their cooking times.

The expenses discussed above would be excluded from the OB and from the indirect portion of the CCT and charged directly to the product, by chart, after all other costs have been computed.

Allocation Inconsistencies

In cost-finding with the MHR, convenient but illogical blanket percentages for allocating overhead are abandoned in favor of the system of apportioning elements of overhead expense to the operating facilities; but the effectiveness of this system rests upon the logic of the base selected for each allocation. As we have pointed out, there are bases which are more equitable than others in making allocations, these depending on the company in which the cost-estimating system is being developed. But, still, the tendency is to select a merely convenient base if it gets to be too much trouble to develop or find an equitable one.

1. Take as an example *repair and maintenance* expenses. Ideally, records should be kept by machine, in what may be called a property ledger, into which additions

to the equipment, as well as the cost of repairs to and maintenance of it, could be entered. For management, such a record provides a fast answer to the question of when to discard a machine. It is recognized, though, that many companies do not have any such record, so are faced with the necessity of apportioning this total expense to facilities on some blanket allocation base.

In a great many cases, we have seen this expense allocated to Production Centers on the basis of the value of the equipment. Immediately, this assumes that the more the machine is worth, the more it will cost annually to repair and maintain. But such may not be the case. It may be that while an expensive facility is inactive, an inexpensive one operates at full capacity. What then? How equitable is that allocation base if the inexpensive machine actually incurs triple the repair and maintenance costs of the expensive one?

In most cases, the allocation factor of annual projected hours has been used to allocate this expense, although in a portion of the cases we used the factor of *dollar-hours* to give effect to the probable higher cost of a single repair on a more expensive machine.

2. In another instance, we discovered that the cost of *stickering* in a lumber mill-work plant (an operation involving the placing of small sticks of wood between long boards of lumber to facilitate the circulation of air for drying in the steam kilns or air drying) was handled as indirect labor and so budgeted in the OB. This meant that all wood products, whether they benefited from the services of drying or not, were loaded with this charge. This millwork company also made products out of plastic laminates and plywood, which were also unfairly charged with stickering.

Obviously, there was a direct relationship between stickering time and the quantity of board-feet dried. The board footage output became the basis for allocation. Since we had obtained stickering time from time study, it became a measurable activity, for which we established a Production Center. The effect was a fairer price for other products and, as a result, sales rose in those product lines. The dropping of the indirect cost of stickering on the other products was much more significant than the slight increase in the cost of the products that utilized the drying services. No sales resistance was encountered, and the company recovered in its selling price of dried stock all of its stickering costs.

3. In companies using patterns, tools and dies as part of specific jobs, ideally the cost of these tools should be tacked onto the order costs either in full, at one time, or over some period in which the quantity is committed. This method, which charges these expenses directly to the product, is, however, not always followed, and occasionally the manufacturer has to absorb the charges and then cost them out to the job on an over-all basis. Obviously, a plant-wide charge for unidentified small tools unfairly burdens the jobs in the plant that do not benefit from these tools.

An equitable way to solve the problem is to depreciate these tools, together with the machinery, at the center which uses them. This is still something of a compromise, since there will be jobs going through one of these centers which do not use the tools. So a further refinement is a fast depreciation of these tools spread over the number of units of production estimated to pass through them.

4. In some foundries the expense of *general plant service* is sometimes charged out on a sales dollar basis. This method assumes that every sales dollar of production benefits from the service to the same extent. This is not true, considering the wide variety of cast shapes and sizes. A more equitable base is tonnage processed.

5. A very common mistake made in facility costing is the development of conversion costs that leave out the *non-manufacturing* segment and then add it in on the basis of a percentage of sales. The assumption is that, as the sales dollars rise, so will the services contributed by this segment of expense. Again, this is not necessarily the case. In some of the more dramatic cases, this method penalized the product cost by the extent of the attainments of the sales department. There is danger particularly in those companies that negotiate a selling price with a customer after being given the product's cost. The activity which varies closest with non-manufacturing expenses is the activity of the plant, and not the margin of profit that salesmen are able to get. Therefore, this expense can be allocated equitably to Production Centers according to the total manufacturing expenses, the annual hours, and so forth.

6. Another mistake often made in MHR systems is to add the *internal handling expenses* to the cost of raw materials and then include the receiving and warehouse personnel in the indirect labor in the CCT and OB. This means a double charge and will artificially inflate all conversion costs. Leave this expense element out of materials cost and include it only in the CCT and OB.

7. A similar error is to include *salesmen's commissions* in the non-manufacturing portion of the OB and then add it in again when calculating selling prices. This expense has no place in conversion costs, since its magnitude is a direct function of the selling price. Omit it completely from the MHR structure, but include it as a percentage of selling price, in accordance with the established sales compensation plan. However, sales service costs, clerks and managers' salaries, and any straight salaries to salesmen, should be included in the OB and thus in the conversion costs.

Typical Expenses and Some Bases Used for Their Allocations

The following list is a tabulation of expenses usually encountered in industry, together with some of the bases on which these expenses are allocated. As we said previously, the base selected for the expense must be meaningful and must be related directly to the characteristics of the operation.

Type of Expense	*Distribution Basis*
Depreciation of machinery and equipment	Present market value Sound insurable value Book value Original capital invested
Building repairs	Area occupied by Center Present value per square foot Volume occupied by Center
Insurance on buildings	Area occupied by Center Investment in Center
Insurance on machinery	Present market value Investment
Insurance on building contents	Inventory values and area occupied by Center
Use and occupancy insurance	Gross budgeted profits generated by Center Direct labor hours at Center Factory payroll
Taxes on machinery and equipment	Assessed valuation
Depreciation of buildings	Area occupied by Center Investment per square or cubic foot
Salaries and expenses of sales department	Manufacturing expenses Product Centers served
Electrical power	Actual consumption (hp-hrs) Direct labor or machine hours
Lighting	Area occupied Number of outlets Electrical power consumption of Center
Heat (not meter-measured)	Area or volume occupied by Center Area of radiation to Center
Water (not meter-measured)	Actual consumption of Center
Group insurance	Employee participation by payroll dollars
Advertising	Products served
Real estate taxes	Area occupied by Center
Insurance on product inventories	Service of warehouse to each Center Inventory values

Type of Expense	*Distribution Basis*
Machinery repairs	Annual hours of Center Machines served Ratio of present value to machine hours
General maintenance	Area occupied by Center Present value of Center Direct labor dollars or hours at Center Annual hours of Center Ratio of present value to machine hours Maintenance hours furnished to Center Units produced at Center
Supervision (plant)	Direct labor employees or dollars at Center
Workmen's Compensation insurance	Direct labor employees or dollars at Center Payroll employees or dollars at Center Indirect labor employees or dollars at Center
Social Security taxes	Direct labor employees or dollars at Center Payroll employees or dollars at Center Indirect labor employees or dollars at Center
Storeroom	Value of materials issued to Center Weight of materials issued to Center Number of units of material issued to Center
Testing laboratory	Units of output Percentage of laboratory hours devoted to making tests for specific Centers
Tool crib	Direct labor hours or dollars of Center Machine hours generated at Center
External transportation service (unless set-up as a separate Center)	Truck hours in relation to units or weight produced at Center Truck miles in relation to units or weight produced at Center Ratio of tonnage hauled to tonnage produced at Center Annual hours of Center Manufacturing expense Sales, if stable product mix

Type of Expense	*Distribution Basis*
Refrigeration	Area refrigerated in Center Temperature and BTU's at Center
Indirect labor	Annual hours at Center Direct labor hours (with care) at Center Units produced at Center (weight, pieces, etc.) Employees in Center Ratio of supervision to direct labor employees at Center
Engineering service	Centers served Manufacturing expense Sales dollars
Machine rentals	Machine in Center involved Royalty additive tied to output
Rental on building	Area occupied by Center Sales (in situations where rental is tied to annual sales)
Cafeteria	Ratio of employees in Center to total employees (only that portion of expenses that exceeds cafeteria income)
Factory accounting service	Number of employees and/or tickets processed
Crane service	Crane hours furnished to Center Weight of materials handled for Center

Section 3

HOW TO APPLY
MHR DATA

13. HOW TO FIND PRODUCT COSTS

14. USING MHR FOR PRICING PRODUCTS

15. USING MHR TO COORDINATE SALES AND PRODUCTION

Chapter 13

HOW TO FIND
PRODUCT COSTS

The machine-hour rates developed in the preceding section represent the cost of owning, maintaining and operating each of the listed facilities for one hour. They show the *rate* at which conversion cost is applied to the order or product, and they determine the cost of the operation according to the amount of time that the order or product benefits from the use of the converting facilities. The MHR represents an hourly cost. In order to get this cost onto the product, we must know how long the product will be in process at the facility or Center.

Production Standards

To get the operational time we must know the direct labor hours and the quantities of production. For this purpose, we must know the standard or anticipated hours for each labor operation in each Production Center. For example, if a worker can perform an operation on a machine at the rate of 500 pieces per hour, after due consideration for fatigue, personal and unavoidable delays, the production standard is 2 hours per thousand pieces. If, at another operation, an operator under the same conditions can produce 2,000 pieces of a different type, the standard for that operation will be .5 hours per thousand. This means that when an order for 2,000 pieces, which uses both of these operations, passes through both Centers, the first Center will be used for 4 hours and the second for 1 hour.

The MHR is the rate at which cost is incurred; the production standard is the rate at which work (or usage of the center) is done. Neither the MHR nor the production standard alone will give the cost of the operation; both must be used together. The operational (conversion) cost is given by the formula:

Operational Cost = MHR × Production Standard

If the MHR of the first center is $12 and that of the second Center is $14, the cost of processing the 2,000-piece order through the two operations would be:

$$\text{First Center} = \$12 \times 4 = \$48$$
$$\text{Second Center} = \$14 \times 1 = \$14$$

These costs, the *conversion costs,* include the total of direct labor and all other expenses (except materials) used in the operation.

Since both figures are multiplied together to form the conversion cost, an accurate production standard is exactly as important as an accurate MHR. Highly accurate machine-hour rates used with "guesstimated" production standards result in production costs which are as inaccurate as the standards. In developing a cost-estimating system, management must drive for the same degree of accuracy in both of the elements used in calculating the conversion costs.

The sum of all of the individual conversion costs at each operation is called the *total conversion cost.* The total order or product cost is obtained simply by adding the materials cost applicable to the order or product to this conversion cost.

Standards

A ruler is a good example of a standard. Without it we would have no consistent way of referring to a unit of length. Imagine the trouble if no one knew how long an inch was, or the quantity in a pound, or of a gallon. What is a standard? In essence, it is a unit of measurement.

A *production* standard is a work measurement, that is, a definite evaluation of the length of time it takes to do a certain amount of work. Without it, there could be no cost-estimating systems, since in order to apply hourly facility costs to an order or product, we must be able to estimate *in advance* how long each facility will be used in its production.

In some industries, the same Center is used for work requiring varying lengths of time per unit. For example, a power press, used for drawing work, can work on jobs which go faster than others. A shallow draw on one piece may permit greater hourly output than a deep draw on another piece. This difference in time has no effect on the MHR of the facility; only the cost of the order is affected. If the shallowly drawn piece has a production standard of 4 hours per thousand (250/hr) and deeper drawn pieces have a production standard of 8 hours per thousand (125/hr), and the MHR of the press center is $18, then the operational or conversion cost *per thousand* is:

$$\text{Shallow piece} = \$18 \times 4 = \$72$$
$$\text{Deep piece} = \$18 \times 8 = \$144$$

This means that irrespective of what orders or parts are processed through a facility, or the speed of production through the center, the cost of making the facility available (MHR) remains the same. In the case above, the deep piece *used* the press facility for twice as long as the shallow piece did. It is necessary to grasp the concept illustrated here before applying the MHR and the production standards to the costing of orders or products.

Development of Production Standards

Production is the result of people working. Measuring their work and then determining what is a fair rate of output or effort is the object of setting production standards. These standards represent the rate at which work is to be performed and the rate at which payroll money is paid to compensate these efforts. When a point in the rate of output is reached where the personnel's efforts are considered equitable for the amount of pay they receive, then the correct standard has been reached. This means, then, that when workers attain their production standard on their particular operations, they have fully earned their base hourly pay. This condition is usually called *100 percent productivity.*

Standards must be realistic. If workers do not attain the standards, then this data cannot be used for cost purposes, since it would falsely convey a lower conversion cost to the estimating sheet. This is generally true in non-incentive daywork plants where workers traditionally give 60 to 75% of the fair day's work level. In incentive shops (piece-work, bonus, quota, bogey, etc.) workers generally earn above the 100 percent mark in order to earn bonus money, and this puts the company in an excellent position, as it can quote lower prices if it has to. It can also retain the profits generated by the higher productivity and, moreover, can have the benefits of expanded machine capacity and lower unit overhead costs.

There are several ways to establish production standards. If you are presently using production standards for incentive purposes or in scheduling or machine loading, these can be used for cost purposes, provided they have been set properly.

Production standards set from time study are the most scientific and reliable. What's more, these standards are highly provable and can be well defended when they are used for incentive purposes. Time-and-motion study is one of the most effective and inexpensive tools that management can acquire. Its uses are many. Usually plants develop what is known as standard elemental time data, with which they build up time information on standard work elements and then apply it to the particular job without having to take time studies constantly. Predetermined time standards, such as MTM (Methods-Time-Measurement), are standard times of motions which are in common to all operations that are performed manually.

Like any other specialty, time study requires skill and maturity on the part of the observer. It is much more than just holding a stopwatch on an operator. In time study, the trained observer subdivides the operation he sees into several elements and obtains an allowed time for each. To the sum of these elemental times he adds time allowances for fatigue, personal needs of the operator, and normal delays which the operator encounters in his job that are beyond his control. From all this the observer gets the standard time for the operation. The purpose of breaking the operation into elements is to analyze the method being used and to expose the operator's tendency to stall or soldier because he knows he is being timed. The same purpose applies to operators who tend to speed up from a nervous reaction to being timed. It is the time study engineer's job to normalize the times he records to make them reflect the fair day's work effort.

Besides scientific methods of developing production standards, there is the traditional foreman's estimate. If no other data are available, these estimates have to be used. But this method is not recommended. First of all, the estimates tend to reflect the level at which the foreman believes he will be protected from managerial action against insufficient production. In effect, the foreman may be checking on himself by setting his own performance standards.

Past performance is also used to develop production standards. It is based on historical data. This practice calls for analyzing time and production tickets of some previous period and then striking an average. "Standards" developed by this method evaluate the level of effort that *has been attained* in the past by workers and has no relationship to the effort that *could be applied* by the same workers. And when these standards are made the basis of wage incentives, they tend to reward the wrong person, namely, the "goldbricks." However, in a cost-finding system we are interested in determining the actual level of production, and sometimes the standard of past performance is the only one available. Historical performance as a base for production standards is better than foremen's estimates, since the former at least indicates the pattern of the future (without wage incentives). However, it is unwise to advertise to the factory workers that this method is being used for estimating standards because, in the mistaken belief that customers will pay for the actual labor costs incurred, these workers will not attempt to better their performance.

If, for some reason, management does not want to use wage incentives, then the company should at least install a plan for measuring worker output. This is called a measured daywork plan. Under this system workers know what is expected of them in order to produce a fair day's work. When output is policed under proper production standards, even though workers may not hit 100% productivity, the average level of output will rise to perhaps 80% and the attained level of output will tend to be more consistent and reliable for cost-estimating purposes.

Dimensions for Tabulating Production Standards

Work output is a function of time and effort. Saying that a worker produces 500 pieces is not a measure of his output or effort. We must know in what period this output was attained. If it was attained in 5 hours, then his rate of productivity is 100 pieces per hour. If done in 30 minutes, his output is 1,000 pieces per hour.

Standards must be expressed in terms of a certain amount of work output—for example, in thousands of pieces or hundreds of pounds—and per unit of time, as per minute, or per hour. Thus, when the normal output of a process serviced by direct labor is 50 gallons per hour, the production standard is 2 hours per hundred gallons or 20 hours per thousand gallons. The rate of the quantity unit (dozens, hundreds, thousands, etc.) is a matter of convenience in the production counting. Very often, this quantity unit will vary on the same cost-estimating sheet, where standards will depend on what seems appropriate for the particular production count of the operation.

In most high fixed-cost industries, the Production Centers, or operations, usually are called upon to process a wide variety of products or different part sizes, styles, colors. It is rare to find exactly the same product passing through all Production Centers. The power press mentioned earlier in this chapter might draw parts from blanks of several areas and depths, and might have to perform this function from steel of different types, from brass, and other sheet metals. A printing press may handle sheets of different sizes and various numbers of "ups" to yield varying blanks per sheet printed. An autoclave will be used for curing high-pressure and low-pressure concrete block.

Obviously, the processing time per unit of product will depend on the specifics of the product; thus, variances, as explained above, must be considered in the production standards, in order to show that they are reflected in the operational conversion cost. Thus, it is common to find not just one production standard for an operation or work center, but a sheet of standards which lists those physical factors of the product or part which affect the operational time.

This book does not deal with the technical methods of developing production standards and the reader is advised to read the many fine texts in the area of work measurement for further information. (Note: Among these are: Marvin E. Mundel, *Motion and Time Study, Principles and Practice*, Prentice-Hall, Inc., 1960; Maynard, Stegmerten and Schwab, *Methods-Time Measurement*, McGraw-Hill Book Co., 1948.)

Formats for Developing Production Standards

Later in this chapter we show how to apply the MHR to products on the estimating sheet, and to do this we need sets of production standards. For this reason, representative formats of production standards are presented in EXHIBITS 13–1 to 13–11.

EXHIBIT 13–1 is a table of production standards for miscellaneous cutting operations in a typical screw-machine plant. In addition to the simple movement of the individual machines, many jobs call for small cutting operations which require hand feed instead of machine feed for a short stroke. This chart of standards is provided to take care of those situations. Minutes per piece are obtained by relating the particular minor operation to the diameter of the stock in the machine. This format of standards is considered elementary and is used generally in addition to the total machining time.

The same is true of Exhibit 13–2, which shows how to alter the basic times of another work standard, depending on the types of clamps and how they are used to hold the piece.

Exhibit 13–3 is a format for production standards used in screw-machine plants to specify the allowed time for loading and unloading stock for turret lathe bar machines. This format is typical where wage incentives are in effect, since it is an attempt to measure repetitive work. For estimating purposes, these production times are added to the times of the various operations performed on the machines so as to simplify the work of estimating without introducing any inaccuracy. Here the time factors are the length of the piece and the diameter of the stock, since they both bear on the weights imposed on the operator and thus affect his fatigue and the time it takes him to do the job. This chart of production standards is another simple form giving standard elementary time data.

Exhibit 13–4 is a chart of setup time standards for screw-machine plants. While it is not all-inclusive, it will give an idea of how even machine "downtime" elements can be measured and estimated with consistency. In this format, various elements of the setup are related to the diametric capacity of single-spindle automatic screw machines. Typically, different functional machines have their own charts of setup standards. Since not all setups require the operator to do all of the elements listed, only those that are required are extracted and used for incentive, scheduling and estimating purposes.

Exhibit 13–5 charts the allowed production time of various sizes of boring mills. Since the time differences are not very great between each size mill, three groups are established as equitable to the company and customers (and operators, if incentives are used). Besides depending upon the capacity of the specific machine, the time taken for operating the mill is a function of the surface speed, the feed, the thickness of the cut taken and the length of the cut. For convenience, a time factor is used to get the linear metal removed, which, together with the speed and feed, determines, the allowed time of the operation. The estimator determines these conditions from the print of the finished piece and the raw stock to be processed. It should be mentioned that even though all the production standards are grouped on the same sheet, the MHR will not necessarily be the same for each of the boring mills.

Exhibit 13–6 is a chart of production standards for a printer-slotter used in a corrugated container plant. The time required is a function of the size of the sheet being fed into the machine, the number of workers in the crew and the type of cor-

PRODUCTION STANDARDS

CHART NO. _____   OPERATION: Misc. Cutting

OPERATION	MINUTES PER PIECE											
	Stock Diameter in inches											
	1/2"	1"	1 1/2"	2"	3"	4"	5"	7"				
Spot drill	.05	.08	.10	.11	.12	.13	.14	.15				
Center drill	.09	.09	.16	.20	.24	.25	.25	.31				
End form - face only	.06	.08	.13	.19								
End form - face, chamf.	.09	.11	.19	.26								
Runout & chamf. hex or sq.	.10	.19	.26	.31	.39	.50						
Prepare end for box tool	.06	.08	.10	.14	.18	.21	.25					

**Exhibit 13–1. Table of Production Standards Used in Screw Machine
Plants: Miscellaneous Cutting**

PRODUCTION STANDARDS

CHART NO. _____

OPERATION: Additives times if
"clamp and unclamp" is performed

OPERATION	MINUTES PER PIECE
Fixed-clamp type with: 1 nut or bolt	.24
2 nuts or bolts	.32
Clamp on and off with: 1 nut or bolt	.32
2 nuts or bolts	.42
Place & remove washer, secure and loosen nut	.21
Place and remove washer and nut	.25
Adjust and loosen set screws	.13

**Exhibit 13–2. Table of Production Standards Used in Screw Machine
Plants: Clamping**

+ depreciation per job

rugated board being processed. As will be noted, as the size of the sheet fed increases, more men are required to man the machine. Overlaps in crew are provided where necessary. In this type of operation, the overhead segment of the MHR will remain the same, but the direct labor portion will vary depending on the size of the crew that the sheet size (determined from the order) requires. As is typical in many production standards, factors are provided to account for variations in the regular method.

EXHIBIT 13–7 charts production standards for a band saw used in corrugated container plants. The factors governing time consumption are the area of the pads and the length of the cut made, these related, in turn, to the number of pads to be cut out of the sheet. The break points of the area and length are largely determined from the past experience of the plant and the specifics of its product mix. In this example, the range of the cut lengths varies between 2 and 45 inches with time standards provided every 5 inches. However, in another plant, where the entire

PRODUCTION STANDARDS

CHART NO. _____   OPERATION: <u>Load and unload stock</u> <u>for Turret Lathe Bar Machines</u>

Stock Diam. in inches	MINUTES PER PIECE Length of piece													
	1''	2''	4''	6''	8''	10''	12''	14''	16''	18''	20''	24''	28''	36''
1/4''	.22	.23	.25	.29	.38	.43	.45	.49	.58	.62	.67	.74	.86	1.04
1/2''	.22	.24	.27	.31	.41	.47	.49	.55	.65	.70	.76	.85	.99	1.20
2''	.28	.32	.40	.49	.58	.76	.82	.93	1.07	1.21	1.32	1.50	1.76	2.17
2 1/4''	.28	.33	.41	.50	.60	.78	.85	.96	1.10	1.26	1.38	1.56	1.84	2.25
4''	.39	.46	.57	.71	.84	1.06	1.18							
4 1/4''	.40	.51	.70	.94	1.15	1.46	1.66							
6 1/2''	.64	.78	1.04											
7''	.65	.80	1.06											
7 1/2''	.66	.82												
8''	.68	.84												

Exhibit 13–3. Table of Production Standards Used in Screw Machine Plants: Turret Lathe Loading

PRODUCTION STANDARDS

CHART NO. _____   OPERATION: Setup
                                          Single Spindle, B & S Automatics

TOOL or OPERATION	MINUTES PER SETUP		
	Machine Capacity		
	1/2''	3/4''	1 1/4''
Remove, replace and time cams, change holders, gears, collet and finger	65	65	65
Box tools (single blade)	22	22	33
Box tools (double blade)	32	42	54
Cut off tools	17	17	21
Centering and facing tools	32	32	36
Drills	22	22	32
Form tools	16	16	22
Knurls, top or bottom	32	32	42
Reamers	33	33	36
Stock stop	5	5	5
Swing tools, turning	32	32	44
Spinning operations	42	42	53
Taps	21	21	26
Thread rolling	42	42	53

Exhibit 13–4. Table of Production Standards Used in Screw Machine Plants: Setup

range is expected to be narrower, it may be more equitable to provide the standards every 3 inches.

EXHIBIT 13–8 charts what is probably considered indirect labor in many plants. The table is presented here to show the type of work that can be measured. Although only rarely would such work be the subject of an estimate, this company makes use of the chart for measuring and rewarding the efforts of the baler.

The warehousing time standards shown in EXHIBIT 13–9 fall into this same indirect labor category and the chart is not used for estimating, unless warehousing is to be set up as a Production Center.

EXHIBIT 13–10 is a chart of production standards in the electrical industry for soldering wires to terminals. The time factors are the heat or wattage of the solder-

PRODUCTION STANDARDS

CHART NO._____   OPERATION: Boring mill--36 to 120''
                                    Material: cast iron
                                    Tooling: high-speed steel

Depth of cut in inches	SIZE OF BORING MILL								
	36- to 42-inch mill			54- to 60-inch mill			72- to 120-inch mill		
	S	F	C	S	F	C	S	F	C
1/8''	47.5	.080	.00135	47.5	.109	.00099	42.5	.25	.00049
1/4''	45.0	.080	.00143	47.5	.083	.00122	45.0	.125	.00091
3/8''	45.0	.062	.00182	47.5	.068	.00159	47.5	.094	.00115
1/2''	42.5	.062	.00192	45.0	.068	.00167	45.0	.094	.00121
5/8''	40.0	.062	.00204	42.5	.068	.00177	42.5	.094	.00128

NOTES: 1. S = Surface speed in feet per minute

2. F = Feed per revolution in inches

3. C = Time factor

TO GET HOURS REQUIRED TO COMPLETE ONE CUT:

multiply C (the time factor) by outside diameter of chip circle and length of cut.

Time factor C includes delay allowances.

Exhibit 13–5. Table of Production Standards for Operating Boring Mill

ing iron, the cross-section area of the terminal and the gauge or heaviness of the wire being soldered to the terminal. This chart is a good example of standard elemental time data. In estimating, the estimator would sum up all the times required for terminal soldering of the piece being costed, convert it to hrs per C or M, and in one step would apply the proper MHR to it to get conversion cost. Notice that the standards are as dependent on the heat of the iron as on the cross-section of the terminal because (in addition to the gauge of the wire) these two factors cause sizeable differences in the time required.

EXHIBIT 13–11 shows production standards for machine wrapping of paper boxes in a setup box plant. The time determinants are the depth of the box and half its perimeter. The depth factor is a function of speed, because of the cam action of the machine. The half-perimeter factor is provided to account for the increasing difficulty of handling larger sizes of paper and boxes.

The Estimate or Cost Sheet

The estimating or costing sheet is the place for gathering all costs of the product or order. A cost sheet accumulates the costs of a regular item carried in the com-

PRODUCTION STANDARDS

CHART NO. _____   OPERATION: Run: Printer-Slotter (Hooper) _____

STANDARD MAN-MINUTES PER 1000 SHEETS FED									
Square ft. area of sheet fed	No. of workers in crew			No. of workers in crew			No. of workers in crew		
	200 lb. test			275-350 lb. test			Double wall		
	2	3	4	2	3	4	2	3	4
up to 5.00	8.2			9.7			12.2		
5.01 to 7.00	8.8			10.6			13.1		
7.01 to 9.00	9.8	8.0		11.5	10.1		14.3	12.5	
9.01 to 11.00	11.0	8.9		12.7	11.0	8.5	15.7	13.5	11.0
11.01 to 13.00	12.3	9.8	8.0	14.2	11.9	10.2	17.2	14.8	12.6
13.01 to 15.00	13.7	10.8	9.3	16.0	12.8	11.7	19.0	15.9	14.5
15.01 to 18.00		12.3	11.4			14.0			17.6
18.01 to 21.00			13.6			15.8			19.1
21.01 to 24.00			15.2			17.5			21.9
24.01 to 27.00			17.0			19.3			24.5
27.01 to 30.00			19.0			21.3			27.3
30.01 to 33.00			21.2			23.6			30.4
33.01 to 36.00			23.8			26.4			34.0

Additive factors:

1. For 2 out add 22 percent to above standards
2. For 3 out add 33 percent to above standards
3. For skip feed add 20 percent to above standards

Exhibit 13–6. Table of Production Standards Used in Corrugated
Container Plants: Run Printer-Slotter

pany's product line, and from it a price list is developed. The estimate sheet, on the other hand, accumulates the *probable* costs of an order. The estimate sheet is initiated by an inquiry from a customer or prospect, and results in a quotation, usually before the order is run in production.

Estimate or cost sheets must have provision for the listing of all the raw materials that enter into the product, the net yield from the material, or waste allowances leading to the direct material cost per unit of product. This is usually a straightforward procedure and is not a subject of discussion in this book. The manufacturing portion of the estimate sheet includes a listing of the operations that may be required to produce the article, the estimated hours required at each operation, or Production Center, for the quantity of product being estimated, and the MHR for each of the Centers entering into the process. Multiplying the production hours at each Center by that Center's MHR and totaling the results gives the total conver-

PRODUCTION STANDARDS

CHART NO. _____   OPERATION: Cut Pads (20 at a time)
                                              Equipment: Band & Gang Saws

Square foot area per M	STANDARD MAN-MINUTES PER 1000 SHEETS								
	Length of out in inches								
	0 to 5	5.01 to 10	10.01 to 15	15.01 to 20	20.01 to 25	25.01 to 30	30.01 to 35	35.01 to 40	40.01 to 45
ONE OUT:									
0 - 400	12.53	13.06	13.38	13.75	14.13	14.50	15.00	15.50	16.00
400.01 - 800	13.03	13.56	13.88	14.25	14.63	15.00	15.50	16.00	16.50
800.01 -1200	13.28	13.81	14.00	14.50	14.88	15.25	15.75	16.25	16.75
1200.01 -1600	13.75	14.31	14.63	15.00	15.38	15.75	16.25	16.75	17.25
1600.01 -2000	14.28	14.81	15.13	15.50	15.88	16.25	16.75	17.25	17.75
FOUR OUT:									
0 - 400	5.90	6.44	6.75	7.13	7.50	7.89	8.38	8.88	9.38
400.01 - 800	6.19	6.73	7.04	7.41	7.79	8.16	8.66	9.16	9.66
800.01 -1200	6.46	7.00	7.31	7.69	8.06	8.44	8.94	9.44	9.94
1200.01 -1600	6.84	7.38	7.69	8.06	8.44	8.81	9.31	9.81	10.31
1600.01 -2000	7.13	7.66	7.98	8.35	8.73	9.10	9.60	10.10	10.60
SEVEN OUT:									
0 - 400	4.95	5.49	5.80	6.18	6.55	6.93	7.43	7.93	8.43
400.01 - 800	5.28	5.81	6.13	6.50	6.88	7.25	7.75	8.25	8.75
800.01 -1200	5.60	6.14	6.45	6.83	7.20	7.58	8.08	8.58	9.08
1200.01 -1600	6.03	6.56	6.88	7.25	7.63	8.00	8.50	9.00	9.50
1600.01 -2000	6.35	6.89	7.20	7.58	7.95	8.33	8.83	9.33	9.83

Exhibit 13–7. Table of Production Standards Used in Corrugated
Container Plants: Band Saw Cut Pads

PRODUCTION STANDARDS

CHART NO. _____   OPERATION: Bale Waste
                                      (one-man operation)

Finished Bale Weight	Standard man-minutes per bale
300 lb. to 400 lb.	33
401 lb. to 500 lb.	42
501 lb. to 600 lb.	46
601 lb. to 700 lb.	52
701 lb. to 800 lb.	56
801 lb. to 900 lb.	61
901 lb. to 1000 lb.	65

Exhibit 13–8. Table of Production Standards Used in Corrugated
Container Plants: Bale Waste

PRODUCTION STANDARDS

CHART NO. _____   OPERATION: Warehousing

Work Performed	STANDARD MINUTES PER ROLL		
	To Bays 1 to 6	To Bays 7 to 12	To Bays 13 to 19
From truck at Main Bldg. - 1 man	3.65	4.28	4.81
From truck at Main Bldg. - 2 men	3.32	3.94	4.85
Put rolls away previously dropped:			
Area outside of Main Bldg. - 1 man	2.61	3.25	3.88
Area outside of Main Bldg. - 2 men	2.28	2.91	3.54
Servicing rolls to Corrugator - 1 man	2.78	2.68	3.66
Servicing rolls to Corrugator - 2 men	2.50	2.38	3.38
Move rolls between bays:			
from bays 1 to 6 - 1 man	1.87	2.50	3.14
from bays 7 to 12 - 1 man	2.50	1.87	2.50
from bays 13 to 19 - 1 man	3.14	2.50	1.87
Drop rolls from truck - 1 man	2.61 minutes per roll		
Move butts to get ones used - 1 man	1.48 minutes per butt		
Load bales at bale room (not topped)	2.16 minutes per bale		
Check damaged rolls	2.76 minutes per roll		

Exhibit 13–9. Table of Production Standards Used in Corrugated
Container Plants: Warehousing

sion cost of the product. When this figure is added to the direct material costs, the sum is the total cost of the product.

Provision then should be made for makeready or setup times, since it must be recognized that a substantial portion of the cost varies with the quantity of product manufactured, while some costs do not vary with volume and are considered fixed. Also, for the same reason, space should be provided for estimating the cost of different quantities of the product.

In addition to these direct costs, space should be allowed for extraordinary expenses, viz.: long deliveries, royalties, salesmen's commissions, license fees directly applicable to the product estimated. Also, a separate section should be provided for the cost of tools, dies, patterns, plates, and forms.

Needless to say, when the inquiry is transferred to the estimate sheet, the specifications should be clear and detailed to avoid later misunderstandings. In some industries, the customer submits a sample; in others, the manufacturer submits a sample as evidence of his understanding of the customer's requirements. Special arrangements, such as who pays for the tools, or the samples made, should be explicit. How the deliveries are to be made should also be clearly described in writing on the estimate sheet. Such expenses may play a large role in cost-estimating.

On some estimate sheets provision is made for listing actual costs after the order has been run. With MHR, this is done only where management wishes to spot check the profitability of some particular order.

PRODUCTION STANDARDS

CHART NO. _____

OPERATION: Solder Terminals
30/70 solder; 12 to 26 gauge wire

Soldering Iron Wattage	Terminal Cross-Section in Sq. In.	TIME IN MINUTES TO SOLDER ONE SIDE ONLY							Add for Solder
		Gauge of Wire Soldered to Terminal							All Around Terminal
		12	14	16	18	19	20	22 to 26	
95 to 200	.0000 to .0070	.041	.038	.036	.034	.033	.032	.030	.004
150 to 200	.0070 to .0115	.047	.043	.038	.034	.033	.032	.030	.004
120	.0070 to .0115	.047	.043	.038	.034	.033	.032	.030	.009
95	.0070 to .0115	.062	.056	.049	.043	.041	.038	.034	.012
62 to 75	.0000 to .0030	.047	.043	.038	.034	.033	.032	.030	.004
62 to 75	.0030 to .0050	.051	.047	.043	.038	.036	.034	.030	.007
62 to 75	.0050 to .0070	.087	.071	.056	.041	.039	.037	.033	.010
62	.0070 to .0115	.089	.080	.070	.060	.057	.055	.049	.041
75	.0070 to .0115	.060	.056	.051	.047	.045	.043	.038	.022

Exhibit 13–10. Table of Production Standards for Soldering Electrical Terminals

PRODUCTION STANDARDS

CHART NO. _____   OPERATION: Machine Wrapping
Stokes & Smith, Model "H-NS"

D E P T H	STANDARD NUMBER OF UNITS PER HOUR						
	Length + Width						
	Under 10''	10'' to 15''	15'' to 20''	20'' to 25''	25'' to 30''	30'' & over	
Under 1/2''	1100	1060	1010	950	880	800	
1/2'' to 3/4''	1090	1050	1000	940	870	790	
3/4'' to 1''	1075	1035	985	925	855	775	
1'' to 1 1/2''	1055	1015	965	905	835	755	
1 1/2'' to 2''	1030	990	940	880	810	730	
2'' to 2 1/2''	1000	960	910	850	780	700	
2 1/2'' to 3''	960	920	870	810	740	660	
3'' to 3 1/2''	910	870	820	760	690	610	
3 1/2'' & over	850	810	760	700	630	550	

Allowances:

1. Setup time = .40 hour per day
2. Cleanup time = None (included in above standards)

Exhibit 13–11. Table of Production Standards for Machine Wrapping
of Setup Boxes

Fixed and Variable Costs

Besides the element of cost that is fixed regardless of the volume of the order (set-ups, makereadies), the conversion cost also has elements of out-of-pocket costs and fixed costs for each level of volume estimated. Provision should be made for the separation of these on the estimate sheet so that the conversion cost can be for full, as well as variable or direct, costs. The importance of making this separation will become more apparent in the following chapter on pricing.

Sample Estimate Sheets

EXHIBITS 13–12 to 13–14 show "full cost" estimate sheets now in use in various industries.

EXHIBITS 13–12 and 13–12a show the first and second sides of a skeletonized estimating form used in the screw-machine industries. This sheet is presented in simplified form to show the application of the MHR. Of course, in practice, provision would have to be made for listing the specific equipment used. In this case, the estimate is for one part made completely on a multiple-spindle automatic screw machine that carries an MHR of $22. Since multiple-spindle equipment can have four, five, six or more spindles, it is necessary to identify the equipment on which work is placed. This practice will insure application of the proper MHR.

Those operations following the screw-machine listings are known as secondary operations, for which the hours per thousand are taken from sheets of production standards. For shop use, those forms would require the insertion of a sketch suitable

ESTIMATE SHEET
(side 1)

Sketch of Part to be Estimated

SEQUENCE OF PRODUCTION OPERATIONS	SETUP OPERATIONS	
1st position: Spot, Form & Rough Face	1. Change collets and pushers	1.7 hrs.
2nd position: Drill	2. Change tool slide cam	.6 hrs.
3rd position: Drill & Form	3. Change cross slide cams	.7 hrs.
4th position: Drill & Shave	4. Change spindle gear	.3 hrs.
5th position: Recess, c'off b-down, fin.	5. Change feed gears	.3 hrs.
6th position: Accelerate Ream & Cutoff	6. Install reaming attachments	1.6 hrs.
	7. Install recess fixture	.9 hrs.
	8. Set up stock stop	.3 hrs.
	9. Change stock feed cams	.35 hrs.
	10. Tool setting, adjusting and test pieces	9.35 hrs.
	TOTAL SETUP TIME = 16.00 hrs.	

MACHINE DATA	MATERIAL DATA	
1. Surface feet per minute: 240		
2. Spindle speed: 509 rpm		
3. Feed: .0025		
4. Longest cam: 1/4"		
5. Gross production per hour: 267		
6. Net production per hour: 200	TOTAL MATERIAL COST = $120 per M	
7. Standard hours per M pieces = 5		

EQUIPMENT	TOOLING
Piece processed on Multiple Spindle Auto.	

Exhibit 13–12. Front Side of Sample Screw Machine Shop's
Estimating Sheet

for use in planning the sequence of operations, also a complete listing of tools required to perform the operations that have to be made up specifically for the part.

Tooling charges that are to be amortized or charged over a given quantity of production are handled in the same way as the setup charge in the exhibit. That is, the cost will remain the same with limited changes in quantities but will be reduced on a per thousand basis as the quoted quantity increases.

Some forms used in this industry make provision for the reject rate encountered in such operations. Also included sometimes are comparisons between the estimated and the actual time taken. Thus the estimate sheet becomes a job record card as well. This is a costly practice and, if done for all jobs, creates a duplicate costing system (job costing). It is helpful, however, to have space for this information on the sheet, to enable the recording of a *spot check* on order profitability.

Exhibit 13–13 shows an estimating form used in the folding carton industries. Instead of providing quotations for varying quantities, this form estimates a specific order quantity (100,000) and then lists the actual performance times together with the gains or losses made at each operation. Again, it is not necessary to job cost each order; however, certain areas of profit- and loss-producing operations can be uncovered by the procedure. Notice that the over-all conversion loss is only 50 cents, about .1 percent of the total conversion costs. However, the ingredients of this small loss are $43.70 of losses and $43.20 of gain. Obviously, due note should be made of this fact in giving subsequent quotations to the same customer. What happened on this particular order for the centers making the gains was that, while the estimated time was listed at "standard," the workers on incentive beat this time, produced the order in less than the allowed time, boosted their earnings, and earned more profits for the company, thereby justifying the existence of the wage incentive plan. This gain should be retained by the company. However, on the loss operations, either the workers did not try to make the standard—which is a negative evaluation of the bonus-earning opportunity provided at these centers by the incentive— or there was some difficulty at those operations. While immediate investigation should be taken into the causes of this circumstance, do not overlook the fact that the estimator could have made a mistake in the listing of the standards—which then places the company in the position of having undercosted this order. Even if such has been the case here since, the order cost would have been inflated by hardly more than 8 percent, there is little likelihood that price resistance would have been encountered.

Note that the variance technique was applied to the amount estimated for materials and the actual sum spent. Often the waste percentage figure, used in arriving at materials cost, has been understated. Again, a discrepancy is cause for investigation.

Exhibit 13–14 is an example of a cost sheet for a proprietary product made by a

ESTIMATE SHEET
(side 2)

CUSTOMER DATA:
    (Name, address, purchasing agent, salesman, rating, terms, freight, comission, etc.)

SPECIAL DATA:
    (outside tool expenses, outside purchases of services, labor, parts, etc.)

PRODUCTION CENTER	Operation	M. H. R.	CONVERSION COST									
			1M		5M		10M		25M		M	
			Hrs.	$	Hrs.	$	Hrs.	$	Hrs.	$	Hrs.	$
Single Spindle												
Multiple Spindle	setup	22	16	352	16	352	16	352	16	352		
1-6-side 1	run	22	5	110	25	550	50	1100	125	2750		
Horiz. Drill												
Mill												
Lathes												
Tapper												
Grinder												
TOTAL CONVERSION COSTS			462		902		1452		3102			
TOTAL MATERIAL COSTS			120		600		1200		3000			
TOTAL COSTS			582		1502		2652		6102			
TOTAL COST PER M PIECES			$582		$300.67		$265.20		$244.08			
PROFIT												
PRICE QUOTED												

Exhibit 13–12a. Back Side of Sample Screw Machine Shop's
Estimating Sheet

manufacturer of novelties. Since this sheet applies to a stock product, it is referred to as a cost sheet rather than as an estimating sheet. Generally, an estimating sheet is prepared in response to an order inquiry or a request for a quotation. In this case, a record is maintained as a cost control reference, whether or not there are customers ordering the article.

Usually, each time an order for this item is run, the reverse of such a form is used for the posting of actual times and other variances from planned costs. In this way, management is able periodically to revise and purify the reported costs of the

X Y Z FOLDING CARTON COMPANY

Customer:

Description:

Quantity: 100,000

ESTIMATE & JOB COST ANALYSIS						
OPERATIONS	MHR	Standard Order Time	ESTIMATED COST	ACTUAL CONVERSION		Gain or (Excess Cost)
				Time	Cost	
PREPARATION:						
Composition	$4.00	5	$20.00	4	$16.00	$4.00
Die Making	3.50	7	24.50	7	24.50	----
Makereadies:						
Printing	12.00	5.5	66.00	6.5	78.00	(12.00)
Cut & Crease	10.00	2.5	25.00	4.0	40.00	(15.00)
Glueing	18.00	6.0	108.00	4.5	81.00	27.00
RUN: EQPT:						
Print 1/C LP	12.00	4.0	48.00	4.6	55.20	(7.20)
Varnish						
Cut & Crease CYL.	10.00	4.5	45.00	5.0	50.00	(5.00)
Cello.						
Strip hand	3.20	10.0	32.00	9.0	28.80	3.20
Guillotine						
Punch						
Glue Staude Master	18.00	7.0	126.00	6.5	117.00	9.00
Wax						
Stitch						
Tape						
Wrap hand	3.00	6.0	18.00	7.5	22.50	(4.50)
TOTALS			$512.50	$513.00		($.50)
Materials Cost			411.00	423.00		(12.00)
Total Costs			923.50	936.00		(12.50)
Add: Sales Commissions, extraordinary delivery, etc.						
Total						
Profit						
Quote						

Exhibit 13–13. Sample of Estimate and Job Cost Analysis of
Folding-Carton Order

product. Reference is made to the latest cost sheet when the time comes to review and alter price lists.

Deficiency of Forms

We have made reference to the fact that there are various interpretations and variations in the application of the MHR concept. They apply to how the rates are to be established as well as to how they are to be implemented for managerial use and for product-pricing purposes. Exhibits 13–12 to 13–14 showed examples of MHR in its simplest and least effective form—a form which did not bring out the information that management needs to price most effectively in its markets. We refer to the lack of fixed and variable cost segregation on the estimates—which made it impossible to determine the out-of-pocket cost "floor" for the products.

Since price is rarely based directly on cost, the MHR becomes effective for pricing only after these two segments stand out clearly. Otherwise, proper managerial

---

A B C NOVELTY MANUFACTURING COMPANY

Product: Proprietary

COST SHEET

OPERATION SEQUENCE	STD. PROD'N/Hr.	STD. HRS./C	PRODUCTION CENTER	M.H.R.	CONVERSION COST PER C
Blank & draw base	1200	.0833	Power press	$ 11.20	$ .933
Form rod	2200	.0454	Foot press	5.15	.234
Weld rod to base	320	.3125	Spot welding	7.30	2.281
Degrease assembly	9200	.0108	Degreasing	4.10	.044
Cut & notch channel	840	.1190	Foot press	5.15	.613
Form channel	410	.2440	Foot press	5.15	1.257
Cut & color	165	.6204	Polishing	7.65	4.746
Degrease channel	11200	.0089	Degreasing	4.10	.036
Plate	1800	.5555	Plating room	17.70	9.832
Final assembly	35	2.857	Assembly dep't.	3.90	11.142
			TOTAL CONVERSION COSTS/C		$31.118
			TOTAL MATERIALS COSTS/C		119.202
			TOTAL COST/C		$150.32
			TOTAL COST EACH		$ 1.503

Exhibit 13–14. **Sample of Cost Sheet of Proprietary Novelty Product**

decision becomes difficult. Only where management knows that its pricing can realistically follow its costs is this segregation unnecessary. In all other situations, the order estimate must show how a proposed price relates to out-of-pocket costs and the contribution it makes to a recovery of fixed charges.

In order to estimate the cost of a product or order, MHR must be developed by its fixed and variable segments. These are discussed in Chapter 14. Exhibit 14–6 shows in condensed form the recommended method of estimating product costs for these two vital elements.

Chapter 14

USING MHR FOR PRICING PRODUCTS

Pricing is a profit-planning effort in which management analyzes alternatives and compares them against each other to select the one that promises to be the most advantageous—the one that promises full recovery of fixed and variable costs and that returns to the company a profit large enough to justify the investment made in its facilities.

Price Acceptability

The price that a buyer is willing to pay for a product will not be a function of the article's production cost, but of the services that this item will provide, its expected future price, and the availability of substitutes and their usefulness.

What advantages will the purchaser get from possession of the product? Will the article give him pleasure or prestige? Will it provide a special service to him? These and similar considerations will determine the price that the buyer will be willing to pay. For a sale to be made it is essential that, in the mind of the buyer, the advantages obtained justify the price to be paid. Costs only indicate the minimum sales price at which production costs will be recovered; they do not show the profit margin that the market is ready to accept.

Costs Start the Pricing Process

Cost is actually the starting point in pricing a company's products. Since competition and customer demand must also be considered in pricing, selling prices rarely have a rigid relationship to cost.

Current or anticipated costs are vital for pricing, because pricing decisions deal with sales to be made in the future. Historical and "standard" costs only provide a *guide* to current or future costs. When costs of material, labor, facilities and services change, costs previously recorded have to be restated in dollars having the same

162

purchasing power as the dollars in which the selling prices are being quoted. We have talked about economic depreciation earlier, but it must be emphasized again that differences in the dollar's purchasing power must be reflected in any current pricing decision.

As it has been said earlier in this book, it is essential to develop an adequate costing system to obtain a good pricing system. When a product seems to be unprofitable, the reason may very well be found in the methods used to ascertain its cost.

The most efficient manufacturer with plenty of sales may well lose money if the gap between actual and quoted costs is large. When quoted costs are higher, the company eventually will price itself out of its markets. In contrast, when actual costs are greater than quoted costs, products are underpriced, and although sales are brisk, the company loses money because its business is unprofitable.

Nature of Costs

To be valuable, any cost system has to be flexible enough to be able to provide the information required at different times as a response to changing conditions. It has to be remembered always that no cost system will produce consistently the same results and, of course, that different cost-finding procedures will never do so. A cost system represents only an assembly of facts presented in an orderly manner for the purpose of obtaining some predetermined answer. Consequently, if the methods used in organizing the data are changed, the results will also differ. For this reason, the cost of a product is never a single, precisely calculated figure; it is a figure obtained to fulfill a specific function in a company, whether in pricing, profitability calculations or control. This is why it is of the utmost importance to decide in advance, before organizing any cost-finding system, what will be the purpose of the system and which objectives the company will try to reach with it.

Knowing the real costs becomes essential when prices for products have to be determined. Naturally, a company that has a good costing system will tend to give costs a greater emphasis in its pricing policies than a company that is not so fully acquainted with the actual costs of its products.

Although costs may constitute an important factor in a price determination system, they can be used only as a *guide* and a *point of reference*. In constructing a price list, the price estimator will apply the cost facts more or less conscientiously, depending on his philosophy and his circumstances.

Pricing Influences

Although pricing usually boils down to the economic laws of supply and demand, the most important elements that will affect the price to be charged are competition and price elasticity. This latter element is directly related to volume.

Competition is an element that has possibly the greatest effect on any pricing system, as usually the smaller companies follow the price leadership of the larger firms. This is because a larger company generally has more facilities available for obtaining reliable cost information to guide its pricing decisions. Lack of cost knowledge on the part of the smaller companies could alter the pricing system in the industry, but usually it does not, as the smaller companies are forced to price their products along the levels already set by the larger manufacturers. The fact that even if inadvertently, they may be setting the price levels for the industry as a whole emphasizes the importance of the larger companies having an adequate knowledge of their costs. Otherwise, it becomes almost impossible for other members of the industry to guide their pricing policies by their own cost.

To prevent the problems that such a situation could bring about, many trade associations have developed, and make available to their members, costing procedures for the industry based on good accounting practices. These educational practices differ from earlier trade association efforts directed principally toward promoting uniformity in pricing practices.

When the demand for a product does not vary considerably with changes in price, it is said that the demand is inelastic. Products illustrating this condition are wheat and sugar. Competition does not generally play an important role in an inelastic market, as suppliers are so many that they cannot independently influence or control the total market, or, as in the mining industry, capacity is relatively fixed and producers are few. In such cases, contrary to prevailing opinion, competitors do not get involved in dangerous price wars to gain the market, but try to develop and maintain their own share of total sales.

On the other hand, an elastic market is usually characteristic of industrial activities. In such a market, small changes in price have a direct influence on the number of units sold, and if the price increases, sales are lost to the competition, and vice versa.

Costs and Pricing

Cost-estimating for pricing purposes may be defined as the process of calculating the expected cost of articles to be produced when past experience does not provide the historical cost of identical items produced under similar conditions. Usually these expected costs should include all expenses other than income taxes and profits.

All pricing problems have both long- and short-range components. While fixed costs must be allocated to provide a complete recovery of expenses at the end of a given period, the short-range impact also must be given consideration. Both long- and short-range volume differentials in cost must be available to permit accurate pricing decisions.

Product costs based upon normal volume and mix of facilities are not sufficient for short-range pricing. The term "short-range" does not mean a short period of time but refers to any period in which there are costs that do not change with production or sales volume. This period may be as long as one or two years, and it is characterized by stability of fixed costs. It is also characterized by the facts that usually the industrial manager cannot adapt his productive capacity to take advantage of sudden increases in the demand for his product, nor can he substantially change his production costs.

Academic approaches to product costing state that every price should cover the full cost of the product. Yet, the amount of overhead apportioned to a product is never precisely measurable, and there are always degrees of interpolation existing between even the closest allocation bases. Besides, customers do not know how much annual activity was projected in a plant and the proportion of each Production Center's activity to that of the others. That is why the amount of overhead carried by each unit product cannot really be known until after the number of product units is known. *Getting or losing a particular order may in itself affect the cost of filling it.* Unit profit is a function of volume and velocity of expense recovery, and not necessarily of the difference between fully allocated product cost and selling price.

The machine-hour rates developed in the previous chapters showed how the expenses allocated to the Production Centers by the EAW became hourly composite rates that included all costs (except materials). The MHR Summary Sheets represent the end in a chain of arithmetical steps including the Converting Facilities Classification Sheet, the Crew Composition Table, the Operating Budget and, finally, the Expense Assignment worksheet.

In essence, what the rates on the Summary Sheet show is that if, by reason of the product mix sold, all of the activity projected comes to fruition in each of the Centers, and the expenses remain reasonably well within the limits budgeted, then the company will recover all of its costs.

The machine-hour rate method provides the means for equitably apportioning overhead expenses to a product so that a full product cost can be developed. When all facilities operate as projected, this product cost will recover all of the company's costs. However, bases of allocation chosen as "equitable" for accounting purposes are sometimes found unsatisfactory for pricing. Unit product costs figures based upon normal volume are not very helpful when management is faced with these questions: "How much will it cost to produce additional product units?" "How much will this specific order add to the company's over-all profits?"

Over the long run, the full cost of all facilities must be recovered in the selling prices to avoid an operating loss. MHR developed at proper operating volume provides control over the long-range pricing objectives. However, long-range recovery depends upon how fixed costs are reflected in the selling prices of specific products or in the selling prices of all products at different times; and these factors are related to the number of products sold and the cost recovery transmitted from the selling prices. In industry, management must find the combination of prices and volume for individual products that provides the largest profit.

This is to say that while a certain group of orders may bring in selling prices based on a planned profit margin over fully allocated costs, these profits only become real profit dollars when the remaining facilities are used somewhere near their capacity or annual activity projected for the coming period. When the remaining activity is under-utilized, then the unrecovered fixed costs act to decrease the profit dollars in the company's total profits, in spite of the actual profit obtained on a particular group of orders.

Adjusting Historical Costs to Current Price Levels

When one considers the purchasing power of money received rather than the mere excess of incoming dollars over outgoing dollars, it is evident that the purchasing power of the capital invested in a business must be maintained before there can be any real income for the owner. For this reason, cost for pricing should be stated in dollars of the same purchasing power as those current in the period to which the prices in question will apply.

Lower selling prices may be adequate to maintain the same productive facilities and the purchasing power of the capital invested in the assets, even when such prices do not replace the number of dollars invested at a higher price level. Prices should depend upon the rapidity with which the purchasing power of money decreases and upon the length of the period of turnover of capital employed in the business.

Some companies, in computing product costs for pricing, figure the cost of materials used in manufacturing at current market or at anticipated replacement prices. Cost of materials so determined for pricing purposes usually differs from cost of materials determined for inventory purposes, because the latter reflect prices in the past rather than current prices.

Pricing of Marginal Business

As we mentioned already, full expense recovery is essential for long-range pricing policies, since, if the company does not make a complete recovery of its costs over a given period, it will cease to exist as a going concern. To attain complete recovery, it is sometimes necessary to make pricing decisions according to a knowledge of the elements, in the conversion cost, sunk fixed costs, such as depreciation, current cash outlay fixed costs, such as salaries, and the out-of-pocket, fully variable costs, which change directly with sales or production volume.

Here is a simple example of a pricing decision based on this type of information: Let's say, a certain product's cost breaks down into:

Material	$ 3.00
Conversion	
Labor	3.00
Overhead	5.00
TOTAL COST	$11.00

A sales forecast shows that a company expects to sell 900 units of this product at $13.75 per unit during the coming period. This goal will require operating at 90% of standard volume. Based on the forecast, the following budgeted income statement is prepared:

BUDGETED INCOME STATEMENT

Sales (900 units at $13.75)		$12,375.00
Cost of goods sold (900 units at $11.00)		9,900.00
GROSS PROFIT MARGIN		$ 2,475.00
Less underabsorbed overhead:		
Overhead Costs		
Variable (900 units at $1.00)	900	
Fixed	4,000	
Total Actual Overhead	4,900	
Applied to production (900 units at $5.00)	4,500	
Underabsorbed balance		400.00
NET PROFIT		$ 2,075.00

Now, the company has been offered an order to enable it to perform converting operations on 150 units of material to be supplied by the customer. Management wishes to know how much, if any, profit can be made by accepting this order at a price of $8.00 per unit.

With normal volume costs available to it, management might conclude that no profit can be made from this order because the total of overhead and labor is shown to be $8.00 per unit. Although most management officials would prefer that the rate of overhead recovery be accelerated, it would require analysis to bring out the correct information.

The data would appear as follows:

Sales, regular product, 900 units at $13.75		$12,375.00
Proposed order, 150 units processed at $8.00		1,200.00
Total Sales		$13,575.00
Cost of goods sold:		
Regular product, 900 units at $11.00	$9,900.00	
Proposed order, 150 units at $8.00	1,200.00	
Total Cost		$11,100.00
GROSS PROFIT MARGIN		2,475.00
Add overabsorbed overhead:		
Overhead Costs		
Variable (1,050 units at $1.00)	$1,050.00	
Fixed	4,000.00	
Total Actual Overhead	5,050.00	
Applied to production		
(1,050 units at $5.00)	5,250.00	
Overabsorbed balance		200.00
NET PROFIT		$ 2,675.00

The above analysis shows that the order for 150 units at $8.00 per unit will add $600 to net profits for the period. While it is quite simple to prepare this type of analysis, it becomes time-consuming where overhead costs have not been segregated into fixed and variable expense segments. Fixed-variable separation of costs, essential to strategic pricing, is discussed later in this chapter. Another concept of marginal pricing stemming from overrecovery is discussed in Chapter 16.

Marginal Pricing Considerations

As marginal business (described above) is acquired, it is necessary to distinguish between volume which adds to the peaks and that which fills the valleys in the output—those orders that improve the balance and those that create bottlenecks in the flow of work through the plant. Some business should be abandoned when more attractive opportunities are available.

While it may be possible to increase over-all profit by getting additional sales volume, even though some increments in the total volume contribute less than others towards fixed costs and profits, control over sales mix must be maintained to make sure that prices are not cut, or low margin products sold, when the factory capacity could be used for more profitable work.

The previous example shows that it sometimes pays to vary the rate at which the fixed costs are reflected in the selling prices. The contribution to fixed costs and profits depends on the volume of units sold and the amount of cost recovered in the selling price of each unit.

MHR is a method for determining full product costs, acts as a guide to pricing and helps management to avoid quoting prices which fail to recover production costs. However important recovery of costs might be over a time period, it may not be significant on individual products. Recovery of full product costs will not bring in profits unless all fixed expenses are recovered first.

Since pricing decisions deal with alternatives, cost data must be prepared to enable management to evaluate the effects of these decisions. One step in this direction is provided by the breakdown of all expenses into their fixed and variable components. One of the difficult problems in determining product costs is that the activity of facilities used in manufacturing and selling cannot, as a practical matter, be varied in proportion to the immediate need for these facilities. As a result, the costs of operating these facilities are fixed irrespective of volume, provided such volume does not exceed the capacity of this equipment.

The cost data needed by management to provide answers to pricing questions are (a) flexible budgets for varying capacity levels, which produce (b) EAW's and (c) sets of MHR's for each operating level; and (d) a stating of conversion cost by the *fixed* and *variable* elements contained in the manufacturing and non-manufacturing cost categories, and of the break-even analysis applied to individual Production Centers.

Fixed and Variable Costs, and Volume of Production

Since, for developing an EAW to be used in pricing decisions, a fixed-variable *flexible* budget is necessary, it might be wise to review briefly what is meant by fixed and variable costs. Variable costs, which are also known as "direct" or "volume" costs, are those costs which vary, in a practical sense, directly with variations in level of activity, or output. As activity increases, variable costs rise, and when volume falls, they decrease. Examples of variable costs are direct materials and labor, overhead expenses, such as maintenance expenses and electricity (energy charges above the demand charge), delivery expenses, sales commissions and the like.

Fixed costs are those which remain at the same level during a period regardless of output. Examples of fixed expenses are machinery depreciation, rent, property taxes, and top management salaries.

In terms of unit cost, these characteristics mean, of course, just the reverse. With a fixed product-volume mix, when variable costs increase with volume, then unit variable costs remain the same. And when volume increases within the framework of fixed charges, the more the volume, the less the unit fixed costs. With varying product mix, the unit variable cost is more elusive of measurement.

Most business decisions result in volume changes: new products are introduced, price revisions are planned, new markets are developed, sales efforts are pegged to certain products. In addition to affecting income, volume changes affect fixed costs in one way and variable costs in another, as stated above. In short, decisions affect volume; volume affects costs and incomes; and costs and selling prices affect decisions in a never-ending circle.

When fixed and variable costs are scrambled together into a total unit cost, it is almost impossible to relate volume to costs, and pricing and other decision-making are also weakened. This problem can be solved by obtaining costs that have been subdivided into their fixed and variable elements. Then the effect of volume changes on the fixed and variable elements of a company's costs becomes immediately apparent. A cost breakdown indicates the profit or loss at any assumed volume of sales and selling prices, as was illustrated earlier in this chapter in the example of a management accepting additional units at less than their total "full" cost level.

As we mentioned in different ways earlier, the "total" unit costing concept can mislead management as to the nature of profit and how it develops in the company's economy. In total unit costing, profit ostensibly accrues at x dollars per unit, as the difference between the selling price received and the total unit cost. But profit is not a function of profit margins—not until fixed costs are all recovered. And even after fixed costs have been recovered, profit is not dependent upon the margin; instead, it accrues with additional volume depending upon the margin between *variable* costs and prices. The fixed costs remain fixed regardless of the volume (provided the volume increase does not exceed the capacities of existing equipment). If this concept is not recognized and integrated with pricing decisions, the company might be led into the adoption of relatively unprofitable policies.

(a) *The Fixed-Variable Flexible Budget:* One of the first steps in arriving at fixed and variable conversion costs is the flexible budget. Not only must the budget be flexible for different capacity levels, it must also distinguish between the fixed and variable elements of the expense classifications. It will thus produce an EAW for each level and a set of MHR's having the ability to give full and variable conversion costs. This information, needed by management to price opportunely in the company's markets, can be used in a direct-costing or absorption-costing framework.

EXHIBIT 14–1 shows such an Operating Budget for three levels of activity: 50%, 70% and 90%. Note that while the major expense classifications follow the OB shown in Chapter 9, each has been expanded to include fixed and variable components. This extension, as we shall see later, is necessary in making break-even charts for any Production Center.

You will notice that both variable and fixed costs are found in every expense classification. The following tabulation will make this clearer:

OPERATING BUDGET

EXPENSE CLASSIFICATION	ACTIVITY LEVEL		
	50%	70%	90%
MANUFACTURING COSTS:			
Space:	$10,000	$11,000	$11,500
Fixed	9,000	9,000	9,000
Variable	1,000	2,000	2,500
Power:	2,500	3,380	4,260
Fixed	300	300	300
Variable	2,200	3,080	3,960
Machinery:	27,000	29,800	32,600
Fixed	20,000	20,000	20,000
Variable	7,000	9,800	12,600
Fringe Benefits:	8,250	11,200	14,150
Fixed	850	850	850
Variable	7,400	10,350	13,300
Indirect Labor:	18,000	20,400	22,800
Fixed	12,000	12,000	12,000
Variable	6,000	8,400	10,800
MFG. COSTS TOTAL:	65,750	75,780	85,310
Fixed	42,150	42,150	42,150
Variable	23,600	33,630	43,160
NON-MANUFACTURING COSTS:			
Selling & Delivery:	45,500	56,500	67,500
Fixed	18,000	18,000	18,000
Variable	27,500	38,500	49,500
(commissions not included)			
Administration:	62,000	57,200	72,400
Fixed	49,000	49,000	49,000
Variable	13,000	18,200	23,400
NON-MFG. COSTS TOTAL:	107,500	123,700	139,900
Fixed	67,000	67,000	67,000
Variable	40,500	56,700	72,900
TOTAL OVERHEAD COSTS:	173,250	199,480	225,210
Fixed	109,150	109,150	109,150
Variable	64,100	90,330	116,060

Exhibit 14–1. Fixed-Variable, Multi-Level Operating Budget

Examples of:

Expense Classification	Fixed Elements	Variable Elements
Space	Building depreciation	Building heat
Power	Minimum demand charge	Energy charges
Machinery	Depreciation	Maintenance
Fringe Benefits	Compensation Insurance	Incentive premium
Indirect Labor	Plant superintendent's pay	Materials handler's pay
Selling & Delivery	Warehouse depreciation	Sales expenses
Administration	Manager's pay	Advertising

(b) *The Fixed-Variable Expense Assignment Worksheet:* Exhibit 14–2 shows the EAW constructed for Company *ABC* according to the fixed-variable multi-level budget shown in Exhibit 14–1. The data is the same as in the EAW's shown in Exhibits 10–3 and 10–4 (in Step 4 of Section 2), except that they have been refined to show two capacity levels, and the fixed and variable expenses for each. As we said earlier, this work is in preparation for the development of machine-hour rates which will produce a product cost with all expenses fully allocated, as well as a total cost separated between fixed costs and variable or out-of-pocket costs. This product cost will be the least amount the selling price must recover to avoid a cash loss on the order. Direct-costing *proponents* will use just the variable segment of the MHR to determine cash contributions of orders.

(c) *The Fixed-Variable Flexible MHR Summary Sheet:* Exhibit 14–3 shows how the above EAW reflects itself in the final rates. As you will notice, the total MHR for each level of activity is subdivided into its fixed and variable components. The fixed portion represents the full charge to the product for fixed expenses, assuming that the planned activity is realized. The variable portion represents that sum which the manufacturer must pay out of his own pocket per hour to sustain each center for the indicated activity. In a limited sense, the variable cost is the hourly cash cost of the center, but this condition is not a fixed one in multi-product manufacture that has a variable product-volume mix.

If all orders are obtained at this variable cost level or price, at the planned level of operation, the company recovers all of its out-of-pocket costs but sustains the loss of its fixed expenses—moneys paid out in the past. If this condition continues over the useful life of its facilities, then the company loses the asset value of the facilities. But if the activity and product mix is such as to permit some orders to recover fixed expenses fully, then recovering only the variable costs on some orders still provides the company with an over-all profit. On the latter orders, variable cost recovery is above the break-even point of the company's total sales.

(d) *Fixed-Variable Product Cost:* Exhibit 14–4 shows a three-operation product estimated at the composite MHR and Exhibit 14–5 shows the same product estimated according to the fixed and variable MHR. In the first exhibit, the total order cost shows all costs fully allocated. In the second, management can see which portion of its total cost represents out-of-pocket costs—the minimum it must recover without sustaining a loss of cash outlay. The decision of whether or not to accept such an order at times is a complex one, since it revolves around a forecast of expected volume and revenue on the rest of its product-manufacturing capacity.

If activity turns out to be higher than projected and the fixed-cost allocations remain constant, management might recover enough (overrecovery) on other work to make up for the fixed cost underrecovery on this order. As we have said before, after fixed costs have been covered, profit is the difference between variable costs

EXPENSE ASSIGNMENT WORKSHEET – FIXED & VARIABLE

(for 50 Percent and 90 Percent Activity Levels)

PRODUCTION CENTER	% ACTIVITY LEVEL	ASSIGNED ANNUAL HOURS	SPACE F	SPACE V	POWER F	POWER V	MACHINERY F	MACHINERY V	FRINGE BENEFITS F	FRINGE BENEFITS V	INDIRECT LABOR F	INDIRECT LABOR V	TOTALS: MFG. COSTS F	TOTALS: MFG. COSTS V	NON-MFG. COSTS F	NON-MFG. COSTS V	TOTAL COSTS F	TOTAL COSTS V
PRINTER–SLOTTER	50	1,800	2,250	250	147	1,073	9,000	3,150	168	1,459	1,845	922	13,410	6,854	21,321	11,764	34,731	18,618
	90	3,200	2,250	623	151	2,005	9,000	5,670	170	2,692	1,901	1,712	13,472	12,702	21,420	21,429	34,892	34,131
PARTITION SLOTTER	50	1,000	1,250	139	20	147	1,500	525	78	673	1,025	512	3,873	1,996	6,158	3,425	10,031	5,421
	90	1,700	1,250	348	19	256	1,500	945	76	1,187	1,010	910	3,855	3,646	6,129	6,161	9,984	9,807
SLITTER	50	1,800	1,250	139	30	221	1,000	350	195	1,710	1,845	922	4,320	3,342	6,868	5,735	11,188	9,077
	90	3,000	1,250	348	29	377	1,000	630	188	2,954	1,782	1,605	4,249	5,914	6,740	9,994	10,989	15,908
SEMI–AUTO. TAPER	50	3,700	3,000	334	61	450	4,500	1,575	210	1,819	3,799	1,904	11,570	6,082	18,380	10,437	29,950	16,519
	90	5,900	3,000	834	57	740	4,500	2,835	193	3,000	3,505	3,149	11,255	10,558	17,895	17,843	29,150	28,401
MANUAL STITCHER	50	1,200	375	41	20	147	500	175	43	373	1,230	614	2,168	1,350	3,447	2,317	5,615	3,667
	90	2,000	375	104	20	251	500	315	41	644	1,188	1,070	2,124	2,384	3,377	4,028	5,501	6,412
PLATEN DIE CUTTER	50	1,700	500	56	17	125	3,000	1,050	120	1,056	1,743	870	5,380	3,157	8,554	5,417	13,934	8,574
	90	3,200	500	139	18	241	3,000	1,890	133	2,050	1,901	1,712	5,552	6,032	8,827	10,194	14,379	16,226
BAND SAW	50	500	375	41	5	37	500	175	36	310	513	256	1,429	819	2,272	1,405	3,701	2,224
	90	1,200	375	104	6	90	500	315	49	773	713	642	1,643	1,924	2,612	3,251	4,255	5,175
TOTALS	50%	11,700	$9,000	$1,000	$300	$2,200	$20,000	$7,000	$850	$7,400	$12,000	$6,000	$42,150	$23,600	$67,000	$40,500	$109,150	$64,100
	90%	20,200	$9,000	$2,500	$300	$3,960	$20,000	$12,600	$850	$13,300	$12,000	$10,800	$42,150	$43,160	$67,000	$72,900	$109,150	$116,060

Exhibit 14-2. Fixed-Variable, Multi-Level Expense Assignment Worksheet

MHR SUMMARY SHEET

| PRODUCTION CENTER | % ACTIVITY LEVEL | ASSIGNED ANNUAL HOURS | HOURLY COSTS | | | COMPOSITE MHR | | TOTAL MHR |
| | | | TOTAL OVERHEAD | | DIRECT LABOR | | | |
			FIXED	VARIABLE		FIXED	VARIABLE	
Printer-Slotter	50 90	1800 3200	$19.30 10.91	$10.33 10.65	$4.70 4.70	$19.30 10.91	$15.03 15.35	$34.33 26.26
Partition Slotter	50 90	1000 1700	10.03 5.87	5.42 5.76	3.90 3.90	10.03 5.87	9.32 9.66	19.35 15.53
Slitter	50 90	1800 3000	6.20 3.66	5.04 5.30	5.50 5.50	6.20 3.66	10.54 10.80	16.74 14.46
Semi-Auto. Taper	50 90	3700 5900	8.09 4.94	4.48 4.81	2.85 2.85	8.09 4.94	7.33 7.66	15.42 12.60
Manual Stitcher	50 90	1200 2000	4.59 2.75	1.83 3.20	1.80 1.80	4.59 2.75	3.63 5.00	8.22 7.75
Platen Die Cutter	50 90	1700 3200	8.20 4.49	5.14 5.07	3.60 3.60	8.20 4.49	8.74 8.67	16.94 13.16
Band Saw	50 90	500 1200	7.40 3.55	4.45 4.31	3.60 3.60	7.40 3.55	8.05 7.91	15.45 11.46

Exhibit 14–3. Fixed-Variable, Multi-Level MHR Summary Sheet

and revenue. However, before it makes any decision with respect to pricing, management must know its cost "floor" or price floor.

From this pricing floor, management knows how much the order contributes to recovery of its fixed charges and, thus, can judge its selling price in the light of the activity of its facilities, the desirability of the customer, and the effect of the order on peaks, valleys, bottlenecks and displacements of more profitable business. Without this analysis, management can only judge the fixed-cost content of specific orders and could be misled when materials costs or other variable costs comprise unusually large or small segments of the sales dollar.

EXHIBIT 14–6 shows how a product is estimated according to fixed and variable

OPERATION	Hours Expected to run	MHR	Conversion Cost
Print	10	$22	$220
Cut & Crease	8	16	128
Glue	6	16	96
		TOTAL CONVERSION COST	$444
		TOTAL MATERIALS COST	240
		Total Order Cost	$684

Exhibit 14–4. Three-Operation Full Conversion Cost Estimate

OPERATION	Hours Expected to Run	Machine-Hour Rates Fixed	Machine-Hour Rates Variable	Conversion Cost Fixed	Conversion Cost Variable
Print	10	$14	$8	$140	$80
Cut & Crease	8	10	6	80	48
Glue	6	10	6	60	36
				$280	$164
		TOTAL MATERIALS COST		////	240
		Total Fixed Cost		$280	////
		Total Variable Cost		////	$404
		TOTAL ORDER COST =		$280 +	$404 = $684

Exhibit 14–5. Three-Operation Fixed-Variable Conversion Cost Estimate

conversion costs provided by the MHR so segregated. The bottom of the form shows the analysis of costs after the order has been run and sold. The first important question requiring analysis (and pre-analysis before the quotation is given) is whether at least the out-of-pocket or direct costs will be recovered. They equal the sum of $362 and $216. According to the estimate, when management decides to sell the order at $842, a balance of $264 as a contribution to fixed expenses is left. As it turned out, the actual conversion cost was $569 instead of $544—which adds $25 to the amount of fixed expense recovery required.

The revenue of $842 paid for the actual materials cost of $362 and left $480 to pay for conversion costs. In effect, $569 worth of conversion cost was "sold" at $480, leaving $89 as unrecovered fixed expenses. That is, the $480 easily took care of the $244 actually spent on variable costs and left over $236 for the fixed expenses. Since the fixed expense required (on the basis of "full" costs) is $569 less $244, or $325, the remaining $89 was unrecovered.

To the casual observer, this situation might appear to be untenable. But such may not be the case, as was pointed out in the marginal pricing example earlier in this chapter. The $89 may be considered an order loss, but may not be a company-wide loss until it is known what the state of fixed-expense recovery is to date in the activity period and what the future recovery is likely to be. For example, if at the time this order is processed, the company recovered all of its fixed expenses in pricing, then this order will carry a profit of $256. And, at the other extreme, if this is the first order of the activity period, then the loss on this order will be $89, plus the entire fixed-expense load for the activity period.

The pricing of this order, as we have said previously, should be based on good judgment formed from analyzing the variables of the company's economy and the market. However, before intelligent judgment can be applied, it is first vital to see in total costs, their fixed and variable elements.

A Philosophy of Pricing

Competition, market shifts, product changes and the individual company's needs for revenue are always present and volatile, especially in multi-product companies. It is vital that management know intimately the ingredients of the company's costs and characteristics, in order to be able to price products most advantageously, regardless of this turbulence, to improve cost recovery, to evaluate proposals to change selling prices, to segment the market to gain advantage of different layers of customer demand, to select most profitable business when capacity is limited, and to determine the price at which to refuse an order.

Costs do not control prices; they may affect them. The one exception is service contracts and cost-plus manufacturing. Prices in manufacturing are based principally on customer demand and competition. Because a company has developed a full product cost with the best cost system in the universe does not mean it will

Production Center	Estim. Order Time	Composite M.H.R.	Composite Estimated Conversion Cost	M. H. R.		Conversion Cost		Actual Conversion		Variable Recovery
				Fixed	Variable	Fixed	Variable	Hours	Cost	
100	9	$17	$153	$9	$8	$81	$72	8	$126	$64
300	7	9	63	5	4	35	28	7	63	28
500	10	28	280	19	9	190	90	12	336	108
600	2	12	24	5	7	10	14	2	24	14
900	6	4	24	2	2	12	12	5	20	10

Total Est. Conversion Cost		$544			$328	$216
Estimated Materials Cost		362			XXX	362
Total Estimated Cost		$906				
Total FIXED costs					$328	XXX
Total VARIABLE costs					XXX	$578

SUMMARY JOB COST ANALYSIS

Actual Conversion Cost		$569
Product sold at	$842	
Less: Actual Matls. Cost	362	
Conversion Cost sold at		480
Loss on order, based on fully-allocated costs		89

Variable Recovery of Conversion Costs	$224
Fixed Expense Contribution	256
Unrecovered Fixed Expenses	89
Actual Conversion Cost	$569

Exhibit 14–6. Fixed-Variable Order Estimate and Job Cost Analysis

sell its products, because, in fact, its costs may be far above competitors' selling prices. Of course, if the company makes a unique product not available elsewhere, it has an excellent chance of developing a pricing policy based on its costs. The primary task of the cost administrator is to have the cost tools to warn management when the profit picture is poor. This does not mean summarily raising prices, for the competition factor still exists. It does mean that management can be led to emphasize the volume and the economic aspects of the operation; that is, to direct effort toward improving profits at the total sales end rather than on an individual order or product.

Customers do not care what a company's costs are. This makes the normal market a buyers' market. Customers will determine prices, because if prices do not suit them, they will not buy the products. Thus, only after a saleable price is reached does the question of cost arise. This leaves the big question: Can the product be made and sold at a cost which will leave a profit in the *total* sales picture? The perfect example is the five-cent candy bar, which has remained at five cents because of fixed consumer habit. The solution for candy manufacturers in *making the cost fit the price* was to reduce the size and weight of the candy bar.

Good cost information, as developed by the facility-costing (MHR) concept, plays an important part in pricing. It tells whether the product can be made and sold profitably at any price. But it does not indicate the amount of mark-up (or mark-down) on cost that will be accepted by the buyers in the market.

Elasticity of Demand

A product that will have a higher volume when prices are reduced and will have a lower volume when prices are increased is said to have *elasticity of demand*. Table salt, for example, is inelastic. That is, price changes will have little effect on its sales volume. Elasticity of demand and the fixed-variable cost ratio determine whether products lower priced with a higher volume will produce more profits than products higher priced with lower volume. In every company there is an optimum point where maximum profits will accrue, and this is not necessarily at prices that "the market will bear." To determine this optimum point, the company must have sound and accurate cost information, overhead fairly apportioned to products, and product costs separated into their fixed and variable elements. However, the benefit resulting from higher volume at lower unit profit margins (costs fully allocated) is greater where the company's fixed costs are a relatively large proportion of total costs. Proper cost information in these companies also determines whether, in a weak market, the manufacturer loses less by accepting marginal business than he would lose by shutting down.

Management's Guide to Pricing

Sound marginal-pricing decisions depend on keeping track of the cumulative state of fixed-expense recovery at any time, as well as on the actual level of out-of-pocket expenses committed on previously booked orders. Exhibit 14–7 shows how to provide management with this essential information.

Actually, this form is a continuous log of orders booked, showing these individual and cumulative recoveries: over the out-of-pocket level, which is a contribution to fixed expenses and profits; and, over the "full" cost level which is a contribution to profits. Since this is a log of *committed* selling prices (orders booked but not necessarily run or completed), and *estimated* expenses, contributions to either/or fixed expenses and profits are estimates.

At best the contribution figures will provide management with an estimate of the

MONTH OF: <u>August</u>

ESTIMATED

Order No.	Booked S.P. of order	O.O.P. Costs	Full Costs	Recovery over O.O.P.	Recovery over Full	Cum. Recovery over O.O.P.	Cum. Recovery over Full
6706	$ 9120	$6170	$ 7071	$2950	$2049	$ 2950	$ 2049
6707	5150	3080	3540	2070	3080	5020	5129
6708	4970	4230	5080	740	(110)	5760	5019
6709	10510	5860	6845	4650	3665	10410	8684
6748	8740	8020	9115	720	(375)	79818	41372
6749	11360	7115	11420	4245	(60)	84063	41312
6750	7390	6112	6214	1278	1176	85341	42488

Total Sales Booked in month = $404,873

Estimated Cumulative Recovery over Full = $\dfrac{42,488}{362,385}$ = 10.49%

Total Estimated Full Costs =

Estimated Cash Flow = $85,341

Less 42,488

Estimated Contribution to Fixed Expenses = 42,853

Period Variances:
a) Materials usages = $(927)
b) Performances = (2171)
c) Activity (volume) = 2003
   NET VARIANCE = $(1095)

NET PROFIT TREND: = $42,488 + $(1095) = $41,393 = 10.22%

Exhibit 14–7. Table Showing Net Profit Trend Based on Committed Selling Prices and Estimated Expenses.

effect of their marginal pricing to date. With this information at hand, management is in a much firmer position to make future pricing decisions based on what fixed expenses have been recovered to date, the balance to be recovered, and the time-position of their budget-activity period.

With proper cost control, this form is useful in presenting valid profit-trend data well in advance of the profit-and-loss statement. When variance information is available (as discussed in Chapter 17) the period's overrecovery, shown on EXHIBIT 14–7, can be adjusted using actual materials usages, performance and activity variations, to produce realistic profit information. That is, the overrecovery shown becomes a real profit only if the materials, labor and overhead expenses estimated are equal to actual. Still, the profit thus produced may not correspond to that shown by the auditors on period profit-and-loss statements. This is because of time overlaps and inventory adjustments. But for day-to-day managerial control and pricing guidance, this form is most effective.

The information shown on EXHIBIT 14–7 is condensed but shows the estimated data on 51 orders booked in the month of August. As we have said throughout the book, profits on individual orders are not realistic because no one knows if they will ever produce an actual profit. Obviously, this is a function of what has happened in the past and what will occur in the future. What is significant are period profits or a continuing trend towards profits.

For example, order #6708 was booked below full costs but during a rising state of recovery over full costs. Before management is in a position to know whether they can afford this type of marginal pricing, some data on what has happened in the previous periods must be available. This is especially true when one looks at order #6748, which is also sold below full costs, but again decided within the framework of a rising, and perhaps satisfactory, overrecovery picture.

A number of interesting comparisons come to light when information is presented in this way. While both orders #6708 and #6748 are marginally priced, the first order makes a contribution to fixed expense recovery of $850 on the booked sale of $4,970, while the second order contributes $720 on the sale of $8,740. Obviously, the second order has little conversion-cost content and in addition, involves the company in a high level of inventory and other out-of-pocket costs. This is where a company can employ selective selling in guiding their economic structures to safe and healthy waters.

There still may be valid reasons for accepting order #6748. Perhaps at this period the company is operating above their break-even point. In that case, profits are the difference between the out-of-pocket costs and their booked sales price. Or, maybe the company wishes to accommodate an important customer, or penetrate a new market, etc. Regardless of the particular reason, this log tells management how safe they are in making this sales commitment.

Speaking of selective selling, compare this order #6748 with order #6709 which makes a large contribution to fixed expenses while involving the company in a relatively low level of out-of-pocket costs.

Order #6749 seems also to be a worthwhile booking in spite of the fact that it is somewhat marginally priced. The question is one of degree. Compare the contribution to fixed expenses of $4,245 on the booking of $11,360 with order #6708. If volume variances prove to be favorable at the end of the period, it is perfectly possible for order #6749 to result in a profit.

The estimated results from the August bookings show a healthy estimated cash flow and a reasonable overrecovery above full costs. Going back at the end of August, to modify the overrecovery with the aforementioned variances, shows the net profit trend to be a trifle below the recover over full costs.

EXHIBIT 14–7a shows these same data for a three-month period. The comparison of the fixed recovery at the end of three months with their operating budget gives management some idea of the speed at which they will reach and pass their breakeven points, and future pricing decisions can safely be based on whatever estimated recoveries have been made to date.

Pricing Strategy

The price decision-maker must be a strategist using, of course, the best objective cost information available to him. If he makes a new or unusual product, then, as we said before, the chances are that his pricing will be allowed to follow his costs. But to what extent? If he prices high in order to recover his costs quickly, he may generate new competitors because of the high profit margin. If he prices on the low side to discourage new competitors, he will recover his costs over a longer period of time.

Month	Total Sales Booked	Cum. Recov. over O.O.P.	Cum. Recov. over Full	Net Profit Trend	Net Profit Trend; % of Booked Sales
August	$ 404,873	$ 85,341	$ 42,488	$ 41,393	10.22%
September	418,112	94,814	43,872	44,002	10.52%
October	416,327	85,617	40,714	43,511	10.69%
Cumulative Sales Booked	$1,239,312				
Cumulative Cash Flow		$265,772			
Cumulative Net Profit Trend				$128,906	
Cumulative Net Profit Trend %					10.4%

Exhibit 14–7a. Comparison of Fixed Recovery with Operating Budget
at End of Three Months

If the demand for a product is elastic, sales activity can be increased only by increasing output. Conversely, profits can be increased by reducing output only if the reduction in sales is exceeded by the reduction in cost. Total profits can be increased by expanding volume only if the expansion adds more to sales than to cost. In multi-product manufacturing, probably the greatest influence on profits is the selection of the appropriate product mix. Because of the existence of the product mix and its volatility, there is really no such thing as constant variable unit costs. Products vary in material and labor content; equipment and workers vary in skill and costs; selling and distribution costs vary depending on the class of product, class of customer, market territory, and so forth. Certain equipment, for example, may come into use to increase capacity and may force up unit variable costs as output is increased, and the material content may also rise coincidentally. Overtime and shift premiums are sometimes necessary to achieve higher output; inexperienced workers may be added to the labor force. In some plants, the increase in output of one product may be accomplished by using equipment intended for other products, and without variable overhead expenses increasing directly at the same rate as volume. All these factors go to increase or decrease unit variable costs at these higher production levels.

Therefore, one has to amend the statement that higher volume increases the difference between variable costs and sales for a maximization of profits. The difference—this profit maximum—is determined by optimizing the volume with the product mix. Increasing volume of an uneconomical product mix may *lower* the difference between selling prices and actual variable costs. The MHR indicates accurately the contributions of product activity at the most expensive pulse of converter-manufacturing where the high fixed costs of converting facilities exist. Thus an optimum selection of product mix becomes possible.

Pricing and Costing Methods

It must occur to the reader thus far, that the principles of pricing discussed in this chapter are basically applicable to any costing method. This statement is true as far as it goes, but it does not go quite far enough. For if traditional overhead allocations are used, then the resulting fixed and variable elements of cost may be in fact just paper-developed. Developing a pricing method, however sensible, will be lost motion if the method is based only upon traditional data.

Pricing revolves around the separation of the fixed and variable costs, a recognition of varying product mix and its impact on overhead allocations, and the volume effect on variable and fixed costs. This information is not reliably produced by traditional cost systems, which make these delineations on an average or convenient basis. The MHR system allows management to price most advantageously in its market, provided a sound pricing policy accompanies it. Imposing a sensibly developed concept for pricing on top of an illogical cost system is like having a Rembrandt paint a portrait on tissue paper. The skills, talents and judgments of the artist will be faithfully applied, but because of the basis selected for communicating this talent to others, the resultant product will fall apart under the slightest pressure.

Chapter 15

USING MHR TO
COORDINATE
SALES AND PRODUCTION

The cost of a product is not necessarily some exact, specific sum. Its amount depends on concurrent manufacture of other products and on the activity of the facilities involved in their production. Cost determination is based on many variables, not the least of which is allocation of overhead to the product. Usually, when an executive inquires about the cost of a specific product, he is given a full allocated figure developed by the orthodox accounting approach. While this figure is useful for many internal managerial decisions and for control, it tends to be inadequate for sales purposes, for the reasons explained in the previous section. For to base prices completely on fully allocated costs is to deny the existence of customer need, competition, and elasticity of demand.

Sales activity is the link between production and the manufacturer's markets. To function most effectively, the selling effort must be keyed to the market needs and the economic requirements of production. Sound cost information, properly used, will enable management judiciously to decide upon such basic sales questions as whether to add to capacity in order to produce an existing product, whether to close down a plant or division, whether to drop a product, and the types of products to add to a line.

Separate Functions

Just as in some companies, methods improvement programs are developed without attention to the cost-estimating function, so we have companies whose production and sales divisions go in separate and autonomous directions. For maximum profits, production and sales must support each other and not work at cross pur-

184

poses. Thus, while high sales productivity in a specific product is a thing of joy to the sales manager, it does little for the company (and may do the company harm) if the product is uneconomical to produce, or if its sale causes an uneconomical duplication of facilities, or taxes the capital structure to the extent of the inventory that must be stocked to support its production. And while the plant manager may be pleased with the highspeed production of an item, the production could be meaningless if the item does not sell well or if it costs excessively to promote the item in the open market. Obviously, emphasizing either producing or selling as a thing apart can have negative effect on the over-all economy of the company.

Costs and Profits

Costs are inextricably interwoven with sales and production. In most multi-product manufacturing, each dollar of sales does not yield the same profit, but different products bring in different profits. This occurs for many reasons: sometimes the price pattern built up over the years has the characteristic of low total cost in relationship to selling prices, a condition which it may be impractical to disturb; some products may use expensive facilities at a low capacity; some products may move quickly, leaving little profit but involving considerable inventory-support capital; some identical products may have sizeable differences in distribution costs based on the class of customers, territories, and so forth.

Many executives use the product's profitability as the criterion for assigning sales effort. If a product shows a high profit margin (as revealed by a cost sheet), then they gang up sales efforts in the attempt to boost company profits. Sometimes they wind up with a loss instead. Even if the estimated profit of a product has been the result of a considered pricing policy, such as was described in the previous chapter, pushing sales might still result in an uneconomical duplication of expensive facilities. Emphasis on one product line might mean owning underactive duplicated facilities, which could cost the company more in unrecovered fixed expenses than the gains of keeping its original facility at full capacity. And, if the profit has been developed from the difference between traditionally developed costs and selling prices, the management might even wind up with facilities duplicated to support a loss-producing product.

Product-Volume Mix

The activity of a given product in the total sales picture of a company is called the product-mix, as has been described earlier. Companies that control this mix by controlling the individual efforts of sales and production are the ones that create the greatest profit potential. With information on product-mix costs, management is able to direct, appraise and reward properly the efforts of its salesmen. Thus production and sales work toward the same goal.

Product mix has its effect both on production and sales economy; that is, selection of the optimum product mix with proper implementation by the sales department can produce the greatest profit. In most multi-product manufacturing, not all products contain the same elements of direct labor costs, factory expenses, materials costs, administrative expenses, and profit. Some products require more direct labor than others. Some involve more machinery than others. These variances play an important part in determining the economy of the plant and the direction which sales must take.

There can be, in two identical periods with total sales the same, different product mixes. One mix may recover fixed expenses more than the other. One may involve principally handwork, the other mostly machine work; yet the direct labor percentage of the sales dollar may be the same in both. In the same manner, each period can yield a different profit, depending on the *nature* of the product mix. This means that not all products do yield or are expected to yield the same unit profit.

Sales management must integrate sales activity and the type of mix yielding the highest profit. This mix should be consistent with the expense recovery needs of the factory, and with its need to develop new customer markets, products and territories.

The managerial direction of sales contacts must not neglect the relationship between the product and the Centers used in its manufacture. Normally, salesmen tend to think in terms of product sales rather than machinery capacity sales, and that is as it should be. Therefore, this chapter contains illustrations of how conversion is made from products to Production Centers. Only after this conversion is made can we see to what extent the selling effort is effective in recovering Production Center expenses.

Just as each dollar of sales may not bring in the same amount of profit, so it may not produce the same amount of expense recovery. Direction of sales therefore must consider the gross volume of sales, the expenses for obtaining this volume, and the product mix or blend of the gross sales.

Sales Integrated with Production

The first crossover point between sales and production is the product. The sales department regards the product as a whole entity, but the factory does not. To the production department, the product is a combination of individual parts, processes, and operations. As a matter of fact, it is in this crossover area that the sales forecast and the production activity budget begin to clash. After preparation of the yearly sales forecast, the Production Center activity has to be projected. But before that step can be taken, the products have to be divided into the Production Centers that are involved in their manufacture. In addition, the Centers have to be evaluated for the activity the products will impose on them. In other words, product sales dollars have to be converted into Production Center activity hours.

Production Center Costs

EXHIBIT 15–1 shows the annual overhead cost of each of the five production centers A to E, the number of hours during the year each Center is expected to operate, and the hourly overhead cost of each facility. The annual overhead cost of each center includes every expense in the operation, maintenance and ownership of the business, except that of materials and direct labor. These costs are not included because they are variable, that is, they vary directly with volume, and would only distort the examples given.

The hourly overhead costs shown are developed from the machine-hour rate structure detailed in Section 2, and they represent the overhead segment of the composite rate. The projected hours are taken from the CFCS or the EAW and ideally represent the conversion of expected product sales (taken from a sales forecast) into Production Center activity.

Products Converted to Operational Hours

EXHIBIT 15–2 shows the breakdown of each product into the Production Centers that are involved in their manufacture. The sales of each product are represented by the number of hours each Production Center must operate to produce that sales level. In other words, when $20,700 of product *ab* is sold, it keeps Production Centers A, B, C, and D active 240, 20, 150, and 30 hours, respectively.

The exhibit shows condition A, the state of affairs at the end of the first quarter,

PRODUCTION CENTER	ANNUAL COST TO MAKE CENTER AVAILABLE (ALL EXCEPT DIRECT LABOR)	PROJ. ANNUAL HOURS	HOURLY O H COST
A	$ 8,000	2000	$4.00
B	16,000	1600	10.00
C	30,000	1000	30.00
D	64,000	1600	40.00
E	72,000	1800	40.00
TOTAL	$190,000		

Exhibit 15–1. Production Center Costs

a three-month period when there was a lack of integration between sales and production. Also shown on this tabulation are the actual hours for each Production Center as a result of the listed product sales; the actual recovery for each center, that is, the extension of the actual hours times the hourly cost figure of EXHIBIT 15–1; and the projected hours for the quarter.

Because of the seasonal fluctuations present in many businesses, a three-month period in a company's activity is not necessarily one-fourth of the yearly activity. This will be discussed in detail in the testing of the MHR in Section 4. However, for the purposes of our illustration, we consider that this quarter's activity *is* one-fourth of the annual projection and that this rate of activity will obtain on a yearly basis.

Note that Center A is overrecovering in a way that will require a duplication of facilities. (We assume 2,000 hours per year, without considering the multishift aspect, on the premise that facilities duplication can take place even with three

| Product | Quarterly Sales | Activity of Production Center in hours | | | | |
		A	B	C	D	E
Projected Hours		500	400	250	400	450
Hourly Cost		$ 4	$10	$30	$40	$40
Actual Hours		600	200	400	225	675
ab	$20,700	240	20	150	30	-
ac	9,792	-	-	75	30	75
bc	37,900	160	-	25	-	250
cd	10,500	-	50	75	45	50
WW	27,050	100	10	65	-	250
YY	14,000	80	60	-	80	50
ZZ	3,330	20	60	10	40	-
TOTAL	$ 123,222	600	200	400	225	675
Quarterly Actual Recovery		$2,400	$2,000	$12,000	$9,000	$27,000
Yearly Actual Recovery		9,600	8,000	48,000	36,000	108,000
Needed Actual Recovery		8,000	16,000	30,000	64,000	72,000
Quarterly Actual Recovery		2,000	4,000	7,500	16,000	18,000
Maximum Tolerable Recovery (before Duplication) Quarterly		2,000	5,000	15,000	20,000	20,000

Exhibit 15–2. **Conversion of Product Sales to Production-Center Activity (Condition A)**

eight-hour shifts. This duplication would be obtained if Center *A* is projected at 1,500 hours for the quarter and has an actual activity of 1,800 hours.)

However, if Center *A* is duplicated, it is not serious, since the annual cost is low ($8,000) compared with that of the other Centers. Production Center *B* is active 50 percent of its expected activity. This underrecovery is not very costly to the company since its hourly cost is fairly low ($10 per hour) compared with that of Centers *C*, *D*, and *E*.

Note another fact: Center *B* is projected at 400 hours. This center has the capability of 500 hours per linear quarter before the duplication of facilities sets in. Therefore this center should be a target for sales action because of the underrecovery and the *opportunity* for increased profit. If the sales function can integrate itself with the needs of production by selling 500 hours at the $10-per-hour figure, then the *overrecovery will be a direct contribution to profits.* If, because of the higher activity, the sales department wishes to price marginally in the hope of attracting more business, then it can reduce that rate to $16,000/2,000, or $8 per hour (see EXHIBIT 15–1), without affecting the profit margin.

Production Center *C* appears to be a profitable center. It is projected at 250 hours and is operating 400 hours per quarter. This represents an overrecovery of 150 hours, or a 60 percent excess recovery. If the activity of the Center was originally projected at too low a rate, the overrecovery will result in higher selling prices and probable sales resistance. However, if the Center is budgeted to achieve a specific rate which the company considers to be competitive, and the sales department obtains more than enough activity to keep it busy on that basis, then the overrecovery adds to profits.

The latter appears to be the case in this example. To make this point a little clearer, let us say that, if the $30 MHR is close to competitive pricing, it would not make sense for the company to create a new hourly cost just because 1,600 hours (instead of 1,000 hours) divided into $30,000 equals $18.75 (instead of $30). Here again, considering an elastic demand, the reduction of a selling price can cause an increase in sales and total profit. In addition, Center *C* still has a target for additional recovery from the 400-hour level up to its maximum capacity at 500 hours, a potential increase which amounts to an additional 25 percent of activity.

Let's stop a minute and compare the circumstances at Centers *B* and *C*. Both provide the additional sales target of increasing activity from 400 to 500 hours, but for different reasons. The difference lies in the accidental nature of the activity, the fact that the activity was not planned to support the needs of expense recovery in production. On the one hand, for Center *B*, the 400 hours is the activity projected, the actual activity being 200. For Center *C*, the 400 hours is an activity attainment exceeding the projection of 250 hours.

The situation in Center *D* is serious. It is like the situation experienced at *B*, but with worse consequences, since annual costs are four times greater than at *B*. The underrecovery here is expensive. Here again, sales integration is needed, first, to recover the unavoidable expenses incurred in making this facility available and, second, to attempt to keep the center operating in the most profitable area, the one providing opportunity for marginal pricing, namely, the area between the 400- and 500-hour slot.

The situation at Center *E* is also serious and dangerous to the economy of the company. It is similar to the condition in Center *A* in that it is one of overrecovery beyond maximum capacity that will require a duplication of facilities, but here the cost will be nine times greater than for Center *A*. Whereas duplicating Center *A* costs only an extra $8,000 per year, duplicating Center *E* costs $72,000 per year.

(In order not to cloud the issue by sophisticated calculations, a duplication of a facility is added at the same rate as that of maintaining the first facility per year. In actual practice, the cost of the duplicated facility will be somewhat lower than the original because of the reallocation of fixed expenses to a greater number of facilities.)

There is no doubt that the company analyzed in Exhibit 15–2 is headed for trouble. That sales are not supporting the needs of production is obvious. However, more must be known about the product before the proper steps can be taken.

Product Cost Breakdown

The first step necessary to obtain additional information is the examination of the cost sheet of each product. This is done in Exhibit 15–3. Here, in condensed form, are shown all the elements of cost: total overhead cost, direct labor cost, plus the materials cost. To simplify matters, all the products carry a profit margin of 10 percent of selling price. The total overhead cost is, of course, the sum of all the conversion costs for each of the Production centers involved in each product. Thus, for product *ab:*

Production Center Used	No. of Hours in Use	Hourly Cost	Cost
A	240	$ 4	$ 960
B	20	10	200
C	150	30	4,500
D	30	40	1,200
Total Overhead Cost			$6,860

When a dollar's worth of a product is sold, this sale can affect the company in several ways, as not all sales dollars produce the same amount of economy. (They all do not produce the same amount of profit either, but that is another matter.) In some products there are more cents devoted to material costs, as in product *bc.* In others, there are more cents devoted to paying the fixed expenses of the company, as in product ZZ. Needless to state, there are infinite variations on this theme.

The volume of sales of product *bc,* while the largest of all the products sold, actually harms the company by being so high. First of all, this product plays give-and-take with its raw-material supplier. It has to commit its financial structure to a large inventory in order to meet its material-content needs; it takes risks in holding this inventory for any length of time because of raw-material market fluctuations; it is the cause of the duplication of the $72,000-per-year production facility of Center *E;* and it probably is helping toward the duplication of Center *A.* Center *C* surely does not need the increased activity; so, on economic grounds alone, why continue to sell product *bc?*

Of course, few companies can discontinue overnight a product that customers demand. But should there not be an attempt to reduce drives on this product in favor of others that will have a more positive effect on the over-all economy?

Obviously, product ZZ recovers more fixed expenses in the sales dollar than any of the rest; thus, increasing the sales drive for product ZZ would aid the recovery of Production Center *B,* and especially of Center *D,* which so desperately needs help and yet should not drive Center *C* to uneconomical activity.

Sales Targets

The reader should now glance at EXHIBIT 15–4, which shows the profitability potential of each of the five Production Centers and the degree in which the major

Cost	PRODUCT						
	ab	ac	bc	cd	WW	YY	ZZ
Overhead	$ 6,860	$ 6,450	$ 11,390	$ 6,550	$ 2,450	$ 6,126	$ 2,580
Direct Labor	750	360	790	415	795	470	220
Conversion Cost	7,610	6,810	12,180	6,965	13,245	6,590	2,800
Material Cost	11,000	2,000	22,000	2,500	11,000	6,000	200
Total Cost	18,610	8,810	34,180	9,465	24,245	12,590	3,000

Total Cost All Items = $110,900 × 4 = $443,600 (Total Cost of Product Mix)

N.P. 10 percent = 49,288

S.P. $492,888

Exhibit 15–3. Condensed Cost Sheet (Condition A)

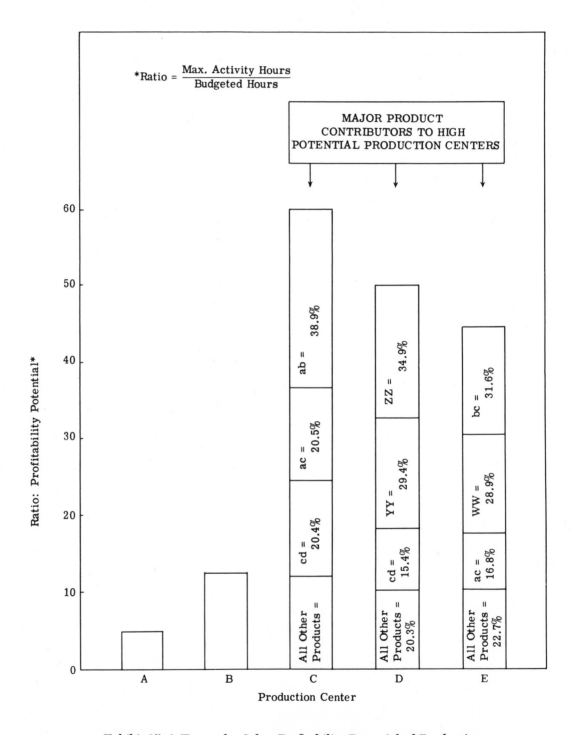

Exhibit 15–4. Target for Sales: Profitability Potential of Production
Centers

PRODUCT	PRODUCTION CENTER										Sales Dollar
	A		B		C		D		E		
	%	$	%	$	%	$	%	$	%	$	
ab	45.1		6.5		38.9		9.8		-		$
		.141		.029		.655		.175		-	1.00
ac	-		-		20.5		10.4		16.8		
		-		-		.349		.186		.465	1.00
bc	17.9		-		3.9		-		31.6		
		.056		-		.066		-		.878	1.00
cd	-		17.2		20.4		15.4	-	11		
		-		.076		.344		.275		.305	1.00
WW	10.3		1.8		9.4		-		28.9		
		.032		.008		.157		-		.803	1.00
YY	16.7		22.1		-		29.4		11.8		
		.052		.098		-		.523		.327	1.00
ZZ	10		52.5		6.9		34.9		-		
		.031		.232		.116		.621		-	1.00
Production Center Usage	100		100		100		100		100		

Exhibit 15–5. Recovery Characteristics of Products and Production Centers

products contribute to each. The background data are shown on Exhibit 15–5. The curve shows that Center *C* offers the greatest potential for contributing profits. This potentiality is a function of the yearly projection and of the cost of the Center.

The profitability potential ratio (Exhibit 15–4) is obtained by dividing the current budgeted hours into the maximum activity hours available, before duplication of the facility is required. This is done on a quarterly basis. Even though Center *C* is not the most expensive Center, it has the capacity for operating twice as much as it does presently, and this places it in the forefront with an index of 60.

The major contributors to Center *C* are shown below the mark of the curve. Of the six products that use Center *C*'s services, product *ab* will use it 38.9 percent, product *ac* 20.5 percent, and product *cd* 20.4 percent, the other three products to use up the balance of 20.2 percent. Center *D*, which has the next highest profitability potential—and, again, this means profit as a result of activity exceeding budget—uses product *ZZ* 34.9 percent, product *YY* 29.4 percent, and product *cd* 15.4 percent.

This curve presents a target for sales, but it is not remedial for the situation depicted in condition *A*. In other words, after sales activities have been adjusted to provide the needed expense recovery in production, sales effort can then be concentrated elsewhere to bring in extra profits. A word of caution on the data shown in EXHIBITS 15–4 and 15–5: because of the different content of the sales dollar for each of the seven products, it would be fallacious to peg these percentages directly to the sales dollar; they should more properly be pegged to the expense recovery represented in each product sales dollar.

EXHIBIT 15–6 shows the relationship among the three recovery figures: budgeted, actual, and maximum economic. The budgeted is the *needed* recovery, which the company must obtain in total before it can make a long-term profit.

Product Expense-Recovering Ability

EXHIBIT 15–7 shows a tabulation of the sales of the seven products for condition A and the amount of recovery each product brings. The total recovery data come

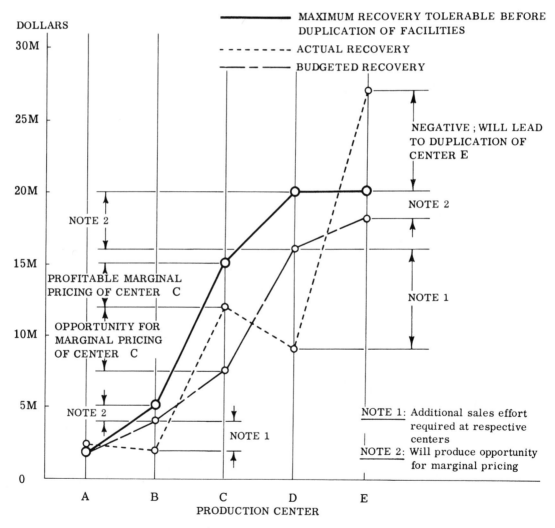

**Exhibit 15–6. Actual vs. Budgeted Recovery vs. Maximum Recovery
Before Duplication of Facilities**

Product	Sales	Percent	Total Recovery	Percent of Product Recovery / Total Recovery	Recovery Ability of Product Per Sales $	Percent of Recovery Per $7 Worth of Sales ($1 from each of 7)
ab	$20,700	16.8	$6,860	13.1	$ .331	9.2
ac	9,792	7.9	6,450	12.3	.658	18.4
bc	37,900	30.8	11,390	21.7	.300	8.4
cd	10,500	8.5	6,550	12.5	.624	17.3
WW	27,000	21.9	12,450	23.8	.461	12.8
YY	14,000	11.4	6,120	11.7	.437	12.3
ZZ	3,330	2.7	2,580	4.9	.775	21.6
Total	$123,222	100%	$52,400	100%	$3.586	100%

Exhibit 15–7. Product Recovery Ability (Condition A)

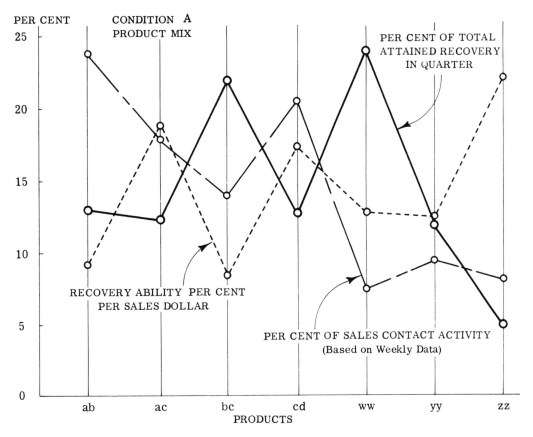

Exhibit 15–8. Recovery Ability of Products vs. Recovery Attained by
Sales (Sales Working at Cross Purposes with Production)

from the data in Exhibit 15–3. The next column is a ratio of the amount of recovery percentage of the total that each product contributes at the sales level shown. The next shows what portion of the sales dollar each product can contribute to expense recovery. The one labeled "percent" shows what percentage of the total recovery each product contributes.

It is clear that there is no coordination. Product ZZ, which can contribute $0.775 out of each of its sales dollars to "paying the freight," or 21.6 percent of the total of the seven products' capacity, is only contributing 4.9 percent. Product *bc*, which only has $0.30 of each of its sales dollars to give to the expense cause, or 8.4 percent of the total of the seven products' capacity, is being made to donate 21.7 percent—an uneconomically high level, as we have said before.

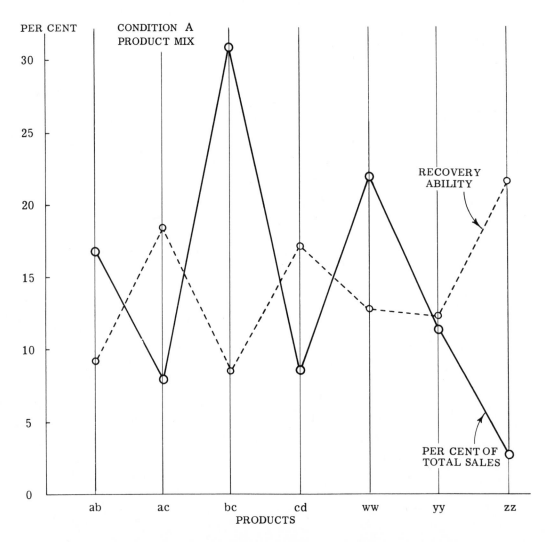

Exhibit 15–9. Recovery Ability of Products vs. Products' Sales (Sales
Not Supporting Needs of Production Recovery)

Needed versus Attained Recovery

EXHIBIT 15–8 shows the relationship between the recovery ability of each product and the level attained. It is different from EXHIBIT 15–6 in that the latter shows actual recovery against that needed by each Production Center, whereas EXHIBIT 15–8 shows the attained recovery against the potential or latent ability to recover offered by the seven products. This curve shows that the sales efforts, besides working at cross purposes to Production Center needs, are also working illogically with respect to positive *potential*.

EXHIBIT 15–9 shows the relationship between the recovery ability of each product (and total product recovery ability) and the percentage of total sales attained by each product. This is based on data from EXHIBIT 15–7. Even with the influence of direct labor and materials cost, there is little alignment between the

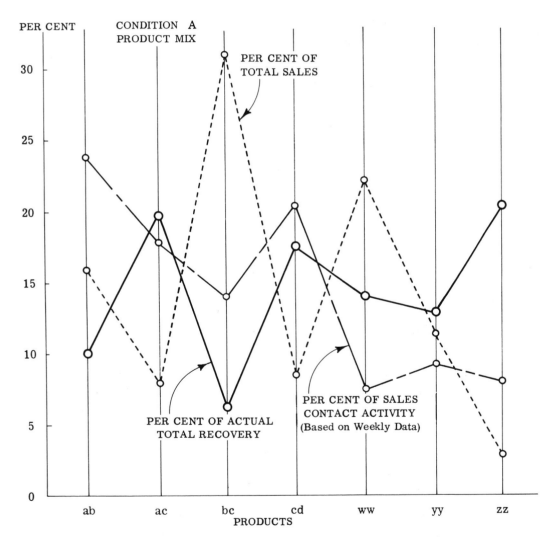

Exhibit 15–10. The Influence on Recovery of the Drive for
Commissions

Production Center	Ratio Value:				Activity Hours × Hourly OH Rate / Product Sales			
	ab	ac	bc	cd	WW	YY	ZZ	Total
A	$ .0491	$ -	$ .0169	$ -	$ .0148	$ .0228	$ .024	$ .1276
B	.0153	-	-	.0476	.0037	.0428	.21	.3194
C	.23	.23	.0198	.214	.072	-	.09	.8558
D	.0614	.123	-	.171	-	.228	.48	1.066
E	-	.307	.264	.191	.37	.143	-	1.275
Total Exp. Recovered Per Sales $	$ .3558	$ .66	$ .3007	$ .6236	$ .4605	$ .4366	$ .804	$ 3.6412
Less: Selling Expen/Sales $	.04	.07	.12	.091	.028	.046	.184	.579
Net Recovery	$ .3158	$ .59	$ .1807	$ .5326	$ .4325	$ .3906	$ .620	$ 3.0622
Recovery Percent of Total	10	19.4	5.9	17.5	14.1	12.8	20.3	100%
Percent of Sales	16	8	31	8.6	22.2	11.5	2.7	100%
Percent of Sales Contact (Based on Weekly Data)	23.7	17.7	13.8	20.4	7.3	9.2	7.9	100%

Exhibit 15–11. Expense Recovery per Dollar of Sales (Condition A)

sales effort and the ability of sold products to recover expenses. Of course, only with cost charged to the respective Centers, as in Exhibit 15–8, is the lack of alignment clearly shown.

The reader must keep in mind constantly throughout this section the difference between the *need* for recovery (as represented by total cost of the profit-and-loss statement) and the degree of *ability* for recovery that products have inherently. The *need* for recovery is expressed by Production Centers, since that is the manner in which overhead costs are apportioned, and not by products. The *ability* is a characteristic of a specific product. Besides keying sales effort to production's needs by insuring that sales fully recover expenses without uneconomical expansion, management should also consider the desirability of accomplishing this task without burdening the capital structure, space occupancy, and so forth.

Exhibit 15–10, based on the data of Exhibit 15–11, is somewhat similar to Exhibit 15–9. Another interpretation that can be made is that these curves show to some extent the drive for commissions, irrespective of needs in production. This can be an added factor in a proper sales compensation plan.

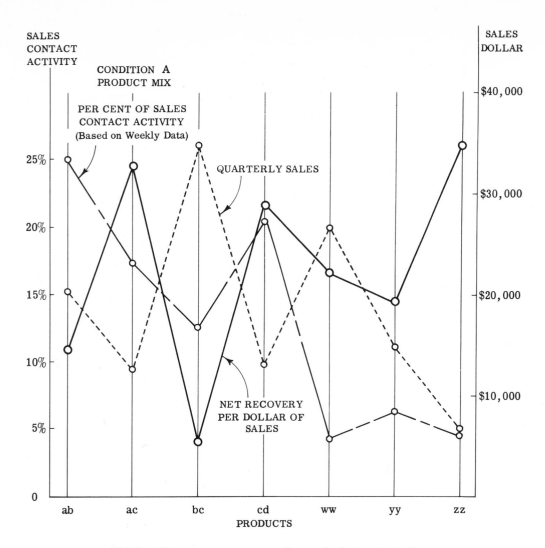

Exhibit 15–12. Recovery vs. Sales Booked vs. Sales Efforts

That the sales department working at cross purposes with production is demonstrated clearly in Exhibit 15–12, which shows sales contact effort, net recovery, and sales.

How to Integrate Sales with Production

The economical integration of sales and production rests upon the way the product mix is cast, plus consistency in the level of sales expenses required to generate that mix. There actually are an infinite number of product mixes in multiproduct manufacturing, as it is possible, within the same total sales volume boundary, to sell varying amounts of the seven products now under discussion. And each variation has a different state of expense recovery, serves the need of recovery differently, affects the potentiality of profits differently, and earns for each product different margins of profit or loss.

The Impact of Product Mix: As an example, let us consider three products, *a, b* and *c,* in a company having three Production Centers, I, II and III. The sales of products *a, b,* and *c* of ⅓, ⅓, and ⅓ may not fully recover at Center I, may generate an uneconomical overrecovery at Center II, and may recover evenly at Center III. But a proportion of 80:10:10 may overrecover uneconomically at Center I, evenly recover at Center II, and underrecover at Center III. Which mix is worse depends on the cost of operating the respective Production Centers and the amount of sales expenses involved in selling the three products. We can also have the proportion of 40:20:20, or 20:20:40, and so on to infinity, each combination causing a different impact on the economy of the company.

Two different combinations can be selected which have almost an identical effect on the cost-recovery needs of the company but whose selling-expense levels are different. Then again, there are differences in profit opportunity under the same product-mix recoveries, and sales effort might be influenced in the direction of a somewhat lower production expense recovery rate, for the sake of higher profit margins.

This concept of sales profits is not fully appreciated by managements. The fact is that each major department in the company should be considered as a separate profit-making, or loss-reducing, entity.

Selling-Price Latitude

Not only is the sales effort supposed to perform economically within its own budget of expenses, it should also be charged with maintaining a fair and reasonable profit margin. This principle especially applies to companies that allow their salesmen a certain amount of latitude in establishing selling prices. In such situations, without controls, the tendency is to sell the easiest way in order to roll up a large sales figure against which the sales commission would apply. Very often the "easiest" way is to exercise the right of reducing selling prices for the sake of obtaining the sale and the commission. In a high-materials-cost product, the result of this practice is that the manufacturer is placed in the position of merchandising raw materials from his supplier, through his facilities, to his customers, without obtaining any profits from the transaction. Often, even if only two percent is deducted from the selling price, it can be more than the gains from automating the direct labor operations in production, and sometimes more than the entire labor cost in high-materials-cost products.

There are also profit differentials because of the traditional price line attached to some products. This element should likewise have a bearing on how the proportions in the product mix are selected: whether they are to be at an optimum based on recovery needs, or at an optimum based on externals beyond the control of the company, or a combination of both.

New Product Mix Selected: The product mix selected as condition *B* (EXHIBIT

Product	Condition A Sales Multiplied by	Quarterly Sales	ACTIVITY OF PRODUCTION CENTER IN HOURS				
			A	B	C	D	E
ab	1	$20,700	240	20	150	30	-
ac	2	19,584	-	-	150	90	150
bc	.1	3,790	16	-	2.5	-	25
cd	2	21,000	-	150	150	90	100
WW	.33	9,000	33	3	22	-	83
YY	2	28,000	160	120	-	160	100
ZZ	3	9,990	60	180	30	120	-
Total		$112,064					
Quarterly Activity ⟶			509	473	504.5	490	458
			× 4	× 4	× 4	× 4	× 4
Annual Activity =			2036	1892	2018	1960	1832

Exhibit 15–13. Conversion of Product Sales to Production Center
Activity (Condition B)

Product	Sales	Percent	Total Recovery	Percent of Product Recovery / Total Recovery	Recovery Ability of Product Per Sales $	Percent of Recovery Per $7 Worth of Sales ($1 from each of 7)
ab	$20,700	18.5	$6,860	11.8	$ .331	9.2
ac	19,584	17.4	12,900	22.2	.658	18.4
bc	3,790	3.4	1,139	1.9	.300	8.4
cd	21,000	18.8	13,100	22.6	.624	17.3
WW	9,000	8.1	4,150	7.2	.461	12.8
YY	28,000	25	12,240	21.1	.437	12.3
ZZ	9,990	8.8	7,740	13.3	.775	21.6
Total	$112,064	100%	$58,129	100%	$3.586	100%

Exhibit 15–14. Product Recovery Ability (Condition B)

15–13) was devised in less than five minutes by looking closely at Exhibit 15–2 and then applying the multiplying factors by which condition A's sales were raised or lowered or maintained. The estimate thus obtained achieved satisfactory results in terms of recovery and Production Center expenses, without requiring a duplication of facilities. No doubt a closer calculation would have provided an even better score.

Notice that the sales level for condition B is $112,064, whereas for condition A it was $123,222. Yet this lower sales level produced far more profits, with every other facet of the company remaining the same as it was for condition A.

The product mix shown in Exhibit 15–13 not only satisfies the needs of production in terms of the budgeted activity, but exceeds the activity (profitability potential) where the budget is below its economical maximum. Here the sales of product ac are doubled, of product bc cut to one-tenth, of product WW cut to one-third and increased three times for product ZZ.

Recovery Ability: Condition B: Exhibit 15–14 is the equivalent of Exhibit 15–7. Exhibit 15–15 shows the relationship between the attained recovery and the product's ability to recover expenses for the product mix of condition B. This alignment is close to what it should be, but it should be policed regularly. Note that where the two curves go off in different directions, the divergence is not great; therefore, the effect is not serious.

Exhibit 15–16 is a summary of the economic effect of both conditions of product mix, on a yearly basis. Under- and over-recovery are expressed on a yearly basis, and the gain or loss on an hourly basis. Exhibit 15–17 shows both conditions of product mix and their effect on the economy of the company. The graph is constructed to show which Centers in conditions A and B operate in the profit or the loss areas. As can be seen, no Center operates in the "red" for condition B, whereas all except Center C run at a loss in condition A. This circumstance leads to the underrecovery of $60,400 for condition A and, for condition B, an over-recovery, which is added to profit because facility duplication is not necessary.

Hourly Recovery Volatility: On an hourly basis, the same economy under the two condition is shown in Exhibit 15–18. It is important to show the hourly as well as the dollar recovery data, because one is usually more volatile than the other. Exhibit 15–18 shows that Center C's recovery is more responsive to the total recovery than it is to the hourly additive necessary. Where such a difference occurs, it is indicative of profit potentiality, that is, how far the budgeted activity is from the maximum economic activity. Notice, for example, the change experienced by Production Center E for condition A. This change should be a signal for the sales department to make an intensive drive to fill up the doubled capacity of Center E, if the facility has been duplicated. This presents, in fact, the greatest opportunity for expense recovery, once the second facility is purchased.

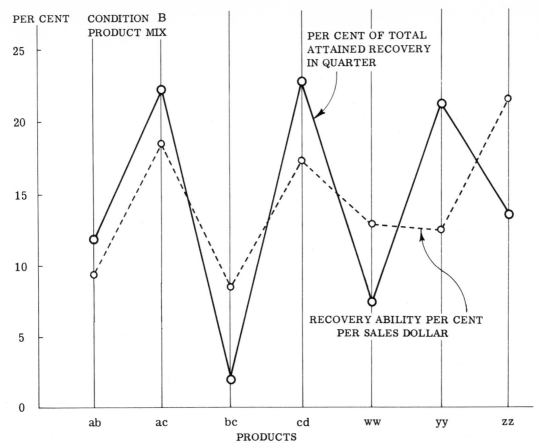

Exhibit 15–15. Recovery Ability of Products vs. Recovery Attained by Sales (Sales Supporting Production Economy)

Production's Needs versus Actual Attainment: EXHIBIT 15–19 compares the two conditions, their respective break-even recovery needs and actual recovery. EXHIBIT 15–19a shows the P & L statement for each mix. These are the results, and this is the type of data, which must be developed frequently; it is the proof of the pudding. Here is a side-by-side condensed profit-and-loss statement of an assumed year's operations under two conditions of product mix. Note that the higher profit was produced with about 10% less sales and a higher direct labor figure. Uniform productivity under both conditions is assumed.

The obvious comment is that more profit was produced because the materials usage was lower. Certainly, a glance at the statement will show that approximately $65,000 less materials was used. But that is not the answer. Failing to look behind P & L statements, or using them solely for managerial control, is fallacious policy, as we have said throughout the book. The answer is that the product mix selected happened to have materials content that added up to that figure. That is why it was possible to make more profits on lower sales. If the mix had been chosen to equal the materials usage of $218,800 for condition *B*, then the sales would neces-

Production Center	Annual Cost of Facilities	Annual Activity	Cost/Hour Charged	Actual Recovery	Over or (Under) Recovery	Gain or (Loss) Per Hour
Condition A						
A	$16,000	2,400	$4	$9,600	$ (6,400)	$ (2.67)
B	16,000	800	10	8,000	(8,000)	(10.00)
C	30,000	1,600	30	48,000	18,000	11.25
D	64,000	900	40	36,000	(28,000)	(31.10)
E	144,000	2,700	40	108,000	(36,000)	(13.32)
					NET $ (60,400)	
Condition B						
A	8,000	2,036	4	8,144	144	.71
B	16,000	1,892	10	18,920	2,920	1.54
C	30,000	2,018	30	60,540	30,540	15.13
D	64,000	1,960	40	78,400	14,400	7.36
E	72,000	1,832	40	73,280	1,280	.70
					NET $49,284	

Exhibit 15–16. Economic Effect of Product Mix (Yearly Basis)

sarily have been more. The important consideration, however, is that, irrespective of materials usage (remember that the materials-usage figure also carries a profit that contributes to the net profit listed), a profit based on more economical use of fixed and semifixed expenses would have been much more significant. *Don't pay salesmen to sell raw material!*

The real *operating* gains, if profit is an incorrect term in this context, is the difference between the $270,000 and the $190,000, less difference in the labor cost. These gains are called "real," because the profit on the materials should not be credited to operating since that sum came along beyond anyone's control.

A Ratio Integrating Production and Sales: The reader is invited to examine the characteristics of his own manufacturing company and then to construct meaningful ratios to assist him in evaluating the relationship between production and sales. One is given below to stimulate him in this direction.

HIGH-PROFIT-TREND RATIO =
Productivity attained at Production Center
$$\times \frac{\text{max. economic activity hr. (before duplication)}}{\text{budgeted hours}}$$

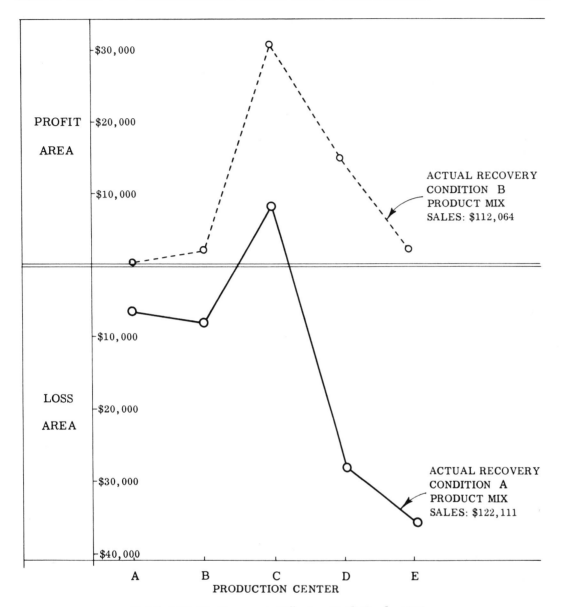

PROFIT AREA

LOSS AREA

ACTUAL RECOVERY
CONDITION B
PRODUCT MIX
SALES: $112,064

ACTUAL RECOVERY
CONDITION A
PRODUCT MIX
SALES: $122,111

PRODUCTION CENTER

Exhibit 15–17. Economic Effect on Both Product Mixes

In this ratio manufacturing productivity is used, to give consideration to the fact that worker effort can raise the effective maximum economic activity hours (before duplication), and thereby increase the profitability potential (shown on EXHIBIT 15–4). The projection of Production Center activity hours is generally done "at standard," that is, at a predetermined level of output and worker effort. If workers have been properly stimulated by some form of wage incentive, then the output can increase over standard and the ceiling on the maximum economic activity can be raised.

Therefore, as shown in EXHIBIT 15–4, it is possible for Center E to have a

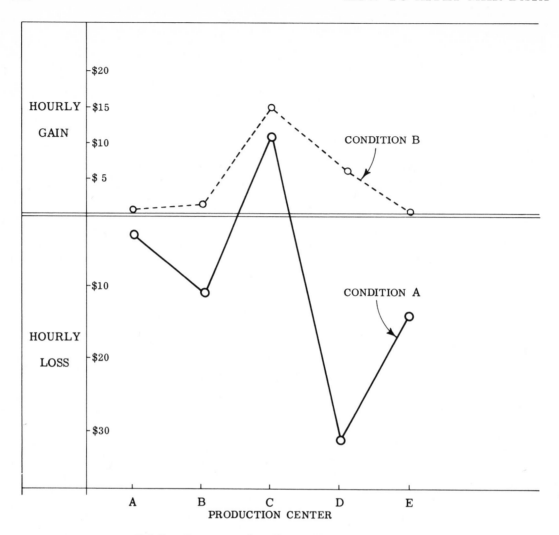

Exhibit 15–18. Hourly Effect of Both Product Mixes

higher profitability trend than Center *D* if Center *E*'s productivity is higher than at Center *D*.

This ratio gives the trend of profitability at each production center, but not for each product. In order to get the profitability trend for each product, it is necessary to add up the above-constructed indices for each Center involved in the making of a product, and to apply the percentage of the sales dollar that the product controls. In EXHIBIT 15–5, the percentage figures for each product are given.

Productivity Increases Capacity: It must be kept in mind that this ratio does not evaluate the sales effort. It evaluates the opportunity that each center has to exceed its budget, and thereby to provide an amount of profits in excess of that expected. A Center has this opportunity according to the number of hours it can run in excess of the budgeted activity up to the limit of its capacity, or before

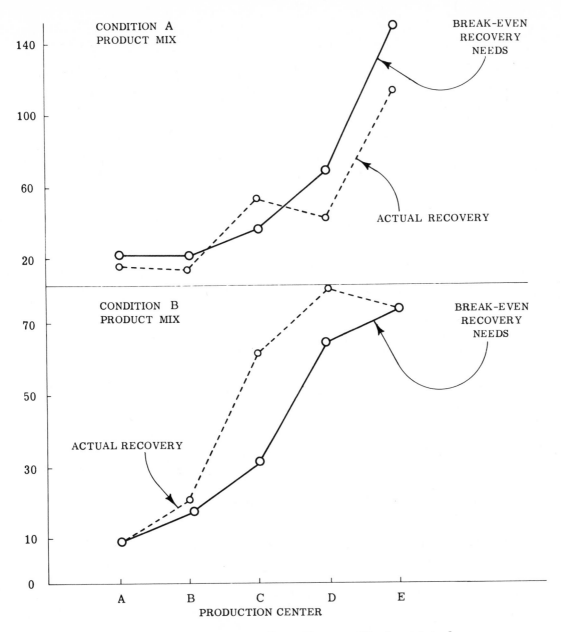

Exhibit 15–19. Annual Breakeven-Recovery Needs vs. Actual Attainment

	Condition A	Condition B
Sales Income	$492,888	$448,256
Total Overhead Costs:		
(All distributed to Production Centers)		
2 - A's --	16,000	1 - A --- 8,000
1 - B --	16,000	1 - B -- 16,000
1 - C --	30,000	1 - C -- 30,000
1 - D --	64,000	1 - D -- 64,000
2 - E's --	144,000	1 - E -- 72,000
Totals	$270,000	$190,000
Direct Labor Costs	15,200	17,512
Materials Costs	218,800	153,868
TOTAL COST	$504,000	$361,380
NET PROFIT or (LOSS)	($11,112)	$86,876

Exhibit 15–19a. Condensed P and L: Conditions A and B

another facility has to be added, and according to the capacity liberated by greater worker effort. Regardless of the amount sold of each product, and considering products only as they contribute to Production Center occupancy, we can arrive at the opportunity that each has for contributing a profit. The pertinent factors, in brief, are:

1. Present worker productivity;
2. Budgeted-to-maximum *product* activity hours.

To illustrate, let's take the data of EXHIBIT 15–5 and arbitrarily assign productivities to the five centers *A* to *E* of 60, 70, 80, 100, and 120 percent, respectively. Let us also use the budgeted or projected hours of EXHIBIT 15–2, 500, 400, 250, 400, and 450 hours, respectively. The values for the profit-trend ratio are:

$$A = 0.60 \times 500/500 = 0.60$$
$$B = 0.70 \times 500/400 = 0.875$$
$$C = 0.80 \times 500/250 = 1.60$$
$$D = 1 \quad \times 500/400 = 1.25$$
$$E = 1.2 \quad \times 500/450 = 1.33$$

This tabulation shows that Center *C* has the greatest opportunity for adding to the company's budgeted profits. These indices are multiplied by the values shown in EXHIBIT 15–5, and footed across. We then have the conversion of the added profitability trend of the *Production Centers* to the added profitability trend of the *seven products*.

These data are shown in EXHIBIT 15–20. The data show that products *ab* and ZZ provide the greatest opportunity to add to the company's budgeted profits.

Sales-Contact Effort: To see to what extent the sales effort is keyed to this high profit trend requires the introduction of contact effort. Let's assume the data in EXHIBIT 15–21 to be representative of the effort of the sales department. And EXHIBIT 15–22 is a comparison of the data in EXHIBITS 15–20 and 15–21. To emphasize a point, we are equating a high profitability of products with the effort made by the sales department to sell those products. It is contact effort, and not the results of the contacts, that is used as the sales activity factor. In other words, we are not considering for the moment the sales or quotations produced, but just the directions that the salesmen are given by their management.

Product *ab* seems to correlate well, this fact indicating that it is being fully exploited. The same is true of product *bc*, but now that we know what we do

High Profit-Trend Ratio	A .6 ×	B .875 ×	C 1.60 ×	D 1.25 ×	E 1.33 ×	Product Total Index
ab	.451 = .27	.065 = .058	.389 = .623	.098 = .123	--	1.074
ac	--	--	.205 = .328	.104 = .13	.168 = .224	.682
bc	.179 = .108	--	.039 = .062	--	.316 = .420	.590
cd	--	.172 = .150	.204 = .326	.154 = .193	.11 = .146	.815
WW	.103 = .062	.018 = .016	.094 = .15	--	.289 = .384	.612
YY	.167 = .100	.221 = .192	--	.294 = .368	.118 = .157	.817
ZZ	.10 = .06	.525 = .460	.069 = .11	.349 = .437	--	1.067
TOTALS	.600	.876	1.599	1.251	1.331	

Exhibit 15–20. **Conversion of Production Center Added Profitability to Products**

PRODUCT	CONTACTS				Product
	Jones	Smith	Brown	Greene	Total
ab	4	14	12	12	42
ac	3	20	8	6	37
bc	10	10	4	2	26
cd	1	0	6	8	15
WW	0	12	2	3	17
YY	0	3	10	8	21
ZZ	0	0	2	6	8
Total	18	59	44	45	166

Exhibit 15–21. Sales Contact Effort

about product *bc,* it would seem better to reduce the number of contacts made on its behalf. Product *WW* appears to be well correlated. The major offender is the lack of contact effort on behalf of *ZZ.* Too much effort is being applied on product *ac;* too few contacts are being made on *cd;* and there is not enough sales effort being applied on product *YY.*

An examination of Exhibit 15–21 soon tells which men need counseling. Of course, the real test is the actual sales brought in by each, and the reader is left to make his own tabulations and curves. Since the contact effort is the forerunner of the actual sale, due attention must be given to this curve; it reflects the way in which the men are being directed.

From these data, however, assuming they are later confirmed by actual dollar sales figures, it would seem that product *ZZ* is being sacrificed because of the low volume of sales the typical order for it brings in. There is an extremely low materials cost content in its sales dollar; therefore, when men shy away from pushing this product, the reason is probably that they are "gross dollar selling" instead of "recovery and added profitability" selling. The function of these charts and curves may thus be seen. Management should use them to direct its men to support the over-all economic needs of the company.

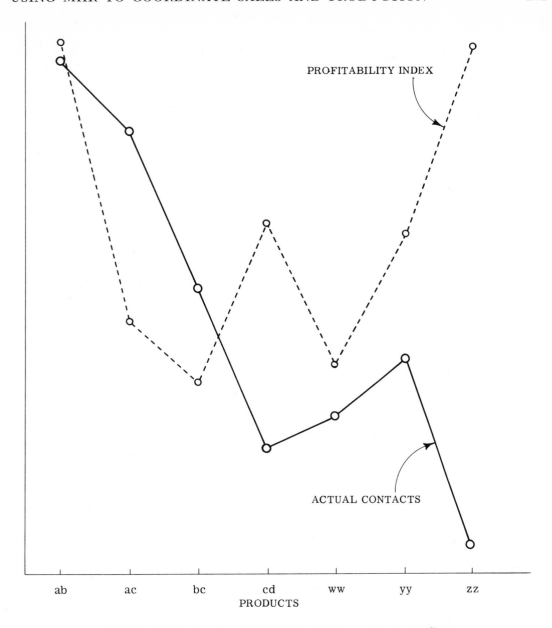

Exhibit 15–22. Products' Profitability Index vs. Contact Effort

Section 4

HOW TO KEEP THE MHR SYSTEM CURRENT

16. PRE-TESTING THE MHR

17. TESTING THE MHR

18. HOW TO CORRECT OR CHANGE THE MHR

Chapter 16

PRE-TESTING THE MHR

The equity of the machine-hour rates is tested by means of a *cost recovery statement*. This tabulation shows whether the estimates are consistently recovering expenses. The purpose of the cost recovery statement is to develop the variation, arising through volume, from planned operations. If the recovery figure and the budgeted costs coincide, there is no activity variation. If budgeted costs and actual costs coincide, there is no cost variation. Then, if the budgeted or planned profit does not coincide with actual profit, it is the result solely of deviations from planned selling prices. In actual practice, it is to be expected that a degree of variation will be found in each element. The extent of the variance will indicate whether the situation is acceptable or needs to be investigated.

Cost Recovery

Converter manufacturing, that type of enterprise which has high initial investments in facilities, is dependent on the *use* of facilities to recover investments. In effect, converter manufacturing is in the business of selling machine and plant time. A proper portion of this total sum must be returned in the sales price of each of the company's products if the company is to recover its investment in the equipment. As we have said before, the magnitude and the velocity of this expense recovery are direct functions of the product mix. That is, the sales dollar will return to the company different amounts of recovery, depending directly upon the product's specific nature as represented by the facilities used in its production. (See the previous chapter.)

Variations in cost recovery stem *principally* from differences between the activity projected and that actually attained. We have seen in the Expense Assignment Worksheet that the MHR varies in inverse proportion with the annual assigned hours. To a lesser extent, variations in recovery result from differences between the actual and projected expenses, where too much, or an insufficient level of, expense was allowed in the Operating Budget. The former type of recovery variance is termed a *volume* variance; the latter, an *efficiency* variance.

While the extent or consistency of the cost recovery will be heavily influenced by the company's pricing policies and its use of "full" or partial costing of the elements of production, it is the purpose of this testing procedure to provide management with a basis for correcting the forecast of their planned production as it was estimated in the EAW.

Check Data

The results obtained will be proportionate to the amount of effort expended in the original work of preparing the MHR. If the original projections were incorrect, the company may wind up with a sizeable amount of unrecovered expenses, a profit-decreasing element, and customers may become the recipients of bargain-priced products. The price "discount" received by customers will be a slice of the company's profits. On the other hand, if projections were made with unrealistically low levels of activity, the company may still suffer the losses of unrecovered expenses, because of overcosted products and the consequent sales resistance.

It is no secret that the average company depends on guesses and averages in projecting the elements of the next year's production. After all, last year's statistics are available as a convenient crutch, and all management has to do is to adjust them up or down to meet the next year's expectations. Also, the tendency in following this practice is to budget a somewhat lower level of expenses and, worse yet, to raise activity levels (without considering inter-Production-Center balances) in a desire to obtain lower (more saleable) machine-hour rates.

Machine-hour rates represent the predeterminations of the company's costs for the coming year and, as such, should be set from soundly considered estimates. While guesswork cannot be completely eliminated, normal errors can be held to a minimum. Judgment, and painstaking checks and crosschecks form the basis for an informed estimate. While a sound approach to the original estimates is no guarantee to the accuracy of the final rates, because of the caprices of the market, and while it might be that the MHR structure developed from properly prepared data will thus turn out no closer to actual results than one pulled out of the air, it is probable that if every facet of the rate structure is carefully prepared, the results will stand the test.

Selection of the Capacity Base

Besides cost recovery variances that develop because of volume changes, there are sums of under- or overrecovered expenses which can be attributed not to variances from planned production, but rather to the way that the capacity was considered in the projections.

Earlier in the book we mentioned the bewildering concepts of capacity used by some people. This discussion dealt largely with the unit by which capacity is measured. In testing the equity of the rates, and in this pre-testing section, we have to examine the policy of the company with respect to the quantitative features of the measurement.

In projecting expenses and activity of the plant, we have to arrive at a normal level of operations, also called *normal capacity*. Basically, there are two interpretations of normal capacity, and it is important that management have a complete understanding of the difference between them, so that the company objectives may be accomplished by the results of applying the proper one.

Years ago, the concept of normal capacity charged to total production all fixed costs, regardless of the rate of activity of the plant. The results of this practice were higher unit costs in periods of low activity, and lower unit costs in periods of high activity. Modern cost practices call for determining manufacturing costs of a *product*—which are unaffected by the rate of plant activity. This product cost, though it may not be the one upon which selling prices are based, is the one that should be obtained at a normal capacity level.

In some companies, normal activity means the level at which the plant is capable of producing. This is its potential operating capacity, also known as *practical* capacity. In some cases, it is thought of as the volume at which the plant is equipped to operate, or the maximum capacity attainable.

In other companies, normal activity means an average expected utilization of plant and equipment based on expected sales orders over a period of years in the future. This concept is known as normal sales expectancy, or *average* capacity, and, sometimes, seems to describe the company's ability to produce and sell.

Practical capacity is greater than average capacity by the difference of *idle* capacity. In other words, average capacity plus idle capacity equals practical capacity. For the sake of completeness, even though the calculation doesn't enter into MHR, we may note that the maximum theoretical capacity attainable is equal to the practical capacity plus capacity lost by operating interruptions.

Practical Capacity: If a plant actually operates at this capacity, then product sales will recover all fixed costs. And if actual capacity is below practical capacity, where activity projections have been made at the higher level, the unrecovered fixed costs act to reduce profits, since customers, for the short term at least, have been undercharged. Where practical capacity is set at a level which leaves unused or excess capacity, resulting from a lack of sales orders to meet the level at which the plant *could* produce, the cost of maintaining this capacity is great. However, it will probably alert management to the nature of the disproportion.

True unit costs are attained, as far as fixed costs are concerned, when unit product costs are based on practical capacity. In this case the product costs are not inflated by costs of idle capacity not involved in their manufacture. This type of unit cost is fine for decision-making. Management can decide more accurately what items to make or buy, what equipment to acquire or dispose of, what procedures to follow in meeting competition, which facilities are not being used to their fullest capacity, and if there are any imbalances among machines.

The major disadvantage to the use of practical capacity in developing MHR is the tendency to use the product unit costs, so developed, as a basis for pricing, without including the fixed costs that arise from unused capacity. If unused capacity is not considered in pricing, the manufacturer will have to absorb these costs, whereas, quite properly, they should be charged to customers. This charge is justified by the existence of stand-by facilities to meet temporary demand peaks of which customers receive the benefit.

However, as was shown in the previous chapter, it is highly desirable for management to be aware of the inherent potential of their equipment so that, even with some price reduction, the higher sold output may result in additional profits. As the reader will recall, this additional sale relates to the concept of elasticity of demand.

MHR costs developed from a practical capacity base should be used for pricing purposes only when there is a close relationship between the productive capabilities of the installed factory equipment and the known customer demand. In this case, the practical capacity level is close to the level for average capacity, and there is little or no problem in charging the cost of unused capacity. However, for companies whose sales fluctuate or which are overequipped, the average capacity method is favored.

Average Capacity: The costs reflecting this level of operation include all fixed costs that are charged to products over a specific period. Under this method, when sales expectancy has been realized, even though the plant has been operating below practical capacity, all fixed costs are recovered. Where underrecovery exists, it is the result of an inaccuracy in establishing and projecting this level of capacity and not of excess capacity. Average capacity includes automatically the average expected idleness cost.

For example, suppose the annual cost of operating a Production Center is $36,000 and the practical capacity is 1,800 annual hours, with an average capacity of 1,500 hours. In the first case, the MHR is $20, but for average capacity the MHR is $24. Obviously, the higher average capacity rate includes the cost of the expected unused 300 hours.

Summary of Capacity Base Selection

For pricing purposes and for establishing long-range pricing policies, the use of normal capacity, in the sense of capacity to make and sell (average capacity), based upon the period of future years necessary for the firm to realize its fixed investment, is essential for a sound pricing policy. Its use automatically establishes sounder cost estimates and prevents overexpansion of facilities, because the company is able to evaluate the relationship of customer demand to its facilities. While the use of practical capacity provides management with a better perspective on its productive potentials, it calls for an addition in cost to account for unused facilities, which may get lost in the shuffle when it comes to setting prices. Hence, practical capacity should be used only when provisions to include the costs of unused capacity are consistently applied and understood by price policy makers.

Capacity Balancing

But the problem is not solved that simply. We now must face the problem of qualifying just how the concept of normal capacity will be used. Will it be applied to the capacity of the plant as a whole, or will each department or process be considered separately? Applying the concept to plant-wide capacity involves our old friend, the magic percentage. Many plants take the figure of maximum theoretical capacity and apply a percentage to it to arrive at practical capacity; they then use a lower percentage, which they believe to represent sales expectancy, and call the result average capacity. In any such methods no consideration is given to the facility of least capacity, the bottleneck.

Even though manufacturing capacity as a whole may be greater than selling capacity, certain Production Centers may not be available in the capacity required to manufacture the products listed in the sales program. In that event, the projected sales program is reduced to the required extent, and corresponding reductions are made in the capacity of other Production Centers performing related operations on the products affected. Conversely, while selling capacity as a whole may exceed the ability to produce, it may not be sufficient for certain products. The capacity of operations relating to products sold in limited quantities is therefore reduced to an appropriate level.

In any case, when the available normal capacity of certain Production Centers is disproportionate to that of preceding or subsequent Centers, the capacity of all equipment performing related operations should be reduced to the level of the limiting equipment, unless normalcy can be achieved by subcontracting.

But as a technique for handling the bottleneck, an arbitrary tailoring down of all Production Centers to the capacity of the bottleneck center is wrong, for it denies the existence of product mix and its role in varying the use of equipment. The reader will recall from the previous chapter how, by optimizing the product-volume mix, a company is able to maximize its profits. It should be borne in mind that this condition may be obtained at a fairly low level of capacity. Hence, the entire con-

cept of normal capacity as some specific portion of a maximum theoretical level
becomes open to question.

Effect of Product Mix on Capacity Base

For many years, and throughout hundreds of machine-hour rate installations, we
have never been able to describe just what normal volume is supposed to be.
Volume is like the weather; considering it unchangeable is like building a house
without a roof, on the assumption that it will never rain because the sun is shining
today. As a semantic crutch normal volume has served admirably the interests of
those who, because of laziness, indifference and/or lack of shop knowledge, used
it as a convenient substitute for analysis. For, indeed, if a sales forecast is used as
the basis of activity projections, then the activity of each Production Center must
be projected in order to fulfill the requirement of the mix represented by the sales
forecast (see previous chapter). Then, in turn, each Production Center must be
balanced against all the other Centers to insure sufficient capacity, and adjustments
must be made accordingly. This adjusted activity becomes the level projected,
even though some of the Centers are expected to operate close to maximum theoretical capacity and others at one-half that level. It must be understood, however,
that a change in product mix caused by changing markets, or sales emphasis, can
result in complete reversals of the activity levels required by each Center. This fact,
especially, makes any attempt at defining normal capacity fallacious.

The best way to insure a high level of cost recovery when it comes time to test the
equity of the MHR is to devote care, judgment and thorough analysis to the original
projection of the activity levels.

Operating Budget Pre-Tests

After determining the various activity levels, management must give attention to
the quality of the OB and to its effectiveness in supporting the requirements of the
activity levels of the Production Centers. Arbitrary budget determinations based on
modified historical figures may not be sound, for the needs in the coming period,
if conditioned by a changed product mix, may cause considerable changes in the
supporting expense budget. Management's plans for the future affect future factory
expenses, as well as expenses in the administrative and selling areas. If past experience is used as a base, it must be modified for such considerations as whether new
products or models are planned and the changes they will require in tooling and
facilities; whether there will be changes in departmental operations, responsibili-
ties, locations and/or groupings; whether new machinery is contemplated, either
as replacement or for extended operations; whether new or different building facilities and services will be needed; whether materials handling and warehousing

facilities will be changed; and a host of other considerations normally recognized as accompanying management's plans for the future.

The operating level of the budget is the next pre-test to make. As elementary as this advice may seem, it is wise to question management as to whether they have completed the sales forecast or production schedule. While it is quite normal for conditions during the coming year to change, it is important to know, before developing the rates, whether the planned production is merely a first stab or whether it is representative of the considered judgment of top management. On this point, it is well to question the plant's ability to fulfill the planned production. One quick way of determining this is to find out whether the plant, or any department or Production Center in the plant, has ever operated at the level of activity called for in the new projection. The answer will bear on the Crew Composition Table, if some of the centers are expected to experience a higher level of activity. For this reason, it is valid to question the crew assignment to each center.

The next step in the pre-test is to review very carefully the overhead expenses themselves. Are all the proper overhead expenses in the correct category? Have any direct costs been included? Have any overhead costs been excluded? Proper classification of costs has been discussed in detail earlier in this book, but the point is worth repeating. One special advantage is the ease of expense tracing, which will simplify problems when government contracts are involved. The time to do the classification job is *before* the rates are developed. Postponement only delays the problems and will result in endless confusion.

Make sure about elements of avoidability and unavoidability to permit prompt managerial action. Don't include in the budget transient expenses which occur accidentally or without regularity. The same is true of above-normal defective material, scrap and rework. Only include costs for the normal level. Variances standing out clearly point the way for remedial action. Including them in the budget is tantamount to accepting the variances as normal; their causes will remain buried in falsely favorable variance reports.

The allocation factors (see EAW, Step 4) should reflect as closely as possible the use of facilities and should reflect all known changes, physical or otherwise, expected to take place in the coming year. For example, if space costs are to be allocated on the basis of square footage of occupancy, the allocation factor should be the number of square feet required for a Production Center during the *coming year*.

The next step is the comparison of the overhead expenses that have been projected for each department with the actual expenses for the preceding full year. Differences should be accounted for and investigated, not that past experience is the basis for the new budget but, rather, that this practice will raise points that can be used in the questioning of the new budget. Similar treatment should be made of any other factory expense that has not been assigned to a department or Production Center. Then expand the current level of actual overhead to a full 12-month basis, compare to the new budget and investigate all differences. Finally, compare the actual overhead expenses allocated to Production Centers during the past year with those allocated in the new MHR projection. Major differences should be fairly simple to trace and explain.

Most of the above pre-testing of the budgeted expenses has positive psychological impact on the budgeter as well as on those from whom information is elicited. The objective is to stimulate a higher degree of refined judgment from the people involved, rather than to obtain arithmetic balancing.

Crew Composition Pre-Tests

Labor load determinations can provoke problems in the development of proper rates. In pre-testing the adequacy of the crew composition for each Production Center, the budgeter should reconcile the labor load for each Center against the payroll of the previous year. Usually mistakes occur when partial operators are assigned to more than one Center, and the budgeter may find that he has overages of several fractional "bodies." Of course, there will be differences between past and expected crewing, due to output volume, labor rates, departmental layouts, product mix and seasonal production. After these factors have been accounted for, there should remain no significant gaps in the reconciliation.

In the case of a revised set of machine-hour rates, don't forget to compare the new payroll projection with the past payroll costs, for reasons similar to those explained above.

Chapter 17

TESTING THE MHR

Assuming proper pricing policies, an equitable set of machine-hour rates will return to the company the costs it incurred in producing its products. Other things being equal, when the rates fail to recover these costs, then one or more of the following factors must have been at work:

1. The volume of sold product, or the activity of Production Centers, was less than that projected;
2. Expenditures were in excess of the amount budgeted;
3. Direct productive workers failed to attain the level of performance estimated.

Testing the Equity of the MHR

The difference between actual and budgeted expenses is an efficiency variance, since actual expenditures are within the control of management. The difference between the overhead recovered and the overhead projected, or the difference between the actual and projected activities extended by the respective MHR's, is a volume variance. While actual activity is beyond the control of production management, as it is a function of the market and sales direction, the accuracy of the projection of expected activity *is* within the sphere of management control. Consequently, any difference between the two is a management responsibility.

The difference between the estimated and actual labor hours is a performance variation and is also within the control of production management. The level of performance has impact on fixed expense recovery and therefore affects volume variances. An example will bring out this point. We have said earlier in the book that the MHR of a Production Center remains the same regardless of the labor productivity attained at that Center; and that this is true because the MHR represents the cost per hour of owning and maintaining the facility. However, if substandard productivity is attained, then the expense-recovering ability of the Center is lowered. Thus, if it is estimated that the manufacture of a product will utilize a Center for five hours, implicit in that estimate is the assumption that labor will be producing according to certain work standards. If a worker fails to process the order through that Center in the five hours, and because of lower productivity he must use the Center for seven hours, then the additional two hours of facility use will not be part of the estimated cost that was used as a guide to pricing. Instead of those two hours contributing to additional expense recovery, they only act to occupy unbilled capacity, or they displace capacity that might be applied to more profitable work.

Thus, it must be clearly understood that only standard performance permits the machine hour generated by sales to recover the full hour's value of expense. For example, if a production standard at a Center for a specific operation is 1,000 pieces per hour, and the worker averages only 750 per hour, then the performance variance will be 25% and the number of activity hours accomplished will be 75% of the *machine* hours reported. In other words, because of substandard labor performance, the company will be deprived of the use of its full Production Center hour for expense recovery.

In testing the equity of the rates, and when using them for control purposes, management must also consider seasonal fluctuations in activity.

Production Center's Monthly Activity Report

The first step in testing cost recovery is to make a record of the time in use of each facility. This information is obtained from the daily production tickets, on which provision is made for machine number. (These production tickets were discussed in Chapter 5.) The office should extract from the tickets the amount of time each facility ran per day and post it on a monthly activity form. Such a form is shown in Exhibit 17–1. Include as running time the machine hours and *not* the man-hours. Makereadies and setups are included as part of running time for testing cost recovery. (The payroll analysis should show downtime separately for managerial control purposes.)

At the end of each month, the activity for each Production Center should be totalled.

Cost Recovery Statement

Exhibit 17–2 shows the format for a Cost Recovery Statement.

Post each month's total from the Production Center Monthly Activity Reports to the Monthly Activity column of the Cost Recovery Statement. Insert the segmented MHR, and extend each segment by the Monthly Activity and place each into the appropriate Recovery columns. Then total each of the three Recovery columns.

Insert the amounts for Budgeted Costs as follows:

Direct Labor: from the Direct Labor Budget of the EAW.
The two Overhead segments: from the Operating Budget.

Month of_____

PRODUCTION CENTER MONTHLY ACTIVITY REPORT

PRODUCTION CENTER	Days of the month																															TOTALS
	1	2	3	4	5	6	7	8	9	10	11	12	13	14	15	16	17	18	19	20	21	22	23	24	25	26	27	28	29	30	31	

Exhibit 17–1. Production Center Monthly Activity Report

Insert the amounts for Actual Costs as follows:

Direct Labor: from the payroll adjusted to conform to the inclusive monthly dates.

Overhead: from the general books of account.

Using the Cost Recovery Statement: Compare the elements in the total Recovery with the Budgeted and Actual Costs. If the Recovery is substantially greater than Budgeted Costs, the annual hours assigned to Production Centers might have been too little, resulting in inflated machine-hour rates. Experience has shown that while a small increase in the dollar value of machine-hour rates can be tolerated without any noticeable sales resistance, continual increases will reverse the curve of increasing profits as their impact becomes felt in the selling prices.

Month ended _____

PRODUCTION CENTER	MONTHLY ACTIVITY	MACHINE-HOUR RATE			RECOVERY		
		Mfg	Non-Mfg	Direct Labor	Overhead		Direct Labor
					Mfg	Non-Mfg	
TOTAL RECOVERY					$____	$_____	$_____
Budgeted Costs					$____	$_____	$_____
Actual Costs					$____	$_____	$_____

Exhibit 17–2. Cost Recovery Statement

If Actual Recovery is substantially lower than Budgeted Costs, it may be that too many annual hours were assigned to the Production Centers and that profits are being passed on to customers. This artificial inflation of the annual hours results in low machine-hour rates, typical of Practical Capacity projections. Projected activity is sometimes inflated purposely when a new machine is to be acquired in the coming period and there is not enough sales experience to project a proper level of activity for it. In that case, rather than attempt to penalize customers for the lack of use of new equipment, which may cause some sales resistance anyway (keeping in mind that a competitor's similar equipment may carry a normal activity level), it is wise to project a reasonable activity for it for the first year. The projection can become a function of actual activity and of the sales forecast in the following year.

When the Budgeted and Actual Costs are approximately equal to each other (and, again, we're not looking for down-to-the-last-cent accuracy), the amount recovered above the Budgeted Costs will be a direct contribution to profits. If Actual Costs exceed Budgeted Costs, the MHR may have to be adjusted, but according to changes in budgeted expenses rather than in annual hours.

The foregoing discussion evaluates cost recovery on a total plant basis. As was shown in Section 2, it is possible to obtain full recovery on a plant-wide basis with the individual Production Centers fluctuating widely in under- and overrecovery. Total Recovery on the form is a *net* summation of the recoveries contributed by individual Centers. Hence, while some Production Centers may be overrecovering, and others underrecovering, the net Total Recovery might, through compensating errors, indicate a satisfactory level of activity and expense disbursement.

It is quite prevalent to find two conditions of even recovery: one due to the individual Centers' evenness of recovery, and the other to the recovery turbulence experienced by the individual Centers. This latter state is unsatisfactory, because it occurs by accident and the smallest shifts in product mix will usually produce wide changes in the plant-wide *net* recovery.

Therefore, the test is not complete until cost recovery is tested, policed and evaluated according to individual Production Centers. Here we find the profitability of the individual Centers. This information, in turn, leads to an evaluation of profitability for each product, determined by the state of profitability of the Centers through which the product passes.

Exhibit 17–2a shows a cost recovery statement of a metal-working manufacturer at the end of the first quarter's activity period. This table would actually be a profit-and-loss statement if materials usage figures, and sales figure, were included. But this table is more dynamic than the conventional P & L, because it lends itself to ready trouble-shooting on those activities that will ultimately determine the company's profits or losses.

This statement shows that profits and losses vary widely among the Centers, with production profits and losses resulting. Let's see how management acts on this information in the next quarter. Exhibit 17–2b shows the cost recovery statement at the end of the second quarter's activity period, showing action to improve the first quarter's results.

Here are shown some of the changes made during the second quarter to recover some of the first-quarter losses. A comparison of the tables will show the improvements made. Notice that if there were no cylindrical-grinder Center, profits would have been earned for both quarters, provided that non-related fixed charges (space occupancy) allocated to this Center were absorbed by increased activity at other

Production Center	Projected Annual Hours of Use	Estimated Yearly Expenses	Machine-Hour Rate Jan. 1	First Quarter Activity Hours	Production Profit or (Loss)
Punchpress	2000	$11,000	$5.50	600	$550
Tumbling	600	2,520	4.20	160	—
Plating	1800	43,000	24.00	500	1,250
Brakes	1400	10,080	7.20	300	(360)
Trim, Notch	2000	7,600	3.80	350	(570)
Welding	1000	6,400	6.40	250	—
Assembly	1200	3,360	2.80	300	—
Grinding	500	1,600	3.20	125	—
Spray Room	2000	29,600	14.80	550	740
Lathe	1800	23,760	13.20	500	660
Mill	1600	25,760	16.10	350	(805)
Cylindrical Grinder	(500) 1600	39,200	(78.40)* 24.50**	100	(7,350)
Surface Grinder	1600	18,800	11.80	400	—
Net Under-recovery (Loss) First Quarter					$(5,885)

*True rate based on true projection—unsaleable.

**Contrived rate to stimulate sales, based on increased but unattained activity.

Exhibit 17–2a. First-Quarter Cost Recovery Statement

Centers. If the Center were not in existence, machine depreciation would not exist either; but the space reserved for the machinery would still be present, and the charges for this space would have to be reallocated.

A decision made on April 1 to sell work at the grinding center at cost, lowered the total product cost of items that required cylindrical grinding. Sales increased, and, of course, activity at this Center increased, until the 1,600 annual activity hours became a reality. At this point, the $24.50 hourly rate, contrived to attract business, became a valid reflection of the Center's costs. As a matter of policy, the company had never added profits to the cost of the Center, and it was greatly pleased to recover all the expenses of operating it. The sales department continued to look for subcontract machine time in case activity started to slip. At one point the company had the grinder busy 2,000 hours a year: 1,600 for their own items and 400 for farmed-out parts. The 400 hours provided an overrecovery of $9,800 per

PRODUCTION CENTER Characteristics—Analyses—Action Taken	Revised Machine-Hour Rate April 1	Second Quarter Activity Hours	Production Profit or (Loss)
Punchpress: Insufficient capacity to justify hourly cost reduction. Over-recovery transferred to profits.	$5.50	570	$ 385
Tumbling: Capacity available. Reduce hourly cost to accelerate and attract additional activity to the point of over-recovery, even though present activity fully recovers. Partial gains to customers from marginal pricing.	3.70	250	295*
Plating: Sales reports projection too low causing sales resistance. Adjust to split difference.	22.75	550	1,762.50*
Brakes: Projection set too high. Adjust for even recovery.	8.40	300	---
Trim, Notch: Sales activity low. Cost is lowest based on maximum-activity projection. Push sales; don't adjust rate.	3.80	450	(190)
Welding: Push sales. Gains to be retained by company. Decrease rate slightly and notice effect on recovery.	6.20	310	322*
Assembly: Hold rate; no change.	2.80	320	56
Grinding: Hold rate; no change.	3.20	110	(48)
Spray Room: Take same action as with punchpress.	14.80	525	370
Lathe: Capacity available. Obviously profitable center. Push sales. Hold rate same.	13.20	500	660
Mill: Projection correct. Sales push needed. Hold rate same.	16.10	500	1,610
Cylindrical Grinder: Sell center at cost (no profit) to accelerate recovery of fixed expenses. Hold lower hourly rate.	24.50	350	(1,225)
Surface Grinder: Hold rate; no change	11.80	440	492

*Notice that profit was made even with decrease of hourly charges. Reason: Attraction of greater sales whose expense recovery exceeded decrease in charges.	Net Gain, 2nd Quarter Net Loss, 1st Quarter	$4,489.50 (5,585.00)
	Cumulative Net Loss, 1st Half	($1395.50)

Exhibit 17–2b. Action Taken on Second-Quarter Cost Recovery
Statement

annum. This subcontracted work was the company's sole opportunity for cylindrical grinding profits.

Production Center Recovery Test Form

This form evaluates the monthly profitability potential of each Production Center by comparing its actual activity, and thereby the amount of expenses recovered, with the activity projected. Projected activity is regarded in two ways because of seasonal variations: as Linear activity and Acceptable activity. From these two activities we get a realistic evaluation and control of the Center's role in the total economy of the company.

Because of seasonal effect on activity, when a center is projected at 1,800 annual hours, it does not mean necessarily that each month should show 150 activity hours. 150 hours per month would be a mathematically proportional expectation and would deny the existence of seasonal effect. While Linear measurement is important in judging the velocity of recovery and the chances of full recovery at the end of the year, it is not a fair yardstick in evaluating individual months. This is why we introduce the measurement of Acceptable activity.

The Production Center Recovery Test Form is shown in Exhibit 17–3.

A fair method of assessing monthly activity is by first determining what activity is realistically attainable in a particular month. Whereas a Center projected at 1,800 annual hours has a Linear monthly activity of 150 hours, the Acceptable activity may be as little as 75 hours in the slower portion of the year and may be as high as 300 in the busy season. At the same time, the Linear measurements must be included, so that as the year proceeds, management can form an opinion as to the accuracy of the original annual projection.

Using the Production Center Recovery Test Form: Divide the annual hours of each Production Center by 12 (or 13, if the company operates on a four-week, 13-period basis) and insert, under ACTIVITY: Linear. Then apportion the annual hours of each Production Center to 12 or 13 periods according to what it is reasonable to expect in each, and insert the activity hours for the particular period and Center under ACTIVITY: Acceptable. Then refer to the summary activity form shown in Exhibt 17–1 and insert the actual activity of each Production Center under ACTIVITY: Actual. For each Production Center the prevailing MHR is inserted in the column provided.

Having set these data into a form, by simple inspection management can key sales effort to the lagging Centers by increasing sales efforts on the products that use those Centers. If it is found that the annual projection is incorrect, due either to management having under- or over-projected activity (both mistakes are negative), changes in the MHR can be made before too much pricing precedent has been set. This feature particularly applies to an MHR structure that has been established for the first time in a company.

Insert the difference between columns (1) and (2) in column (4). Insert the difference between columns (2) and (3) in column (5). Show deficiencies in parentheses. Multiply column (6) by column (4) and insert the product in column (7). Multiply column (6) by column (5) and insert the product in column (8).

Columns (9) and (10) are the cumulative results from columns (7) and (8), respectively. Show deficiencies in parentheses.

PRODUCTION CENTER RECOVERY TEST FORM

PRODUCTION CENTER	ACTIVITY			VARIATION IN ACTIVITY Based On:		MHR	COST OF ACTIVITY VARIATION Based On:		CUMULATIVE RECOVERY VARIANCE	
	Lin.	Acc.	Act.	Linear	Accept.		Linear	Accept.	Linear	Acceptable

Exhibit 17–3. Production Center Recovery Test Form

These last two columns, (9) and (10), should be under constant policing to detect some flaw in activity or expense projection. Generally, column (9) is more deficient than (10) when the MHR period starts in the slow season, and the reverse is true when the MHR period commences at a busy time. In either case, the goal for management is a zero in both columns at the end of the calendar or fiscal period—the sign that all expenses have been recovered. Attention should be given periodically to these last two columns to see that the gap between the two figures does not widen appreciably.

In actual practice, the procedure of getting management to think about the monthly acceptable levels of activity for each Production Center usually forms an accurate basis for arriving at the annual projection. And, if it is possible for it to do so before originally establishing the annual activity (usually difficult because of the lack of complete understanding of what is desired in a first MHR), management should deal with the monthly estimate. However, after the first year of MHR's use, especially when the data has been used by management for machinery and product profitability determinations, little difficulty will be encountered. After this initial period, key people will be talking and thinking in terms of activity hours, cost recovery, sales-production coordination, and so on.

To reiterate: a widening between Linear and Acceptable Cumulative Recovery Variation can be a signal for managerial action to improve sales activity or to revise the activity of certain Production Centers to make it more realistic. The degree of widening, the time of occurrences, and the degree of likelihood that deficiencies may be made up by the end of the activity period, are the criteria for such action.

Changes in the MHR affect the order estimate only to the extent that the Production Centers are concerned. Often the price increase resulting from a higher MHR is not felt by the individual customer on his order, but the accumulation of small increases is a step towards insuring the consistent recovery of expenses planned in the budget.

As a practical matter, prices are not generally raised appreciably just because of the lack of activity at certain Centers. Consider that the customer is not a partner in the manufacturer's business and is not concerned about activity, expense budgets, and the like. He is concerned solely about getting the quality and service he requires at a price in keeping with competition, irrespective of cost recovery performances at the manufacturer's plant. At the same time, prices need not be decreased just because of an arithmetic overrecovery. For one thing, until the end of a period, the extent of fixed-expense recovery is not known, and, if savings resulting purely from overrecovery are summarily passed on to customers, the manufacturer loses the benefit of a recovery cushion. Such a cushion may be required later in the period to compensate for unexpected underrecovery stemming from a revised product mix, changes in the market, and mistakes in activity projections elsewhere in the MHR structure. However, considering elasticity of demand, if it is known that marginal pricing will bring in more profits through boosting sales, then it may pay to pass a portion of the overrecovery on in the form of lower prices. Again, though, due consideration must be given to the matter of displacement of more profitable work and to the bottlenecks that are created during busy periods, when this type of marginal pricing is practiced. Control of this procedure is discussed starting on page 178.

Testing of Product and Order Costs

One of the first steps to be taken after the installation of a machine-hour rate system is to recost with the MHR every cost estimate pertaining to current products. Comparing the new costs so determined with the costs estimated in the past will instantly give an appraisal of customer and order profitability. This recosting procedure is a most worthwhile effort, since it will alert management to the need to review prices to certain customers the next time an order from them is received. This recosting work should be done right on the face of the old estimate and a notation made also on the individual customer records.

Often, where a customer buys more than one product, even if it is a variation in size, his order will be more profitable than others. The point is that a customer's total account cannot necessarily be evaluated as totally profitable or totally unprofitable. At the same time, certain products or orders may have, in the past, been undercosted. Unless it does not use expensive equipment for which cost recovery is vital, unprofitable work should be discouraged or, to justify its continuance, increased in price.

Most importantly, once correct costs are known, management can peg its sales emphasis to bring in sales of the products which use the most profitable facilities to the highest practical degree, with due consideration being given to the possible additional burden created by a duplication of facilities.

To save time, and the consequent loss of recovery through the passage of time, tabulate all sizeable orders made in the past period, perhaps involving 75% of the company's product mix, to show the ostensible costs on which their selling prices were based. In a column next to the tabulation can be shown the recosted results of those orders according to the new MHR. The past orders corresponding to these data can be listed in another vertical column showing the customer's name and the products or product lines purchased. Experience has shown that after such a comparative tabulation is made, clear patterns of profit and loss are easily seen.

This information should be eventually turned over to the sales department for implementation.

	MONTHLY SUMMARY OF DIRECT LABOR COSTS					
Production Center: No. A					Period ended: January 31	
PRODUCT CODE NUMBER	ACTUAL		STANDARD		COST VARIANCE	
	HOURS	COST	HOURS	COST	Favorable	Unfavorable
1000	175.0	$172.00	178.0	$180.00	$8.00	
2000	50.0	51.50	48.0	49.00		$2.50
2200	48.0	48.50	47.5	48.00		.50
2500*	41.1	41.94	40.2	41.46		.48
2700	12.9	13.56	13.3	14.00	.44	
3000	20.0	20.00	18.0	18.00		2.00
3200	25.0	27.00	24.0	26.40		.60
3500	110.0	111.00	109.0	110.00		1.00
3700						
4000	35.0	39.00	36.0	42.00	3.00	
4300	15.0	16.00	15.0	16.50	.50	
4600						
5000	55.0	51.00	51.0	49.00		2.00
5500						
6000	13.0	13.00	12.0	12.00		1.00
Totals	600.0	$604.50	592.0	$606.36	$11.94	$10.08
	NET VARIANCE				$1.86	

*hours and costs for this product classification taken from Exhibit 17-6

Exhibit 17–4. Direct-Labor Cost Summary Form

Variance Reports

Different companies use different forms in checking on their variances. As we mentioned earlier, it is important that the performance attained by labor be included as part of every cost variance, because of the impact this labor performance has on the utilization of each facility. Exhibit 17–4 shows a Monthly Summary of Direct Labor Costs, which gives the variance between actual work and the standards allowed for the work at one particular Production Center. This information is developed from a Labor Operation Report, shown in Exhibit 17–5, which is in turn posted to the respective Product and Operation Direct Labor Cost Sheets, as shown in Exhibit 17–6.

Exhibit 17–7 is a Summary of Standard and Actual Conversion Costs, from which the labor cost variances are obtained, by *Production Center;* Exhibit 17–4 shows the variance by *product lines.* Often the difference between the two is expressed as a percentage, which may be used to modify Actual Activity in the

LABOR OPERATION REPORT

Name: George Smith   No. 758   Date: January 14

Production Center: A

DIRECT LABOR OPERATIONS

Job No.	Product Code	Description	Labor Code	Quantity Produced	Time on	Time off	Hours	Pay Rate	Cost
938	2500		101	79	8:00	10:18	2.3	$1.00	$ 2 30
951	4000		101	38	10:18	12:00	1.7	1.00	1 70
953	2000		101	158	2:00	5:00	3.0	1.00	3 00
965	1000		101	38	6:00	7:36	1.6	1.00	1 60
TOTAL DIRECT LABOR				313	/////	//////	8.6	/////	$ 8 60

INDIRECT LABOR OPERATIONS

Prod'n Center	Labor Code	Description	Time on	Time off	Hours	Pay Rate	Cost
A	411	No work	1:00	2:00	1.0	$1.00	$ 1 00
A	412	Clean up	7:36	8:00	.4	1.00	40
Costed by:		TOTAL INDIRECT LABOR			1.4	//////	1 40
		TOTAL DIRECT AND INDIRECT LABOR			10.0	//////	$10 00

Exhibit 17–5. Labor Operation Report Form

Cost Recovery Statement, Exhibit 17–2, and in the Production Center Recovery Test Form, Exhibit 17–3.

A by-product of the variance reports can be the development of profit-and-loss statements by product lines, if such determinations are desirable. From the data of Exhibit 17–4, a Distribution of Current Overhead Expenses by Product Classifications can be made, to form the basis of such analyses. This form is shown in Exhibit 17–8.

Exhibit 17–9 is a form developed for a folding carton plant. On it is assembled all pertinent information regarding Production Center profitability. This report is prepared weekly, as well as quarterly, to give management a picture of the shop's

PRODUCT AND OPERATION DIRECT-LABOR COST SHEET

Production Center: __A__   Product: No. 2500

Date	Operation No. A-100 (machine)			Operation No. A-101 (hand)			Operation No. A-102 (setup)			Total	
JANUARY	Hrs.	Quan.	Cost	Hrs.	Quan.	Cost	Hrs.	Quan.	Cost	Hours	Cost
3	4.7	156	$4.70	3.6	220	$3.96	1.0	200	$ .90	9.3	$9.56
4	7.1	235	7.10	2.0	160	2.20	.9	180	.81	10.0	10.11
14*	2.3	79	2.30	3.4	200	3.74	1.1	210	.99	6.8	7.03
28	9.0	309	9.00	4.2	250	4.62	1.8	260	1.62	15.0	15.24
Actual Cost	23.1	779	$23.10	13.2	830	$14.52	4.8	850	$4.32	41.1	$41.94
Standard: Hours	22.2			12.9			5.1			40.2	
Rate			$1.01			$1.10			$ .95		
Cost			$22.42			$14.19			$4.85		$41.46
VARIANCE	- .9		- $.68	- .3		- $.33	+ .3		+ $.53	- .9	- $.48

* direct-labor hours, production quantity and machine cost taken from Exhibit 17-5

Exhibit 17–6. Product and Operation Direct-Labor Cost Sheet

SUMMARY OF STANDARD AND ACTUAL CONVERSION COSTS

Period Ended: January 31

PRODUCTION CENTER	DIRECT LABOR					OVERHEAD			
	Standard		Actual		Cost Variance	MHR	Standard Cost	Actual Cost	Cost Variance
	Hours	Cost	Hours	Cost					
A*	592	$606.36	600	$604.50	+ $ 1.86	$3.722	$2,203.42	$2,293.20	- $ 89.78
B	285	356.25	290	362.50	- 6.25	4.530	1,291.05	1,306.27	- 15.22
C	620	818.40	610	793.00	+ 25.40	3.967	2,459.54	2,326.45	+ 133.09
D	1200	1,680.00	1300	1,820.00	- 140.00	3.091	3,709.20	3,896.99	- 187.79
E	560	1,120.00	550	1,100.00	+ 20.00	6.750	3,780.00	3,781.56	- 1.56
F	1280	2,688.00	1350	2,835.00	- 147.00	5.715	7,315.20	7,436.05	- 120.85
G	3500	4,375.00	3600	4,500.00	- 125.00	3.507	12,274.50	12,387.57	- 113.07
H	525		550	704.00	- 32.00	4.193	2,201.32	2,179.59	+ 21.73
I	933	1,250.22	950	1,273.00	- 22.78	3.110	2,901.63	2,979.73	- 78.10
J	605	665.50	600		+ 5.50	2.238	1,353.99	1,412.59	- 58.60
Totals	10100	$14,231.73	10400	$14,652.00	-$420.27		$39,489.85	$40,000.00	-$510.15

*standard and actual hours for this production center taken from Exhibit 17-5

Exhibit 17-7. Summary of Standard and Actual Conversion Cost

DISTRIBUTION OF CURRENT OVERHEAD EXPENSES BY PRODUCT CLASSIFICATION

Period ended January 31

Production Center	Direct Labor Hours	Overhead Expenses	MHR	Product 1000		Product 2000		Product 3000		Product 4000		Product 5000		Product 6000		Product 7000		Product 8000		Product 9000	
				Hrs.	Cost	Hrs.	Cost	Hrs.	Cost	Hrs.	Cost	Hrs.	Cost	Hrs.	Cost	Hrs.	Cost	Hrs.	Cost	Hrs.	Cost
A*	600	$2293.20	3.822	175	$668.85	152	$580.94	155	$592.41	50	$191.10	55	$210.21	13	$49.69						
B	290	1306.27	4.504					200	900.80	30	135.12	50	225.20	10	45.15						
C	610	2326.45	3.814	280	1067.92	270	1029.78			60	228.75										
D	1300	3896.99	2.998	100	299.80	200	599.60	500	1499.00	400	1199.20	100	299.39								
E	550	3781.56	6.876									450	3094.20	100	687.36						
F	1350	7436.05	5.508	500	2754.00	400	2203.20	300	1652.40	150	826.45										
G	3600	12387.57	3.441	100	344.10	1100	3785.10	300	1032.30	1000	3441.00	1000	3441.00	100	344.07						
H	550	2179.59	3.963													550	$2,179.59				
I	950	2979.73	3.137			400	1254.80			400	1254.80	150	470.13								
J	600	1412.59	2.354															500	$1,177.00	100	$235.59
Totals	10,400	$40,000.00	///		$5,134.67		$9,453.42		$5676.91		$7,276.42		$7,740.13		$1126.27		$2,179.59		$1,177.00		$235.59

*The actual direct-labor hours for this production center taken from Exhibit 17-4.

Exhibit 17–8. Distribution of Current Overhead Expenses by Product Classifications

Period ended: 9/21

MACHINE CENTERS

100 -- Rate 17.75/hr. (Department B)

[1] Date	[2] Job No.	[3] Non-Prod.	[4] Prep. Setup	[5] Run	[6] Quan	[7] Prep. Setup	[8] Est. Quan.	[9] Std. Run
			ACTUAL			ESTIMATED		
9/15	131	1.0	1.0	3.5	5,000	1.0	1500	3.3
9/15	133	.5	2.0			1.5		
9/16	140	.5	2.5	5.0	8,000	2.5	1800	4.4
9/17	140			8.0	14,000		1800	7.7
9/18	155	3.5	4.5			4.0		
9/19	155			8.0	15,000		1800	8.3
TOTAL		5.5	10.0	24.5	42,000	9.0		23.7
				34.5	1,715			32.7

200 -- Rate 15.02/hr. (Department B)

Date	Job No.	Non-Prod.	Prep. Setup	Run	Quan	Prep. Setup	Est. Quan.	Std. Run
9/15	138		2.5	6.0	6,500	2.0	1400	4.6
9/16	138			5.0	4,900		1400	3.5
9/16	144		5.0					
9/17	144	1.0		4.0	5,500	12.5	1800	3.1
9/17	121		.8	9.2	17,000		1800	9.5
9/19	121	1.0	1.0	6.0	5,900	2.0	1400	4.2
TOTAL		2.0	13.8	30.2	39,800	17.0		24.9
				44.0	1,318			41.9

300 -- Rate 13.21/hr. (Department B)

Date	Job No.	Non-Prod.	Prep. Setup	Run	Quan	Prep. Setup	Est. Quan.	Std. Run
9/15	151		3.4	6.9	14,800	3.0	2000	7.4
9/16	154		2.2	8.8	23,450	2.0	2000	11.7
9/17	169	2.0	3.4	5.6	13,150	4.0	2000	6.6
9/18	169			11.3	29,000		2000	14.5
9/19	169	.7		11.2	27,500		2000	13.8
TOTAL		2.7	9.0	43.8	107,900	9.0		54.0
				52.8	2,463			63.0

400 -- (2) -- Rate 9.15/hr. (Department B)

Date	Job No.	Non-Prod.	Prep. Setup	Run	Quan	Prep. Setup	Est. Quan.	Std. Run
9/15	103			16.0	20,700		2000	10.4
9/16	105	2.9		10.2	15,000		2000	7.5
9/17	105	1.7		12.6	16,430		2000	8.2
9/18	105			16.0	18,100		2000	9.1
9/19	116		16.0			20.0	2000	
9/20	116	.6	6.1	8.6	16,340		2000	8.2
TOTAL		5.2	22.1	63.4	86,570	20.0		43.4
				85.5	1,365			63.4

LABOR CENTERS

	110 [10] Estim.	[11] Actual	210 [12] Estim.	[13] Actual	310 [14] Estim.	[15] Actual	410 [16] Estim.	[17] Actual

SUMMARY

[18] Department	[19] Actual $	[20] Estim. $	[21] Budget $	[22] Perf. Percent	[23] Act'y Percent
A	730	757	695	103.6	108.9
B	2750	2622	2116	95.3	123.9
C	1952	1693	1485	86.7	114.0
D	504	501	444	99.4	112.8
E	1176	1151	1106	97.9	104.1
TOTAL PLANT	7112	6724	5846	94.5	115.0
Handling	865		797		
GRAND TOTAL	7977		6643		
Performance Var.		(-$388)			
Activity Variation		+$878			

Exhibit 17-9. Weekly Production Report

performance. The date and job number are shown in the first two columns. Next, the actual times spent by the Production Centers and their production are shown for each day. This information comes from the daily production tickets. In the next three columns the estimated times are shown, and these data come from the estimate sheet. Estimated running time is computed by dividing actual production by the hourly speed of the machine as calculated in the estimate for that particular job. This estimated running time can be adjusted for over or under runs.

When the actual and estimated times for the whole week have been posted and totalled, the analysis can be started. The total of column (6) divided by the total of column (5) is the average hourly production. The total of columns (4) and (5) is the earned hours figure, which, multiplied by the MHR, gives the earned dollars. Similarly, from columns (7) and (9) we derive the estimated hours and dollars. The dollar figures by departments are summarized in the Summary section of this form. The figures in column (19) are Actual dollars. Column (20) figures are the Estimated dollars, which represent what it *should have* cost to process the jobs through the various Production Centers, had actual production been according to estimate. Column (21) is the product of the budgeted hours in each department multiplied by the appropriate MHR. In this case, the Production Centers are grouped together by department. Then the production of each Center is reduced to a weekly basis by dividing the annual assigned hours by 52.

In using a form of this type, it is necessary to keep in mind that while the form gives convenient performance and activity accomplishments, it in no way accounts for seasonal effect and for normal variations.

Column (21) shows the dollars that would be earned if actual production activity equaled the projection made at the beginning of the activity period. This is equivalent to the Linear Activity figure of Exhibit 17–3.

Performance is measured by comparing Estimated dollars with Actual dollars, and *Activity* (or volume gain) by comparing Estimated dollars with Budgeted dollars. When Performance is greater than 100%, more profit is made (for the week) than was estimated. When Activity exceeds 100%, more profit is made (for the week) by overrecovering budgeted overhead.

This type of report is handy for the production manager. He sees the negative performance variation, the result of low productivity, and he sees which of the departments are the offenders. Department *C*, with the lowest substandard performance, handles the second highest amount of money of any department. By extracting the production tickets of this Center, the manager sees that a particular job pulled down its average. This sets the target for remedial action. Discussion with the foreman about causes and remedies might then prevent the recurrence of a loss that would otherwise have easily passed unnoticed for a long time.

Testing Fixed and Variable Cost Recovery for Pricing Control

Up to this point in our discussion of testing the MHR, there has been no mention of the need for measuring the expense recovery by both the fixed and variable elements of cost. As we established earlier in the book, to become aware of these separate elements is a necessary step toward a sound pricing policy. It is just as necessary to know the speed at which both recoveries are occurring, in order to enable management to direct the efforts of its sales department. While high recovery for products that contain a small element of fixed expense allows the company to make a profit on its labor and materials, selling these products does not provide sufficient revenue to pay for the cost of owning and maintaining facilities. In a sense, the company ends up merchandising only variable expenses. Profit-making calls for a full utilization of facilities, and optimum use may not be accomplished where there is insufficient fixed-expense recovery.

Different companies work this consideration into their forms in different ways. Exhibit 17–10 shows how the Cost Recovery Statement of Exhibit 17–2 is expanded to account for the fixed and variable elements. Exhibit 17–11 does the same for the Production Center Recovery Test Form of Exhibit 17–3.

COST RECOVERY STATEMENT

Production Center	Monthly Activity	MACHINE-HOUR RATE			R E C O V E R Y		
		FIXED	VARIABLE		FIXED	VARIABLE	
			Direct Labor	Overhead		Direct Labor	Overhead
Total Recovery							
Monthly Direct-Labor Cost			////////				////////////
Budgeted Overhead Cost				////////			
Actual Overhead Cost				////////			

Exhibit 17–10. Fixed-Variable Cost Recovery Statement

PRODUCTION CENTER RECOVERY TEST FORM

Production Center	ACTIVITY		VARIATION IN ACTIVITY Based On:		MACHINE-HOUR RATE		COST OF ACTIVITY VARIATION Based On:				CUMULATIVE RECOVERY VARIATION			
	Lin.	Acc.	Act.	Linear	Accept.	Fixed	Varia.	LINEAR		ACCEPTABLE		LINEAR		ACCEPTABLE	
								Fixed	Variable	Fixed	Variable	Fixed	Variable	Fixed	Variable

Exhibit 17–11. Fixed-Variable Production Center Recovery Test Form

Chapter 18

HOW TO CORRECT OR CHANGE THE MHR

Whether or not pricing is to be affected, it is desirable to alter the rates to provide for changes that have taken place since the rates were established. This practice immediately obviates the necessity for calculating new rates at the end of each year. Instead, rates are adjusted periodically to conform to actual operating conditions.

Because of the nature of competition, it may not be advisable to reflect changes in the rates immediately into product costs during any one season or activity period. As a matter of fact, when estimators are familiar with the existing rates, they can almost apply them automatically. This is why MHR estimating is a fast and accurate procedure. Besides the unrealistic effect immediate rate changes would have in the market, they would slow estimating procedure drastically, as estimators would constantly have to be looking through a maze of schedules for revisions. Experience has shown that estimators should be given a new set of rates only once during each activity period. The adjusted rates caused by changes in operating conditions should be the schedule given to management for use in decision-making and profitability determinations.

Why Change or Correct?

Basically, there are nine reasons for adjusting the rates—changes in: activity, machinery disposal, machinery acquisition, machinery replacement, labor rates, labor classifications, expenditures, allocation factors, and occupancy.

From a purely theoretical point of view, changes in any one of the above nine categories would necessitate an entirely new Expense Assignment Worksheet. This is not practical in many cases, because the new MHR so developed might be less than .01 percent different than if certain shortcuts are taken. This matter of revision has to be left to the judgment of the person administering the rates, but the major criteria are the degree of change and the estimated effect of such a change in the rate structure. For example, suppose that activity hours are changed to one-half of the original projection. This is certainly a major change, since it would raise the MHR to approximately double the amount it was previously. But what else would it do? Let's refer back to EXHIBIT 10–3 and see.

Since the overhead segment of the MHR is obtained by dividing column (13) by column (1), obviously, lowering to 1,000 hours the projected activity of the first Production Center, "Printer Slotter," would cut that portion of the MHR exactly in half. But this is not entirely true. Had the original projection been 1,000 hours instead of 2,000, the Direct Labor Budget would have been reduced in proportion, a reduction which, in turn, would have affected the allocation of Fringe Benefits Costs, column (10). This means that all the rates would have to be altered as a result of the change in activity of one Center. Note that the $95,000 total costs would remain unchanged, since the change of activity simply reshuffles the amount of overhead expenses each Production Center is called upon to carry. Of course, these are not the only changes that would occur when the activity of the first Production Center is changed. Since the Assigned Annual Hours are used as an allocation factor for distributing Indirect Labor Costs to the various centers, each of the Centers' allocated amount would likewise change.

Practical Considerations

In some situations, it would pay to make a new EAW to account for a Center's change, because of the serious effect on the other Centers' MHR. In other cases, it is sufficient simply to increase or reduce the MHR in accordance with the change in activity.

While we advocate consistency in rate-setting, we also recommend practical accuracy. We don't believe in spending a dollar to save fifty cents. The accuracy gap between costs and selling prices is subject to variables over which the company has no control—the matching of marginal pricing to the degree of elasticity of demand, competitive influences, market saturation and consumer desires—to the point that it becomes impractical to try and present cost figures to within .01 percent.

Accordingly, we are listing below basic steps which we have found to be practical for making the changes indicated earlier:

Activity: One of the principal reasons for making a change in activity arises from the tendency to make activity projections according to past history rather than by means of a sales forecast. The need to make changes based on activity is usually shown by the Production Center Recovery Test Form. The first thing to decide is whether the variation between Actual and Acceptable activity was due to a poor original projection, or whether it has occurred as a result of a new set of circumstances. The correction should be made if the variation is excessively high, and at this point the monthly apportionment of activity for each Production Center should be reviewed.

If the variation is on the high side of activity, and the sales department is experiencing no resistance on prices, the rate for pricing purposes should be left unchanged. However, management should be informed of a profitable Center, so that it can direct more effectively the time and efforts of its sales force.

Experience has shown that Centers which are severely underprojected will show up with higher conversion costs, depending on the extent of their service contribution in the production of orders. While existing customers may not express opposition, higher prices may hamper penetration into other markets. For this reason, it pays to make immediate changes in the rates where substantial levels of activity have been underprojected.

In the alteration of the rates for changes in activity, the total overhead expense budget (OB) does not change. The expenses are simply shifted. Changes do occur in those ratios which use Assigned Annual Hours as an allocation factor, as in the case of Fringe Benefits of EXHIBIT 10–3, and they also occur in allocation factors affected by the Assigned Annual Hours, such as the factor of Direct-Labor Budget of EXHIBIT 10–3.

Machinery: Here we deal with such matters as disposing of a machine, replacing one machine with another and adding new machinery. In the first case, when a machine is sold, it affects or eliminates the cost of the Production Center of which it was a member. Replacing a machine usually adds to the cost of a Center. When a machine is added, it always affects an existing Center or creates a new Center. That calls for reviewing the elements entering into a Production Center. These are handled in the same way as in the original MHR, according to the instructions given in Section 2: depreciation expenses affect the Operating Budget; changes in workers' pay affect the Crew Composition Table; changes in annual hours have the effect explained in the case of machinery relocation.

If one of the machine units is removed from a center, the practical correction is to reduce space, power, and machinery costs to that Center alone on the EAW, and to leave the other Center costs alone. Remember that in adjusting machinery costs, the price-level adjustments on depreciation become an important consideration. As we said before, there will probably be such little effect on the other Centers that the effort in making an entirely new EAW is not justified.

If one of the machine units is replaced within a Center, this may call for a revision of the space and possibly the power costs, and almost always calls for a new level of depreciation and price-level expenses in machinery costs.

When a machine is added to a Center, space, power and machinery costs must be increased. There must be a corresponding increase in the costs stated in the Operating Budget. In this case, depending on the annual cost of the additional unit, the change may call for a sizeable revision in the EAW.

In any of these machinery cases, if additional workers are added consideration must be given to the indirect labor and fringe benefit costs on the EAW. And, of course, where more workers are added, a change must be made on the Crew Composition Table—which causes a direct change in the direct labor segment of the composite MHR.

Labor: Changes in labor, because of base rate increases or additional crewing, can be made directly on the CCT. The extent to which labor changes affect the Direct Labor Budget allocation factor will be felt in the Fringe Benefits Costs of all Centers. But, again, unless this change takes place throughout the plant, it is usually not practical to change all the rates.

Sometimes, though, the addition of workers together with changes in equipment may change the Assigned Annual Hours. The impact of this combined change may make it pay to revise the entire EAW. Occasionally, in reviewing rates at the start of an activity period, it is found that only the direct labor base rates have changed, while the product mix is expected to remain more or less the same as last year's. Under that circumstance, the practical procedure is to note the changes on the CCT and simply boost the direct labor segment of the composite MHR, by the extent of the increases in the hourly base rates for the crew affected.

Expenditures: Where expenses are found to be considerably different than originally projected in the Operating Budget, and it is desired to change the MHR to reflect these changes, the procedure is simple. Make the changes on the OB and bring them forward to the EAW. From this point on, it is only required to change the allocation ratios (using the same allocation factors)—an adjustment that will change the expenses allocated to each Center. This will call for a new set of rates, because an expense change is an over-all one affecting all Centers.

However, if the expense change is identified with only a specific Center, then the proper cost category for that Center can be changed and a new rate for it developed without, in a practical way, disturbing any of the other Centers' MHR.

Allocation Factors: The necessity for changing allocation factors arises if it is discovered that inequitable allocation factors were used at first. Or the need arises when the nature of the company's business changes to an extent which makes the use of the existing allocation factors unsound. This often happens as a result of an equipment modernization program, or because of interdepartment shifts in location and/or responsibility. In these cases there is no alternative but to revise the entire EAW.

Occupancy: Changes in this category do not refer to occupancy of individual Centers but, rather, to changes in total company occupancy—changes involving the acquisition or disposal of warehouse, store, office and other space. In this type of change, the OB is affected in the Space Costs category—which in turn affects the amount of space costs apportioned to each Center. While all the rates will change under this type of move, it is usually sufficient to change the values of Space Costs only on the EAW.

Summary

By means of the allocation ratios shown on the EAW, it is possible to test in advance the effect of any change. Judgment must be used to determine whether or not the change should be integrated into the rates at the time it occurs, or whether it is small enough to wait for the start of the new activity period. The time required for making changes is small. The mechanics follow those instructions listed in Section 2. In using the technique of allocation ratios, it is common practice to permit the major part of the computation to be done by comptometer operators or by the use of office machine calculators.

INDEX

A

Administrative costs, 7, 34, 52–55, 60, 76, 88, 91
Advertising costs, 87, 128
Amortization
    pricing and, 95
    taxes and, 86
Amortization periods, depreciation and, 94

B

Bad debts, 54
Buildings
    depreciation, 33
    investment, 7
Burden, 50

C

Capital, working, 7, 19
Capital investment, 3, 4, 7, 19, 65
    control of, 39
    inventory-support, 185
    recovery of, 93, 122
    return on, xi
Competition, effects of, ix, xi–xii, 3–4
Cost allocation (see also Expense assignment)
    bases, 32, 132
    conversion cost, 134, 141–142, 150, 152–155, 234
    customer, 127
    direct costs, 25
    direct-indirect ratio, 85
    equipment costs, 67, 74
    equity in, 31–33
    factors for, 110–118, 132–137, 246
    inconsistencies in, 104–105, 112, 132–134
    indirect costs, 7
    inequities in, 112
    job costs, 133–134
    labor, fractional, 77, 82–84
    overhead, 31–35
    present value, 66–68
    production-center, 128, 130
    production-line-center, 129
    proportionate, 73
    services, 126
    traditional, 11–18, 184
    variations in, 116–118, 121

Cost control, 31
Cost estimating
    allocation factors in, 113
    annual hours, 68
    conversion cost in, 142
    cost-finding and, 158
    definition of, vii
    equipment costs, 61, 65
    expense, projection of, 91–92
    full cost, 155
    importance of, 11
    job costs, 150–154
    labor costs, 82, 149
    MHR and, 120
    MHR accuracy and, 216
    management costs, 69
    materials cost, 157
    objective of, 22–26
    product costs, 150–154
    production capacity vs. activity, 216–220
    production center, 68
    rate changes and, 243
    reliability in, 144
    requirements of, 39
    revisions in, 233
    variance technique, 157
    waste percentage, 157
Cost finding, 126, 184
Cost finding, product costs, 141–161, 169
Cost floor, 4
Costing
    analysis of, 3–10
    annual hours, 84, 245
    book value, 74
    composite rates, 120
    downtime, 146
    economic, 194
    fluctuation, seasonal, 188, 224
    fringe benefits, 80, 85
    handwork, 84
    job costing, 63, 65, 74
    job quantity and, 154, 157
    labor, average, 82
    labor, direct vs. indirect, 133
    labor, non-productive, 83
    MHR and, 18
    man hours, 84
    operational hours, 187–190

Costing (*cont.*)
  overhead, 16
  overtime, 83
  practicality in, xi
  present value, 74
  problems in, 19, 104–108
  product, xii
  production activity, 122–124
  production capacity, 122–124, 143
  production-center, 63
  production standards and, 143
  profits and, 20, 21–22
  time, idle, 81
  time, lost, 132–137
  time, operational, 141
  time, setup, 154
  time, unassigned, 85
  time, unearned, 85
  traditional methods, ix, x, 11–18
  transfer of personnel, 81, 82
  use of, x
Costing methods (see also MHR system), 12–17,
    32–33, 129–132, 145–150, 163
  direct-labor, 21, 22, 26, 32
  direct-labor-dollar, 13–15
  direct-labor-hour, 15
  direct-labor vs. MHR, 17–18
  expense-recovery and, 111
  facility costing, 56–57
  job costing, 44, 56–57
  material-cost, 13, 21
  material-weight, 21, 22
  pricing and, 182
  prime-cost, 12–14
  production capacity vs. activity, 105–107
  traditional, 182
  unit-of-product, 15
Costing services, trade-association, 164
Cost recovery, 71, 74, 83, 93, 162, 165, 166, 169,
    188, 189, 200, 215–216, 223–233, 241
Cost reduction vs. cost estimating, 3
Costs (see also Expense)
  actual, 154
  actual vs. budgeted, 215, 227
  actual vs. estimated, 25
  actual vs. quoted, 163
  allocation factors and, 113
  annual, 111
  budget, flexible, and, 169–176
  classification of, 6, 39–40, 88–91
  composite rates, 187
  conversion cost, vii, 16, 56, 59–60
  definition of, 4–5
  direct, vii, 5, 6, 11, 59, 73, 169
  distribution of, 185
  vs. expenses, 3
  factory, 88
  fixed, vii, 5, 6, 85, 122, 155, 160, 165, 169–
    176, 241

Costs (see also Expense) (*cont.*)
  historical, adjustment of, 166
  indirect, 5, 6, 73
  make-ready, machine, 8
  manufacturing, 6–7, 113, 120
  non-manufacturing, 6–7
  operating, 73
  out-of-pocket, 6
  out-of-pocket "floor," 160
  periodical, 6
  prices and, "accuracy gap," 244–245
  product, 184, 190–191
  production-center, 187, 245
  production volume and, xii, 6, 97
  profit and, 185
  projected, 187
  "quiet," 5
  reporting of, 7–8, 86
  stand-by, 6, 97
  standby-facility, 5
  "sunk," 6, 122
  testing of, 233
  total, 85
  variable, vii, 5, 6, 85, 155, 160, 169–176, 241
  variances in, 234–240
  variety of, ix
Cost tracing, 83
Customer reaction, xi

D

Delivery expense, 7, 88, 127–128, 169
Depreciation, 4–6, 8, 12, 33, 50, 52, 54, 65, 66,
    86–87, 100–104, 169, 245
  costing methods for, 107–108
  economic, 92–93, 95
  pricing and, 95
  tax deduction and, 94
  technological, 93, 95
Distribution costs, 127

E

Equipment costs, 5, 7, 17, 19–22, 61, 63, 66, 67,
    90, 111, 245–246
Equipment disposal, vii
Equipment replacement, reserve account, 96
Estimating, requirements of, 5
Expansion, 9–10, 20, 22
Expense (see also Costs)
  actual vs. budgeted, 223
  actual vs. estimated, 180
  actual vs. projected, 246
  budgeting of, 92, 96–108, 215–216
  classification of, 126, 171
  direct-indirect, 91–92
  distribution bases, 34–35, 134–137
  factory, 50–52, 60
  fixed, vii, 50, 54–55, 97, 98, 100, 171
  general, 34, 65

Expense (see also Costs) (*cont.*)
  institutional, 34
  misclassification of, 55–56
  non-manufacturing, 134
  occupancy, 7
  operating, 53
  period, 52, 54
  projection of, 87
  service, 59, 127
  supplies, 59
  total, 97
  types of, 134–137
  unrecovered, 185
  variable, 97, 98, 100, 171
  variations in, 31
Expense assignment, vii, x, 110–118, 126–129,
    142, 165
  factors of, 126–127
  MHR variation and, 215
  production centers and, 111–113
  service, 134
Expense recovery
  ability, product, 194–196, 202
  ability, productivity and, 223–224
  actual, 194
  actual vs. required, 197–199
  budgeting and, 111, 194
  definition, 20
  fixed expense, 22, 106, 107, 161, 169, 178,
    232–233, 241
  job costing and, 88
  overage, 97
  pricing and, 111
  product mix and, 199–200, 215–216
  sales adjustment for, 193–194
  sales dollar and, 186
  unit profit and, 165
  variations in, 215–216
Experimental expense, 51

F

Facility usage, x, 5, 7, 18–30
  overhead and, 26
  profit and, 19–27
Fringe-benefit expense, 7, 80, 84, 85, 90, 120,
    246

G

General accounting, 8

H

Handling, internal, expense, 134
Holiday expense, 76, 80

I

Incentives, 25, 45, 49, 143, 146, 149
Idle-time expense, 77, 82, 83, 120

Inspection expense, 34
Insurance, Workmen's Compensation, 51
Insurance appraisal, 67
Insurance expense, 33, 50, 52, 54
Interest expense, 5, 8
Inventories, 7, 8, 33, 52, 61, 81, 185

L

Labor costs, ix, 4–5, 40–50
  direct, 6, 7, 11, 21, 23, 24, 42, 43, 59, 60, 76,
    82, 85, 111, 120, 142, 234, 246
  fractional, 77, 82–84
  indirect, 7, 42, 51, 59, 76, 82, 83, 85, 90,
    111–112, 128, 134, 149, 246
Labor force, 7

M

Machine-hour rate
  accuracy of, 116
  accuracy, practical, 244–247
  administration, xi
  advantages of, 18
  annual rate, 71
  application of, 141, 156, 160, 243–247
  composition of, 69, 72–73, 87, 113
  computation of, 60
  consistency in, 244
  conversion cost, 84
  correction of, 71, 72, 243–247
  cost-estimating and, 216
  definition of, 17, 58, 59, 125
  development of, x, 58–59, 61–125
  equity of, 215, 223–224
  inflation of, 82
  obtained, 7
  overhead in, 148
  practicality of, xi
  pre-testing of, 215–222
  pricing and, 169
  problems of, 72–74
  product mix and, 182
  testing of, x, 71, 72, 74, 223–241
  vs. traditional methods, 11–18
  updating of, x
  wage rate and, 77
MHR accounting, vii–ix
MHR system
  annual hours, 68, 77–80
  application of, x
  conversion cost, 40
  cost allocation, 111
  cost finding, 87
  costing, traditional, and, 13–18, 21, 26, 33
  equipment replacement, 95–96
  facility duplication, 190
  forms, deficiency of, 160–161

MHR system (*cont.*)
   handling expense, 134
   job costing and, 44
   job profitability, 56
   maintenance, 65
   as managerial tool, x–xi
   power plants, 65
   present value, 66–68, 73–74
   problems, 82–85
   production center, 63–64, 68–72, 76–82
   production control, 65
   sales-production coordination, 184–211
   service-cost center, 64–65
   space costs, 73
   tool rooms, 65
   work stations, 61
Maintenance expense, 34, 60, 133, 169
Management control, 223, 224, 244–245
Management decision, x, 52, 184, 211
Management responsibility, 223
Market demand, xi
Marketing expense, 31
Material costs, ix, 6, 11, 23, 25, 40, 50–51, 59, 73, 87, 142, 157, 169
Methods-time-measurement, 143
Methods-Time Measurement, 145
Monopoly, 8
Motion and Time Study, Principles and Practice, 145

O

Occupancy costs, 5
Out-of-pocket costs, vii
Overhead expense, ix–x, 6, 7, 11–12, 15–16, 18, 19, 23, 25, 31–35, 59, 65, 72, 88, 110, 116, 130, 143, 165, 169, 187, 223
Overtime expense, 51, 80

P

Payroll, 5, 8, 51, 81, 82, 85, 88
Planning, long-range, 9–10
Planning for profit, 19, 20
Power costs, 33–34, 89, 100, 110–111, 169, 245
Pricing
   "accuracy gap," 244–246
   adjustments, 92, 160
   allocation factors and, 111, 133
   capital investment and, 67–68
   committed prices, 178
   competition and, ix, 162–164
   consistency in, 66, 74
   control, 241
   cost allocation and, 23, 32
   cost control and, 31
   costing methods and, 182
   cost recovery and, 26, 216
   cost and, 8, 162–163, 164–166, 244–246

Pricing (*cont.*)
   current-dollar, 94–95
   customer demand, 162
   data required, 169
   depreciation and, 102–104
   direct-labor allocation, 27
   dollar value and, 163
   effective, 39
   equitable, 66
   financial reporting and, 86–87
   factors in, 184
   labor estimating and, 82
   latitude in, 200–211
   MHR, use of, 162–183
   MHR changes and, 232
   marginal, 166–169, 180
   markup, 3–4
   a philosophy of, 176–178
   policy, 185
   practicality in, xi
   price acceptability, 162
   price elasticity, 163
   profit planning and, 5, 7
   sales resistance, 225
   strategy, 181–182
   surplus stocks, 130
   unit-product cost and, 165
   volume and, 163
   volume and demand, 178
Product differences, ix
Product mix
   allocation and, 182
   allocation factors, 111, 112, 121
   allocation variances, 104–105
   capital investment, 65
   control of, 185–186
   costing methods, 21
   cost recovery, 5, 7, 165
   effects of, 199–200, 220
   equipment usage, balanced, 20
   equipment usage, effects on, 26
   estimates, 69
   estimates, composite, 25
   facility activity, comparative, 24
   facility profitability and, 8
   fixed and variable, 169
   forecast, 127
   labor, indirect, and, 85
   optimizing of, 9, 40
   overhead and, **26**
   profit effect of, 19–30
   rate review and, 246
   selection of, 200–202
   shifts in, expense recovery and, 106
Production standards, 141–150
   development of, 143–144
   dimensions for tabulating, 144–145
   formats for developing, 145–150
Production volume and costs, 169–176

Profit inflation, 94
Profit margin, vii, 88
Profits
　cost allocation and, 164
　costs and, 74, 185
　definition of, 3
　departmentalization of, 200
　expense, fixed, recovery and, 241
　facility, 8, 9
　facility activity and, 106
　facility usage and, 241
　vs. fixed costs, 168
　material usage and, 203
　maximization of, 182
　operating risks, 7
　payroll and, 81
　planning for, xi, xii, 3, 4, 7, 19
　product mix and, 26–27, 186
　production standards, 143
　real, 204
　real vs. dollar, 93–94

R

Receiving expense, 34, 129
Rental expense, 5, 52, 54, 59, 169
Repair expense, 60, 87, 127, 132–133
Rest-period expense, 76, 80

S

Salary expense, 169
Sales
　commissions, 134, 169
　contact effort, 208–211

Sales (*cont.*)
　expense, 7, 53, 60, 76, 88, 91, 134, 169
　expense recovery and, 193–194, 197–199
　mixture, 4
　objectives, 191–194
　price latitude, 200–211
　prices, vii
　production integrated with, 199–200
　vs. revenue, 3
Shipping expense, 34, 127
Social security, 51, 54
Space expense, 7, 88, 111, 245–247
Stand-by costs, vii
Storage expense, 5, 7, 34, 128–129
Survival, 7

T

Tax expense, 33, 50, 52, 54, 86, 164, 169
Technology, effects of, xii
Time-and-motion study, 143
Time costs, vii

U

Unemployment compensation, 51, 54

V

Vacation expense, 51, 54, 76, 80
Volume costs, vii
Volume mix, 5, 7

W

Water-consumption expense, 33